Lesson Masters B

THE UNIVERSITY OF CHICAGO SCHOOL MATHEMATICS PROJECT

ADVANCED ALGEBRA

INTEGRATED MATHEMATICS

Further practice on
SPUR objectives

Scott Foresman
Addison Wesley

D1157522

Editorial Offices: Glenview, Illinois • Menlo Park, California
Sales Offices: Reading, Massachusetts • Atlanta, Georgia • Glenview, Illinois
Carrollton, Texas • Menlo Park, California

http://www.sf.aw.com

Contents

ISBN: 0-673-45808-3

3 4 5 6 7-VHG-05 04 03 02 01

LESSON MASTER 1-1 B

Skills Objective A: Evaluate expressions and formulas, including correct units in answer.

In 1 and 2, consider the expression $\dfrac{5 \cdot 2^3 - 4}{9}$.

1. Give the steps, in order, needed to evaluate the expression.

_____

_____

_____

_____

2. Evaluate the expression. _____

In 3–5, evaluate the expression $2n^2 + 4n - 5$ for the given value of n.

3. $n = 3$ _____   **4.** $n = -2$ _____   **5.** $n = \frac{1}{2}$ _____

In 6 and 7, evaluate the expression.

6. $8 \div 2 \cdot 6 - (3 - 9)$ _____   **7.** $(4 - 6)^3 + 12 \div 3 - 7$ _____

In 8–10, evaluate the expression when $x = 4$, $y = -3$, and $z = 2$.

8. $\dfrac{x^2 - 2z}{y}$ _____   **9.** $y^4 - 3xz$ _____   **10.** $\dfrac{x}{(y + z)^3}$ _____

11. The formula for the volume of a sphere is $V = \frac{4}{3} \pi r^3$. Find the volume of a sphere with a 9-cm radius. _____

12. For a polygon with n sides, the sum of the measures of the polygon's interior angles T is given by the formula $T = 180(n - 2)$. Find the value of T for an octagon. _____

13. Near the surface of the moon, the distance d that a rock falls in t seconds is $d = \frac{1}{2} gt^2$. If $g = 5.3 \frac{\text{ft}}{\text{sec}^2}$, how far will a rock fall in 8 seconds? _____

▶ **LESSON MASTER 1-1B** *page 2*

Uses Objective I: Use addition, subtraction, multiplication, and division to write expressions which model real-world situations.

In 14–24, write an expression to describe the situation.

14. The enrollment at Shaw Elementary School was 1164. On Friday, *n* new students enrolled and *w* students withdrew. What is the new school enrollment? _____

15. Sam drove at an average rate of *m* miles per hour for *h* hours. How far did he drive? _____

16. For *D* days, the total attendance at the Rocky Top Museum was *P* people. What was the average attendance per day? _____

17. The model of a ship is one hundredth of the actual size. Find the length of a model ship if the actual ship is *M* meters long. _____

18. *F* feet of paper was taken from a roll of wrapping paper containing *W* feet. How much paper is left on the roll? _____

19. At North High School, the faculty *f* increased by *t* teachers. How many teachers are now on the faculty? _____

20. The water level in Long Lake was *L* inches in 1992. It dropped *I* inches in 1993 and then rose *K* inches in 1994. What was the water level at the end of 1994? _____

21. Yesterday, *s* students were present at Wee Wons Nursery School. Today, 4 fewer students were present. What was the total attendance yesterday and today? _____

22. Cutweld International ordered *T* tons of steel which came in *s* sheets of equal weight. What was the weight of each sheet of steel? _____

23. The original price of a compact disc was *C* dollars. What is the sale price after a 25% discount? _____

24. If the markup on furniture is *p* percent, what is the selling price of a chair that cost the dealer *d* dollars? _____

LESSON MASTER 1-2 B

Vocabulary

1. A function is a correspondence between two variables such

   that each value of the _____ variable corresponds

   to exactly one value of the _____ variable.

2. For the function with equation $y = \dfrac{1}{x^2}$, give

   a. the *domain.* _____   **b.** the *range.* _____

Skills Objective A: Evaluate expressions and formulas and use correct units in answers.

3. In the formula $d = \dfrac{n(n-2)}{2}$, find d when $n = -10$. _____

4. If $T = kPV$, find T when $k = 0.68$, $P = 2.5$, and $V = 120$. _____

5. If $x = \dfrac{2b}{a}$, find x when $a = -1.2$ and $b = 0.45$. _____

6. A cone of radius r and height h has volume $V = \dfrac{1}{3}\pi r^3 h$. Find the volume of a cone with radius 6 inches and height 10 inches. _____

7. Total surface area of a right circular cylinder is $S = 2\pi rh + 2\pi r^2$. Find the total surface area of a tin can 15 cm high if its radius is 3 cm. _____

In 8–10, evaluate the formula for the given value of the independent variable.

8. $r = 200(3)^n$, $n = -2$ 9. $y = 4x^2 - 3x - 7$, $x = -3$ 10. $p = \dfrac{48}{n^3}$, if $n = -2$

_____   _____   _____

Properties Objective G: Determine whether a relation defined by a table, a list of ordered pairs, or a simple equation is a function.

11. Does the table describe b as a function of a? Justify your answer.

a	0	1	-1	2	-2
b	0	1	-1	8	-8

_____

_____

▶ **LESSON MASTER 1-2 B** *page 2*

12. Is the set $\{(2, 4), (4, 8), (8, 16), (16, 32)\}$ a function?
Why or why not?

_____

_____

In 13–15, tell whether or not the equation describes a function.

13. $y = 12$ _____ **14.** $y = x^3$ _____ **15.** $xy = 0$ _____

Properties Objective H: Determine the domain and the range of
a function defined by a table, a list of ordered pairs,
or a simple equation.

In 16–18, give the domain and the range of the function.

16. $\{(8, 4), (6, 3), (-12, -6), (21, 10.5), (0, 0)\}$

Domain _____ Range _____

17. m is a function of c.

c	0	1	-1	2	-2
m	1	2	2	5	5

Domain _____ Range _____

18. $y = \dfrac{x + 5}{x}$

Domain _____ Range _____

Uses Objective J: Evaluate functions to solve real-world problems.

19. The total surface area of a box is given by the formula
$S = 2(\ell w + \ell h + hw)$. How much gold foil is needed
to cover a brick 8 in. long, 3 in. wide, and 2 in. high? _____

20. John bought a boat with a down payment of $3,000 and
monthly payments of $150.

a. Write a formula for the amount paid p as a function
of the number of months n he has been paying. _____

b. Find the total paid for the boat if payments last
for 3 years. _____

21. The formula $S = m + \dfrac{m^2}{20}$ gives the stopping distances in

feet as a function of the car's speed m in miles per hour.
How far does a car traveling 60 mph skid before it stops? _____

22. Use the formula $V = e^3$ to find the volume of air in a
cube-shaped box with edges 15 centimeters long. _____

LESSON MASTER

1-3 B

Vocabulary

In 1–3, tell how each is read.

1. $f(n)$ _____

2. $A: x \to \dfrac{x^2}{10}$ _____

3. $S(y) = \dfrac{y^2}{8} + 5y + 17$ _____

Skills Objective B: Use function notation.

In 4–6, suppose $B(x) = x^2 - x$. Evaluate the function for the given value of x.

4. $B(4)$ _____

5. $B\left(\dfrac{1}{2}\right)$ _____

6. $B(-3)$ _____

In 7–9, use the description $H: x \to \dfrac{x^2 - 2x}{4}$.

Evaluate the function for the given value.

7. $H: 2 \to$ _____

8. $H: 4 \to$ _____

9. $H: 0 \to$ _____

10. If $g(y) = 3^y$ and $h(y) = y^3$, which is greater, $g(-1)$ or $h(-1)$? Justify your answer.

_____

11. At a speed s, the minimum distance $D(s)$ a car travels between the time a driver decides to stop and the time the car comes to a complete stop is given by the function $D(s) = s + \dfrac{s^2}{20}$.

   a. Complete the table.

Speed s of car (in mph)	10	20	30	40	50	60
Stopping distance $D(s)$ (in feet)						

   b. Determine the stopping distance for a car traveling 55 mph. Does this distance agree with the values you found in Part a? Why or why not?

_____

_____

   c. Find the stopping distance for a car traveling 70 mph. _____

► **LESSON MASTER 1-3 B** *page 2*

Uses Objective J: Use functions to solve real-world problems.

In 12–14, use the table below. $S(x)$ and $U(x)$ are the numbers
of successful space launches by the Soviet Union and the
United States, respectively, for the years 1980 through 1993.

	'80	'81	'82	'83	'84	'85	'86	'87	'88	'89	'90	'91	'92	'93
$S(x)$	89	98	101	98	97	97	91	95	90	74	75	59	54	47
$U(x)$	13	18	18	22	22	17	6	8	12	18	27	18	28	23

12. Describe what $U('87)$ represents.

_____

_____

13. **a.** Calculate $S('88) - U('88)$.   _____

b. What does your answer to Part a represent?

_____

_____

14. **a.** Calculate $\dfrac{U('89) - U('80)}{1989 - 1980}$.   _____

b. What does your answer to Part a represent?

_____

_____

_____

15. The cost of making a phone call from an airplane is $9.50
for the first three minutes, and $2.00 for each additional
minute or fraction thereof. Describe this function

a. using Euler's notation.   _____

b. using mapping notation.   _____

c. Find the cost of a phone call lasting
7 minutes 20 seconds.   _____

16. The cost for gas in Northwoods is $0.4685 per therm
for the first 50 therms and $0.3830 for each therm
thereafter. In addition, there is a customer charge of
$4. Find the amount charged for 105.76 therms.   _____

17. In Northwoods, electricity costs $0.10819 per kwh for
the first 400 kwh and $0.07093 for each kwh over 400.
Find the amount charged for 725 kwh of electricity.
Include a basic service charge of $9.06.   _____

LESSON MASTER 1-4 B

Vocabulary

1. State the *Vertical-Line Test for Functions*.

_____

_____

Uses Objective J: Use functions to solve real-world problems.

2. The graph at the right gives the estimated percent $C(y)$ of high-school seniors, by year y of graduation, who have ever used cigarettes.

   a. Estimate $C(1987)$.

   _____

   b. Estimate $C(1989) - C(1983)$. Tell what this number means.

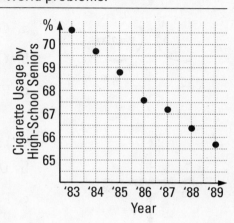

   _____

   _____

3. The table below gives the sources for electric power in the United States for the years 1980-1989. Amounts are given in billions of kilowatt-hours produced. Let y = the year, $C(y)$ the amount produced by coal that year, and $N(y)$ the amount by nuclear sources that year.

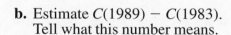

	1980	1981	1982	1983	1984	1985	1986	1987	1988	1989
Coal	1162	1203	1192	1259	1342	1402	1386	1464	1541	1551
Nuclear	251	273	283	294	328	384	414	455	527	529

   a. On the grid at the right, graph the points $(y, C(y))$ and $(y, N(y))$ and connect each set of points with a smooth curve.

   b. Which source for electricity shows a more rapid increase in usage? Use the table or your graph to justify your answer.

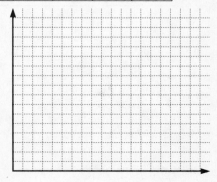

   _____

   _____

Name _____

▶ **LESSON MASTER 1-4 B** *page 2*

Representations Objective L: Determine the domain, the range,
and values of a function from its graph.

In 4–6, a function is graphed.

4.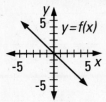

   a. Give its range. _____

   b. Give its domain. _____

   c. For what values
   of x is $f(x) = 0$? _____

5.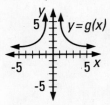

   a. Give its range. _____

   b. Give its domain. _____

   c. Find $g(-2)$. _____

6.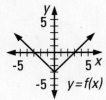

   a. Give its range. _____

   b. Give its domain. _____

   c. For what values
   of x is $f(x) = 1$? _____

Representations Objective M: Apply the Vertical-Line Test for a function.

**In 7–10, determine whether or not the graph
represents a function. How can you tell?**

7.

8.

_____

_____

9.

10.

_____

_____

8

LESSON MASTER  1-5 B

Skills Objective C: Solve and check linear equations.

In 1–12, solve and check the equation.

1. $\frac{1}{4}x = 32$

2. $\frac{3}{5}n - 4 = 56$

3. $25 = \frac{5}{6}(m + 1)$

_____

_____

_____

4. $24 = 1.2y$

5. $20 = \frac{5}{10c}$

6. $4n - (n - 1) = 7$

_____

_____

_____

7. $\frac{d}{4} + \frac{d}{6} = 5$

8. $\frac{1}{6}(60x + 24) = -x$

9. $5y + 42 = 3y + 60$

_____

_____

_____

10. $\frac{6}{F} = 0.2$

11. $8k - 5 = 5 - 8k$

12. $0.4(g - 20) - 0.2g = 36$

_____

_____

_____

13. If $f(q) = 8q - (3 + 4q)$, for what value of q
is $f(q) = 17$?

_____

14. Use the function g defined as $g(e) = \frac{2}{e} - 6$.

    a. Find $g(8)$. _____

    b. If $g(e) = -4$, find e. _____

Uses Objective K: Use linear equations to solve real-world problems.

15. A bag of mixed dried beans for soup contains $\frac{1}{8}$ pinto beans,

    $\frac{3}{8}$ white beans, $\frac{1}{4}$ kidney beans, and 8 ounces of navy beans.
Find the weight of the

    a. entire bag of mix. _____

    b. pinto beans. _____

    c. white beans. _____

    d. kidney beans. _____

16. How many bows each using two thirds of a yard
of ribbon can be made from 20 yards of ribbon?   _____

17. Nancy has 120 cm of wood molding to make a
picture frame. If she wants the frame to be twice as
long as it is wide, what should be the outside
dimensions of the frame?   _____

18. The total bill for a restaurant meal, including 8%
tax and 15% tip (both on only the cost of the meal),
was $9.84. What was the cost of the meal?   _____

19. When Pedro called Gary, the call cost $1.58. If the
rate for the call was 53¢ for the first three minutes
and 15¢ for each additional minute or fraction
thereof, how long did Pedro and Gary talk?   _____

20. Yuko needs materials for a felt banner. She needs a
half yard each of green and blue felt and 1 yard of
white felt. She also needs two wooden dowels at
$1.25 each and cord costing $4. If she has only $12
to spend, how much can she afford to spend per
yard for the felt?   _____

21. Maria wishes to invest in bonds which pay 6%
annual dividends. How much must she invest in
order to realize $2,120 at the end of the first year?   _____

22. After consecutive discounts of 10% and 20%, a
winter coat was sale-priced at $144. What was
the original price of the coat?   _____

LESSON MASTER

1-6
B

Questions on SPUR Objectives

Skills Objective D: Rewrite formulas.

In 1 and 2, use this information: The formula for the distance d an object falls during time t when it is dropped near the earth's surface is $d = \frac{1}{2}gt^2$.

1. What is the ratio of d to t^2? _____

2. Solve this formula for g. _____

3. The sum S of the measures of the angles of a polygon with n sides is $S = 180(n - 2)$. Solve for n. _____

4. Solve for n in the formula $t^2 = 8 - 2n$. _____

5. In the formula for the volume of a sphere,
   $V = \frac{4}{3}\pi r^3$, find the value for π. _____

In 6 and 7, use the formula $A = P + Prt$, which gives the total Amount A when a principal P is invested at a simple-interest rate r for a time of t years. The interest is represented by Prt.

6. Solve the formula for the principal P. _____

7. Solve the formula for the interest rate r. _____

8. The formula $A = P(1 + r)^t$ gives the amount A when a principal P is invested at a compound-interest rate r for a time of t years. Solve the formula for P. _____

9. The formula $C = \frac{5}{9}(F - 32)$ converts a temperature from degrees Fahrenheit to degrees Celsius. Solve for F. _____

10. A formula for the perimeter of a rectangle is $P = 2(\ell + w)$. Solve for w. _____

11. A formula for the area of a triangle is $A = \frac{1}{2}bh$. Solve the formula for the height h of the triangle. _____

12. A formula for the area of a trapezoid is $A = \dfrac{(a + b)h}{2}$.
    Solve the formula for the height h of the trapezoid. _____

► **LESSON MASTER 1-6 B** *page 2*

Uses Objective K: Use linear equations to solve real-word problems.

13. The volume of the Great Pyramid of Cheops in Giza, Egypt,

was about 2,559,900 m³. Use the formula $V = \frac{1}{3}Bh$ to

determine the original height of the pyramid if the area

of its base B was about 52,600 m³. _____

In 14 and 15, use the formulas from Items 6 and 7.

14. Cindy and Tony invested $5,000 at an annual rate
of 3.5%. Determine

    a. the amount of interest at the end of the first year. _____

    b. the total value at the end of the first year. _____

15. The annual rate of Cathy and Mike's investment was 4%.
If the total value of their investment at the end of one
year was $2,600, how much had they invested? _____

16. The temperature given on a bank thermometer was 25°C.

    a. Was this temperature above or below freezing? _____

    b. Give the temperature in degrees Fahrenheit.
    Refer to the formula in Item 9. _____

    c. Try to write a simple "rule of thumb" for estimating
    a Fahrenheit temperature when given a Celsius reading.

_____

_____

17. Young's formula, $C = \left(\frac{g}{g + 12}\right)A$, tells how much medicine C

to give a child of age g under age 13 when the adult dosage A
is known. If the dosage for a 12-year-old child is
600 mg, what is the dosage for someone 18 years old?_____

18. A pine-tree nursery plants each seedling in the center
of a square 4 m on each side. How many seedlings can
be planted in a rectangular field 200 m by 300 m? _____

19. A 4-cubic-foot bag of peat moss is in the shape of a
rectangular solid 32 in. long and 18 in. wide. How
high is a stack of 4 bags if they are stacked on their
largest sides? The formula for volume is $V = \ell wh$. _____

20. The building code for a ramp states that the ratio of
the horizontal distance d to the height h of the ramp
must be at least 12 to 1. How much horizontal
distance must be allowed for a ramp that accompanies
six 8-inch-high stairs? _____

LESSON MASTER **1-7** B

Vocabulary

1. Give an informal definition of the term *sequence*.

_____

_____

2. Consider the sequence 2, 3, 5, 6, 11, 13, 17, 19, ...

a. Tell how "$p_5 = 11$" is read. _____

b. Name the third term. _____

c. Give p_8. _____

Uses Objective E: Evaluate sequences.

3. a. Draw the next term in the following sequence of dots.

b. Give the number of dots in the first
five terms of the sequence in Part a.   _____

c. Predict the number of dots in the tenth
term of the sequence in Parts a and b.   _____

In 4–7, give the first four terms of the sequence.

4. $a_n = 4n - 6$ _____

5. $a_n = n^2 + 8$ _____

6. $a_n = 12n$ _____

7. $a_n = 2^n$ _____

8. Given $p_n = \dfrac{n^2 + n}{2}$, find p_6.   _____

9. Given $T_n = \dfrac{8n}{2n^2 - 1}$, find T_5.   _____

**In 10 and 11, *multiple choice*. Which is a formula
for the *n*th term of the sequence?**

10. 6, 10, 14, 18, 22, ...   _____

    (a) $6 + 4n$ (b) $6 + 4(n - 1)$ (c) $6 + (n - 1)^2$

11. 3, 12, 27, 48, 75, ...

    (a) $3n$ (b) $4n^2 - 1$ (c) $3n^2$ _____

▶ **LESSON MASTER 1-7 B** *page 2*

___

Uses Objective J: Use sequences to solve real-world problems.

___

12. Cary plans to read 3 books a month to help increase
    his reading speed. The sequence $b_n = 3n$ gives the
    number of books he will have read after n months.
    How many books will Cary have read in 8 months? _____

13. Juan, who weighs 110 pounds, plans to lose $1\frac{1}{2}$ pounds
    a week so that he can wrestle in the 103-pound weight class.
    Juan's weight n weeks after he begins his diet is
    $w_n = 110 - 1.5n$.

    a. If Juan diets for 8 weeks, what will he weigh? _____

    b. When should Juan stop dieting in order to
    wrestle at 103 pounds? _____

14. On Sidewalk Day, *Abigail's Designs* has a "sliding-scale"
    sale on all merchandise. At the end of each hour, prices
    are reduced 10%. This means that the sale price of a $100
    dress after hour h is given by $p_h = 100(0.9)^h$.

    a. Find the sale price of the $100 dress after
    4 hours. _____

    b. Find the sale price of a $55 skirt after 7 hours. _____

15. Beth Garcia's beginning annual salary at Dontel was $22,000. She
    was promised an increase of 4% at the end of each year. So,
    $S_n = 22,000(1.04)^{n-1}$ gives Beth's salary in her nth year.

    a. Find Beth's salary for her second year. _____

    b. At this rate, what would Beth's salary be in
    her tenth year with Dontel? _____

16. The number of feet traveled during each second of free fall
    is given by the formula $d_n = 16 + 32(n - 1)$. Suppose a stone
    is dropped from the top of Chicago's Sears Tower, which
    is 1454 feet high.

    a. How far will the stone travel during the
    eighth second? _____

    b. What is the total distance the stone will have
    traveled after eight seconds? _____

    c. How long will it take for the stone to hit
    the ground? _____

LESSON MASTER  1-8 B

Skills Objective E: Evaluate sequences.

1. The first two terms of a sequence are 2 and 2.
   Each term after the second is the sum of the
   previous two terms. Write the next 6 terms. _____

**In 2 and 3, give the first five terms of the sequence
defined by the recursive formula.**

2. The first term is 100. Each term after the
   first is one half of the previous term. _____

3. The first term is -1. Each term after the first
   is 1 more than the cube of the previous term. _____

**In 4–7, give the first six terms of the sequence defined by the
recursive formula. The formula is given for integers $n \geq 2$.**

4. $\begin{cases} s_1 = 5 \\ s_n = \boxed{\text{ANS}} + 6 \end{cases}$

5. $\begin{cases} a_1 = \text{-8} \\ a_n = \boxed{\text{ANS}} + 2 \end{cases}$

_____   _____

6. $\begin{cases} a_1 = 6 \\ a_n = 2 \cdot \boxed{\text{ANS}} \end{cases}$

7. $\begin{cases} t_1 = 1 \\ t_n = (\text{-1})^n \cdot \boxed{\text{ANS}} \end{cases}$

_____   _____

In 8 and 9, *multiple choice*.

8. The explicit formula $x_n = 3(4)^{n-1}$ gives the same _____
   sequence as which recursive formula for integers $n \geq 2$?

   (a) $\begin{cases} x_1 = 6 \\ x_n = 3 + 3 \cdot \boxed{\text{ANS}} \end{cases}$ (b) $\begin{cases} x_1 = 3 \\ x_n = 4 \cdot \boxed{\text{ANS}} \end{cases}$ (c) $\begin{cases} x_1 = 3 \\ x_n = 3 + 4 \cdot \boxed{\text{ANS}} \end{cases}$

9. Which is a recursive definition for the sequence of squares _____
   of integers 1, 4, 9, 16, 25, 36, . . . ?

   (a) $\begin{cases} s_1 = 1 \\ s_n = \boxed{\text{ANS}}^2, \\ \text{for integers } n \geq 2. \end{cases}$ (b) $\begin{cases} s_1 = 1 \\ s_n = \boxed{\text{ANS}} + 3, \\ \text{for integers } n \geq 2. \end{cases}$ (c) $\begin{cases} s_1 = 1 \\ s_n = \boxed{\text{ANS}} + 2n - 1, \\ \text{for integers } n \geq 2. \end{cases}$

▶ **LESSON MASTER 1-8 B** *page 2*

Skills   Objective F: Write a recursive definition for a sequence.

In 10–12, a sequence is given. Write a recursive definition a. in words and b. in symbols.

10. 891, 297, 99, 33, 11, . . .

a. _____   b. _____

_____

_____

11. 1, -5, -11, -17, -23, . . .

a. _____   b. _____

_____

_____

12. 5, 10, 20, 40, 80, . . .

a. _____   b. _____

_____

_____

Uses   Objective J: Use sequences to solve real-world problems.

13. Becky invested $5000 in a savings account that pays 4% compounded annually. She plans to withdraw $100 at the end of each year. The recursive formula at the right gives her account balance at the end of the *n*th year.

$$\begin{cases} B_0 = 5000 \\ B_n = 1.04 \cdot \boxed{\text{ANS}} - 100, \\ \quad \text{for integers } n \geq 1 \end{cases}$$

a. Give the account balance at the end of year 1.   _____

b. Give the account balance at the end of year 3.   _____

c. By how much will Becky's investment have increased after 5 years?   _____

14. Tim received $20 from his parents on his first birthday, $25 on his second birthday, $30 on his third birthday, and so on.

a. Write a recursive formula for this situation.

b. How much did Tim receive on his tenth birthday? _____

c. Find the total amount of money Tim's parents had given him for his ten birthdays.   _____

LESSON MASTER  1-9 B

Skills Objective E: Evaluate sequences.

In 1 and 2, give the first six terms of the sequence defined by the recursive formula.

1. The first term is -2. Each term after the first is -3 times the previous term. _____

2. The first term is $\frac{1}{1000}$. Each term after the first is ten times the previous term. _____

In 3-8, give the first six terms of the sequence defined by the recursive formula. The formula is given for integers $n \geq 2$.

3. $\begin{cases} a_1 = 5 \\ a_n = 3a_{n-1} \end{cases}$ 4. $\begin{cases} C_1 = 3 \\ C_n = 2C_{n-1} + 3 \end{cases}$

_____   _____

5. $\begin{cases} d_1 = -4 \\ d_n = 8 - d_{n-1} \end{cases}$ 6. $\begin{cases} e_1 = 2 \\ e_n = 1 \div e_{n-1} \end{cases}$

_____   _____

7. $\begin{cases} x_1 = 1 \\ x_n = 3x_{n-1} + 1 \end{cases}$ 8. $\begin{cases} m_1 = 3 \\ m_n = 3m_{n-1} \end{cases}$

_____   _____

In 9 and 10, a sequence is defined. Find the designated term.

9. $\begin{cases} P_1 = -3 \\ P_n = (-1)^{n-1} \cdot (3P_{n-1}) \end{cases}$ 10. $\begin{cases} t_1 = -2 \\ t_n = (t_{n-1})^2 - 6 \end{cases}$

$P_6 =$ _____ $t_5 =$ _____

▶ **LESSON MASTER 1-9 B** *page 2*

Skills Objective F: Write a recursive definition for a sequence.

In 11 and 12, write a recursive definition in symbols for the given sequence.

11. 3, 7, 15, 31, 63, . . .

12. 2, 8, 18, 32, 50, . . .

Uses Objective A

13. Jon opened a savings account when he received his first pay check. He started with a deposit of $50 and then deposited $20 each week.

   a. Write a recursive formula to describe this situation.

   b. How much had John deposited after 10 weeks? _____

14. Each year after he retired, Oscar Anderson sold two 20-acre parcels from his 400-acre farm for income.

   a. Write a recursive formula to describe this situation.

   b. How many acres were left after 5 years? _____

   c. In how many years will Oscar have fewer than 100 acres on his farm? _____

In 15–17, use this information: Sara Kim was offered two jobs with a starting salary of $20,000. NA Publishing promised a raise of at least 4.5% every year, and Gary Press promised annual raises of at least $1,000.

15. Write a recursive formula to describe the salary plan

   a. of NA Publishing.

   b. of Gary Press

16. After how many years would Sara's salary reach at least $25,000

   a. at NA Publishing? _____

   b. at Gary Press? _____

17. Which company's annual salary would be higher after 10 years? _____

LESSON MASTER  2-1 B

Vocabulary

In 1–3, use the direct variation equation $V = \frac{4}{3}\pi r^3$.

1. Identify the *constant of variation*. _____

2. Identify the *independent variable*. _____

3. Identify the *dependent variable*. _____

Skills Objective A: Translate direct-variation language into formulas and formulas into direct-variation language.

In 4–8, translate into a variation equation. Let k be the constant of variation.

4. a varies directly as the cube of b. _____

5. T is directly proportional to the fourth power of S. _____

6. The actual distance D between two towns is directly proportional to d, the distance between them on a map. _____

7. A person's weight w varies directly as the cube of his or her height h. _____

8. Real-estate taxes T are directly proportional to property value V. _____

9. Write the variation equation $y = kx^3$ in words.

_____

Skills Objective B: Solve direct-variation problems.

10. m is directly proportional to n. If $m = 48$ when $n = 12$, find m when $n = 3$. _____

11. y varies directly as the square of x. If $y = 63$ when $x = 3$, find y when $x = 9$. _____

12. s varies directly as g^4, and $s = 64$ when $g = 2$.

    a. Find the constant of variation k.   **b.** Find s when $g = 3$.

    _____   _____

13. c varies directly as the cube of d, and $c = 32$ when $d = 4$.

    a. Find the constant of variation k.   **b.** Find c when $d = 5$.

    _____   _____

▶ **LESSON MASTER** 2-1B *page 2*

Uses Objective F: Recognize direct-variation situations.

In 14–16, translate into a variation situation.

14. The price p of a pizza varies directly as the square
    of its diameter d.   _____

15. The rebate r is directly proportional to the
    number n of coupons submitted.   _____

16. The volume V of a spherical helium balloon is
    directly proportional to the cube of its radius r.   _____

Uses Objective G: Solve real-world problems involving direct variation.

17. When lightning strikes 8 miles away, the sound of
    the thunder is heard about 40 seconds later. The
    time it takes for the sound to travel is directly
    proportional to the distance. How long does it take
    the sound to travel if lightning strikes 6 miles away? _____

18. The distance a car travels before stopping after the
    driver brakes varies directly as the square of the speed
    of the car. If a car travels 30 feet after the driver
    brakes when the car's speed is 20 mph, how far will
    the car travel after the driver brakes if the car's speed
    is 60 mph?   _____

19. The designers of the Parthenon, a Greek temple
    completed in 432 B.C., utilized the golden ratio. The
    outline of its face fits into a golden rectangle, in which
    the length varies directly as its height in the ratio 1.618
    to 1. The length of the temple was about 31 m. What
    was the original height of the Parthenon?   _____

22. The rear wheel of a 5-speed bicycle turns 770 times in a
    mile. The table below lists the number of pedal turns
    for rear-wheel turns in each gear. The number of rear-
    wheel turns in each gear is directly proportional to
    the number of pedal turns.

Gear	First	Second	Third	Fourth	Fifth
Pedal turns	9	4	1	3	5
Rear-wheel turns	14	7	2	7	14

How many times must a person pedal in a mile in each gear?

a. First _____   **b.** Second _____   **c.** Third _____

d. Fourth _____   **e.** Fifth _____

LESSON MASTER 2-2 B

Skills Objective A: Translate inverse-variation language into formulas and formulas into inverse-variation language.

In 1–6, translate into a variation equation.

1. P varies inversely with d. _____

2. e is inversely proportional to the cube of g. _____

3. m varies inversely with n^2. _____

4. The number n of baseballs that can fit into a carton is inversely proportional to the cube of a baseball's radius r. _____

5. The number of hours h it takes to travel a given distance varies inversely with the speed s of a car. _____

6. The weight W of a body varies inversely with the square of its distance d from the center of the earth. _____

Skills Objective B: Solve inverse-variation problems.

7. a is inversely proportional to b. If $a = \frac{1}{4}$ when $b = 2$, find a when $b = \frac{1}{2}$. _____

8. y varies inversely as the square of v. If $y = 4$ when $v = -4$, find y when $v = 8$. _____

9. m varies inversely as the cube of n. If $m = -2$ when $n = -5$, find m when $n = -2.5$. _____

Uses Objective F: Recognize inverse-variation situations.

In 10–15, complete with "directly," "inversely," or "neither directly nor inversely."

10. The weight of a magazine varies __?__ as the number of pages it contains. _____

11. The speed of a horse varies __?__ as the time it takes the horse to travel a given distance. _____

12. The temperature in Chicago varies __?__ with the number of the month of the year. _____

13. The number of tiles it takes to tile a floor varies __?__ as the area of the tiles. _____

▶ **LESSON MASTER 2-2B** *page 2*

14. The distance needed to stop a moving vehicle
varies ___?___ as the speed of the vehicle.   _____

15. The amount of sunlight at a given time varies   _____
___?___ as the time of day.

Uses Objective G: Solve real-world problems involving inverse variation.

16. The number *n* of square tiles needed to tile a floor
varies inversely as the square of the length *s* of a side
of each tile. If it takes 180 tiles with 6-in. sides to tile
a floor, how many tiles with 9-in. sides will it take to
tile the same floor?   _____

17. The number *n* of citrus fruit that fit into a carton varies
inversely as the cube of the diameter *d* of each fruit. A
carton that holds 12 grapefruit with diameter 15 cm
holds how many tangerines with diameter 5 cm?   _____

18. A lever is a simple machine which can
be used to raise a weight at one end of
a bar by pushing down at the other end
of the bar. The diagram at the right shows
how a 3-foot-long crowbar is used to pry
an 80-pound boulder out of the ground.
Recall that the weight needed to balance a
lever is inversely proportional to the
distance of the weight from the fulcrum.

a. If the fulcrum is 2 feet from the boulder, how
much weight must be exerted at the other end
of the bar to raise the boulder?   _____

b. Where could the fulcrum be placed in order for
the lever to be more efficient? Justify your answer.

_____

_____

19. It takes 4 workers 6 hours to pick the strawberries in a field.

a. How many hours would it take 6 workers to
pick the strawberries in the same field?   _____

b. What is the constant of variation, and what
does it represent?

_____

_____

LESSON MASTER 2-3 B

Vocabulary

1. If y varies directly as x and x is multiplied by c, then y is multiplied by ___?___ .

   _____

2. If y varies inversely as x^n and x is multiplied by a nonzero constant c, then y is ___?___ by c^n.

   _____

Properties Objective D: Use the Fundamental Theorem of Variation.

In 3–6, suppose that in a variation problem the value of x is doubled. How is the value of y changed

3. if y varies directly as x^3?   _____

4. if y varies directly as x^4?   _____

5. if y varies inversely as x^2?   _____

6. if y varies inversely as $\sqrt{x}$?   _____

In 7–9, suppose that a varies directly as the fourth power of b. How does the value of a change if

7. b is doubled?   _____

8. b is multiplied by 5?   _____

9. b is multiplied by $\frac{1}{4}$?   _____

In 10–12, suppose that m varies inversely as the square root of n. How does the value of m change if

10. n is doubled?   _____

11. n is multiplied by 4?   _____

12. n is multiplied by $\frac{1}{9}$?   _____

In 13–15, tell what effect multiplying the x-values by $\frac{1}{3}$ has on the y values.

13. $y = 5x$ _____

14. $y = 4x^2$ _____

15. $y = \dfrac{8}{x}$ _____

Review Previous course

In 16–21, graph the equation.

16. $4x + 3y = 24$

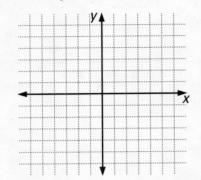

17. $y = \frac{1}{2}x + 6$

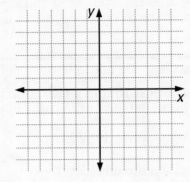

18. $xy = 12$

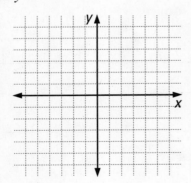

19. $y = x^2$

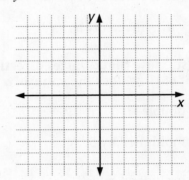

20. $y = 2^x$

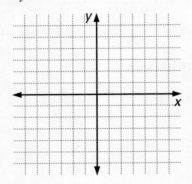

21. $y = \frac{1}{x}$

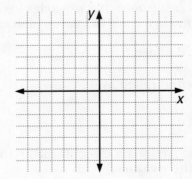

LESSON MASTER 2-4 B

Questions on SPUR Objectives

Vocabulary

1. *Slope* measures the ___?___ of a line.

   _____

2. *Multiple choice.* Tell which of the following
   is *not* a definition of slope.

   _____

   (a) the rate of change of
   y with respect to x

   (b) $\dfrac{\text{change in vertical distance}}{\text{change in horizontal distance}}$

   (c) $\dfrac{\text{change in independent variable}}{\text{change in dependent variable}}$

   (d) $\dfrac{\text{rise}}{\text{run}}$

Skills Objective C: Find slopes.

In 3–5 find the slope of the line through the given points.

3. $(5, -2), (3, 8)$ 4. $(-9, 2), (-4, 0)$ 5. $(12, 8), (6, -3)$

   _____   _____   _____

6. Find the slope of each line
   graphed at the right.

   a. _____

   b. _____

   c. _____

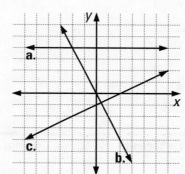

Representations Objective E: Identify properties of variation functions.

**In 7–9, give the slope of the line which is the
graph of the equation.**

7. $y = -7x$ _____   8. $y = \frac{1}{2}x$ _____   9. $y = 0.2x$ _____

Uses Objective I: Graph variation equations

In 10–13, graph the equation.

10. $y = -2x$

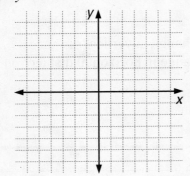

11. $y = \frac{1}{4}x$

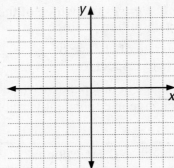

12. $y = 1.5x$

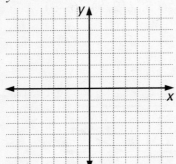

13. $y = 3x$

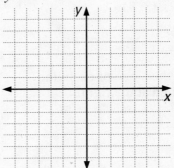

Representations Objective J: Identify variation equations from their graphs.

14. Match each graph with its equation. The axes have the same scale.

   i. $y = 5x$ ii. $y = -5x$ iii. $y = \frac{3}{4}x$ iv. $y = -\frac{3}{4}x$

a. _____

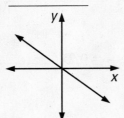

b. _____

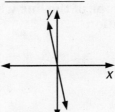

c. _____

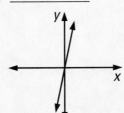

d. _____

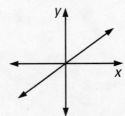

LESSON MASTER 2-5 B

Questions on SPUR Objectives

Vocabulary

1. A graph *symmetric* to the y-axis coincides
   with its ___?___ image over the y-axis.   _____

2. *Multiple choice.* The graph of which equation is a *parabola*?   _____

   (a) $y = x^3$ (b) $y = 2^x$ (c) $y = 2x^2$

Skills Objective C: Find rates of change.

In 3 and 4, $y = 6x^2$.

3. Find the rate of change between $x = 2$ and $x = 5$.   _____

4. Find the rate of change between $x = -2$ and $x = 2$.   _____

In 5 and 6, $y = -2x^2$.

5. Find the rate of change between $x = 4$ and $x = 6$.   _____

6. Find the rate of change between $x = 6$ and $x = 8$.   _____

Properties Objective E: Identify properties of graphs of functions with equations of the form $y = kx^2$.

In 7–9, refer to the following equations.

   (a) $y = -4x$ (b) $y = \frac{1}{4}x$ (c) $y = -4x^2$ (d) $y = \frac{1}{4}x^2$

7. Which equations have a graph which is a parabola?   _____

8. Which equations have a graph which is symmetric
   with respect to the y-axis?   _____

9. Which equations have a straight-line graph?   _____

Uses Objective I: Graph equations of the form $y = kx^2$.

In 10 and 11, graph the equations on the same grid. Label the graphs.

10. **a.** $y = 5x^2$ **b.** $y = -5x^2$ 11. **a.** $y = \frac{1}{2}x^2$ **b.** $y = -\frac{1}{2}x^2$

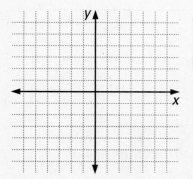   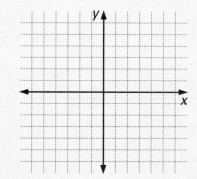

Representations Objective J: Identify variation equations from
their graphs.

---

12. Match each graph with its equation. Axes have the same scale.

   i. $y = -3x$ ii. $y = \frac{1}{3}x^2$ iii. $y = 3x^2$ iv. $y = -\frac{1}{3}x^2$

   a. _____   **b.** _____   **c.** _____

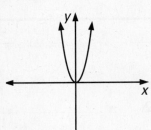 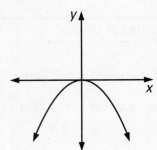 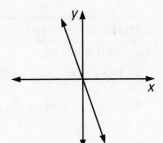

Representations Objective K: Recognize the effects of a change
in scale or viewing window on a graph of a
variation equation.

---

13. In the graph of $y = kx^2$ shown at the right,
   what type of number is k?

   _____

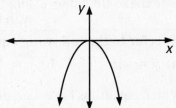

14. **a.** Sketch the graph of $y = 2x + 1$
   on the window at the right.

   b. Sketch the graph of $y = 2x + 1$ on
   the second window at the right.

   c. Does the slope of the line
   $y = 2x + 1$ change when the
   viewing window is changed?
   Explain your answer.

   _____

   _____

   _____

   _____

a.

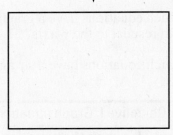

$-2 \leq x \leq 2$, x-scale = 1
$-5 \leq y \leq 5$, y-scale = 1

b.

$-2 \leq x \leq 2$, x-scale = 1
$-10 \leq y \leq 10$, y-scale = 1

LESSON MASTER 2-6 B

Vocabulary

1. *Multiple choice.* Which is an equation for a *hyperbola?* _____
   (a) $y = \dfrac{2}{x}$ (b) $y = \dfrac{x}{2}$ (c) $y = 2x$ (d) $y = \dfrac{2}{x^2}$

2. The parts of a hyperbola are called ___?___.   _____

3. Name the *asymptotes* of the graph of $\dfrac{2}{x^2}$.   _____

Skills Objective C: Find rates of change.

In 4–7, find the rate of change between -2 and 2.

4. $y = \dfrac{8}{x}$ _____

5. $y = \dfrac{8}{x^2}$ _____

6. $y = -\dfrac{8}{x}$ _____

7. $y = -\dfrac{8}{x^2}$ _____

Properties Objective E: Identify properties of variation functions.

8. *True or false* Graphs of all variation functions
   pass through the point (0, 0).   _____

In 9–12, refer to these equations.
   (a) $y = kx$ (b) $y = \dfrac{k}{x}$ (c) $y = kx^2$ (d) $y = \dfrac{k}{x^2}$

9. Which graphs have exactly one line of symmetry?   _____

10. Which graphs have more than one part?   _____

11. When $k < 0$, which graphs have points in the
    fourth quadrant?   _____

12. When $k > 0$, which graphs have points in the
    third quadrant?   _____

▶ **LESSON MASTER 2-6B** *page 2*

Uses Objective I: Graph inverse-linear variation and inverse-square variation equations.

In 13–16, graph the equation.

13. $y = \dfrac{8}{x}$

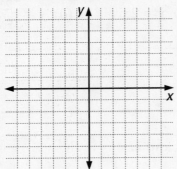

14. $y = -\dfrac{8}{x}$

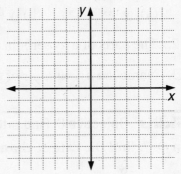

15. $y = \dfrac{8}{x^2}$

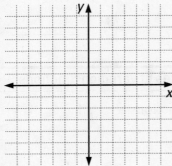

16. $y = -\dfrac{8}{x^2}$

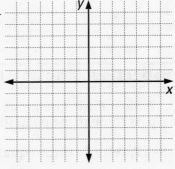

Representations Objective J: Identify inverse-linear and inverse-square functions from their graphs.

In 17–19, *multiple choice*. Choose the equation whose graph is most like that shown. Assume that the axes have the same scale.

17. _____

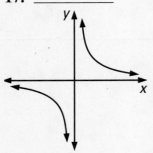

(a) $y = -\dfrac{3}{x}$

(b) $y = 3x^2$

(c) $y = -\dfrac{3}{x^2}$

(d) $y = \dfrac{3}{x}$

18. _____

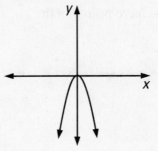

(a) $y = 2x^2$

(b) $y = -2x^2$

(c) $y = \dfrac{2}{x^2}$

(d) $y = \dfrac{2}{x}$

19. _____

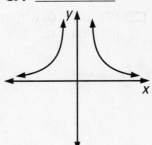

(a) $y = \dfrac{7}{x^2}$

(b) $y = -7x^2$

(c) $y = -\dfrac{7}{x^2}$

(d) $y = 7x^2$

LESSON MASTER

2-7
B

Uses Objective H: Fit an appropriate variation model to data.

In 1 and 2, *multiple choice.* **Tell which equation is the best model for the graph shown at the left.**

1.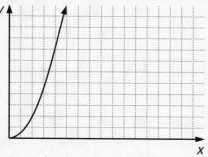

   (a) $y = kx$ _____

   (b) $y = kx^2$

   (c) $y = \dfrac{k}{x}$

   (d) $y = \dfrac{k}{x^2}$

2.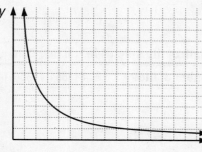

   (a) $y = kx$ _____

   (b) $y = kx^2$

   (c) $y = \dfrac{k}{x}$

   (d) $y = \dfrac{k}{x^2}$

In 3–6, **do steps a through d.**
  a. **Draw a graph to represent the situation.**
  b. **Write a general variation equation for the situation.**
  c. **Find the value of the constant of variation and rewrite the variation equation.**
  d. **Answer the question in the problem.**

3. The amount of force needed to loosen a certain bolt is related to the length of a wrench as given in the table.

Force needed (lb)	3	7	10	15	30
Length of wrench (in.)	630	270	189	126	63

How many pounds of force would be needed to loosen the same bolt with a 21-inch wrench?

a.

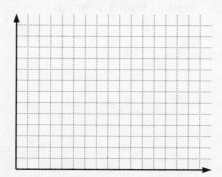

b. _____

c. _____

d. _____

4. While studying gears, a physics class collected the data in the table relating the number of teeth in a gear and the speed of the gear in revolutions per minute. What would be the speed of a gear with 30 teeth?

Number of teeth	10	12	18	24	36
Speed (rpm)	108	90	60	45	30

a.

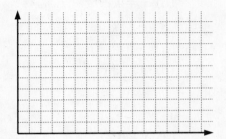

b. _____

c. _____

d. _____

5. The table to the right gives the number of square tiles of various sizes needed to floor a small restaurant kitchen. How many square tiles with 8-in. sides would be needed?

Length of tile side	4 in.	6 in.	9 in.	12 in.
Number of tiles	1944	864	384	216

a.

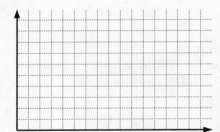

b. _____

c. _____

d. _____

6. A packaging specialist studied the weights of 100 ball bearings of various diameters. The data are in the table.

Diameter of bearing (mm)	3	4	5	6	7	8
Weight of 100 bearings (grams)	12	28	54	93	147	220

What would be the weight of 100 ball bearings with 10-mm diameters?

a.

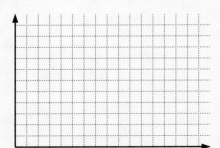

b. _____

c. _____

d. _____

Name _____

LESSON MASTER

2-8 B

Vocabulary

1. If multiplying every x-value of a function by c results in multiplying the corresponding y-value by c^n, then y varies ___?___ as the ___?___ power of x.

_____ _____

2. If multiplying every x-value of a function by c results in dividing the corresponding y-value by c^n, then y varies ___?___ as the ___?___ power of x.

_____ _____

Uses Objective H: Fit an appropriate variation model to data.

In 3 and 4, select the equation that could model the relationship shown in the graphs.

3.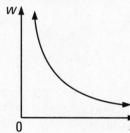

(a) $w = \dfrac{kr}{v}$ _____

(b) $w = \dfrac{kv}{r}$

(c) $w = kvr^2$

(d) $w = \dfrac{kv^2}{r}$

4.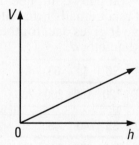

(a) $V = \dfrac{kh}{r^2}$ _____

(b) $V = krh^2$

(c) $V = krh$

(d) $V = kr^2h$

5. A social scientist found a relationship between the average daily number of phone calls C between Unicity and other cities. The left graph displays data relating phone calls and the population P of the cities in millions. The right graph displays data relating phone calls and the distance D in miles between Unicity and the other cities.

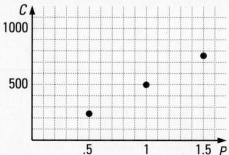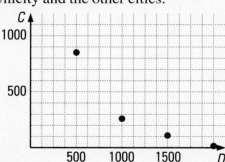

Write an equation relating C, P, and D.
Do *not* find the constant of variation.

_____

6. The Transportation Department studied the length of time traffic was halted as freight trains traveled across a road. The data in Table I relate speed *s* of a 100-car train to time *T*. The data in Table II relate length *ℓ* of a train traveling at 40 mph with time *T*.

I.
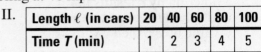

Speed *s* (mph)	20	30	40	50	60
Time *T* (min)	10	7	5	4	3

II.

Length *ℓ* (in cars)	20	40	60	80	100
Time *T* (min)	1	2	3	4	5

a. Graph the points from Table I.   **c.** Graph the points from Table II.

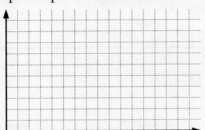   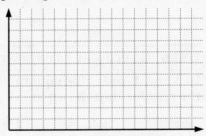

b. How does *T* vary with *S*?   **d.** How does *T* vary with *ℓ*?

_____   _____

e. Write an equation relating *T*, *S*, and *ℓ*. Do *not* find the constant of variation.   _____

7. A packaging specialist for a toy company compiled the following data. Table I gives the data for the number of racquetballs *r* that fit in 30-cm-diameter cylindrical cans of height *h*. Table II gives data for the number of racquetballs *r* that fit in cans 48 cm high with diameter *d*.

I.

Height of can *h* (cm)	30	36	48	60	84
Number of racquetballs *r*	100	120	160	200	280

II.

Diameter of can *d* (cm)	30	35	40	45	50
Number of racquetballs *r*	160	210	270	340	425

a. Graph the points from Table I.   **c.** Graph the points from Table II.

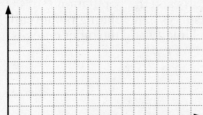   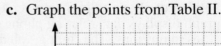

b. How does *r* vary with *h*?   **d.** How does *r* vary with *d*?

_____   _____

e. Write an equation relating *r*, *h*, and *d*. Do *not* find the constant of variation.   _____

LESSON MASTER 2-9 B

Skills Objective A: Translate joint- and combined-variation language into formulas and formulas into joint- and combined-variation language.

In 1–5, translate into a variation equation.

1. The area A of an ellipse varies jointly as its major semiaxis b and its minor semiaxis h. _____

2. The cost C of a square oak butcher block varies jointly as its thickness t and the square of a side s. _____

3. The load L which will buckle a column is inversely proportional to the square of its length ℓ and directly proportional to the fourth power of its radius r. _____

4. In the middle 1800s, the French scientist J. L. Poiseuille found that the rate r at which a fluid flows through a small tube varies directly with the product of the pressure p acting on the fluid and the fourth power of the diameter d of the tube. _____

5. The speed S of a 10-speed bike varies directly with the number of revolutions r per minute, directly with the number f of teeth on the front sprocket, and inversely with the number b of teeth on the back sprocket. _____

6. In the formula $A = \pi ab$, A varies __?__ as __?__ and __?__.

_____ _____ _____

7. If $g = \dfrac{2d}{t^2}$, g varies __?__ as __?__, and __?__ as __?__.

_____ _____ _____

Skills Objective B: Solve problems involving joint or combined variation.

8. a varies directly as b and inversely as the square of c. When $b = -8$ and $c = 2$, $a = -6$.

   a. Find a when $b = 4$ and $c = -2$. _____

   b. Give the constant of variation. _____

9. m varies jointly as n and the cube of p. When $n = 3$ and $p = -2$, $m = -48$.

   a. Find m when $n = -4$ and $p = 5$. _____

   b. Give the constant of variation. _____

Uses Objective G: Solve real-world problems involving joint or combined variation.

10. The wind force F on a sail varies jointly as the area A of the sail and the square of the wind speed W. The force on a sail with area 500 ft^2 is 100 pounds when the wind speed is 20 mph.

   a. What would the force be with a 30-mph wind? _____

   b. What would the force be if the sail is a triangle 20 ft high and 20 ft at the base and the wind speed is 40 mph? _____

In 11 and 12, use this information: The speed s at which water flows through a pipe is directly proportional to the pressure p exerted by a pump and the fourth power of the radius r.

11. What effect will lime deposits on the inside of a pipe have on the speed of the water, if the pressure remains constant? _____

12. If the speed of the water through a 2.5-cm-radius pipe is 600 cm per second when the pressure is 4 kg per cm^2,

   a. what would be the speed if the pressure is doubled? _____

   b. what would be the speed if the radius is 5 cm? _____

13. Bridge columns of a new material are 10 in. in diameter and 10 ft high. These columns are able to support up to 40 tons without collapsing. The weight w that collapses a column varies directly as the fourth power of its diameter d and inversely as the square of its height h. Give the maximum weight each column of this material with the given dimensions can support.

   a. diameter, 20 in.; height, 10 ft _____

   b. diameter, 10 in.; height, 20 ft _____

   c. diameter, 20 in.; height, 20 ft _____

Review Previous course.

In 14–16, solve the system of equations.

14. $\begin{cases} 10y - 20x = 20 \\ 4y + 2x = 28 \end{cases}$

15. $\begin{cases} 3a + 2c = -9 \\ 9a - c = 57 \end{cases}$

16. $\begin{cases} 10x + 2y = 60 \\ 3x - 4y = 41 \end{cases}$

_____   _____   _____

LESSON MASTER 3-1 B

Vocabulary

1. A function with an equation of the form $y = mx + b$ is a __?__ function. _____

2. Give an example of a *constant-decrease* situation.

_____

_____

Skills Objective A: Determine the slope and y-intercept of a line given its equation.

In 3–9, complete the table.

	Equation	Slope	y-intercept
3.	$y = -3x + 8$		
4.	$y = \frac{4}{5}x - 1$		
5.	$y = 6x$		
6.		1	2
7.	$y = \frac{8}{3}x + \frac{2}{3}$		
8.	$y = ax + k$		
9.		d	0

Properties Objective E: Recognize properties of linear functions.

In 10–12, x is the independent variable, y is the dependent variable, and $y = mx + b$.

10. In a constant increase situation, is m positive, negative, or equal to zero? _____

11. In a constant decrease situation, is m positive, negative, or equal to zero? _____

12. The initial value of the independent variable occurs when $x =$ __?__ and $y =$ __?__. _____ _____

Uses Objective G: Model constant-increase or constant-decrease situations.

13. Mr. Reyes bought 100 coffee filters. On the average,
he uses 5 per week. Write an equation relating the
number of filters *f* left after *w* weeks.   _____

14. Lynn has 42 computer magazines. She adds two more each month.

   a. Write an equation relating the number of
   magazines *c* Lynn has after *m* months.   _____

   b. How many magazines are there after 6 months?   _____

   c. After 2 years, will Lynn have 100 computer
   magazines? Why or why not?   _____

   _____

Uses Objective K: Model situations leading to
                piecewise-linear functions.

---

15. Graph this situation. Ai's
temperature at 4:00 P.M. was
99.5°F. It rose at a steady rate
of 0.3°F per hour for 6 hours.
It then stayed constant for 4
hours, and then steadily fell
0.4°F per hour for 4 hours.

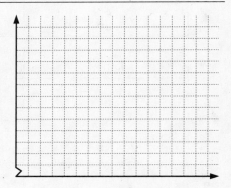

Representations Objective M: Graph or interpret graphs of
                        piecewise-linear functions.

---

16. Refer to the graph below. Max walked to the library
where he studied for awhile and then walked home.

   a. How long did Max
   stay at the library?   _____

   b. Find Max's speed in
   blocks per hour on his
   way to the library.   _____

   c. Find the total
   distance Max walked.   _____

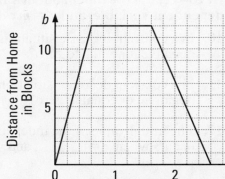

LESSON MASTER 3-2 B

Skills Objective A: Determine the slope and y-intercept of a line given its equation.

In 1–8, complete the table.

	Equation	Slope	y-intercept
1.	$y = 9x + 5$		
2.		$\frac{3}{8}$	-2
3.	$y = 7x$		
4.	$y = 18$		
5.	$2x + 5y = 12$		
6.	$3x - y = 16$		
7.	$6y = 3x - 4$		
8.	$y + 6 = 0$		

Skills Objective B: Find an equation for a line given a point on it and its slope.

9. Find an equation for the line with slope -6 and y-intercept 9. _____

10. Find an equation for the line with slope $\frac{7}{4}$ and y-intercept -3. _____

11. Find an equation for the horizontal line through $(5, -5)$. _____

12. Find an equation for the line with slope -1 and y-intercept 0. _____

13. Find an equation for the line with y-intercept -3 that is parallel to $y = -1.5x + 4$. _____

14. Find an equation for the line with y-intercept 0 that is parallel to $y = 2x - 5$. _____

▶ **LESSON MASTER 3-2B** *page 2*

Properties Objective E: Recognize properties of linear functions.

15. As you move one unit to the right on the line, it rises 6 units. What is the slope of the line? _____

16. As you move one unit to the right on the line, it drops 2 units. What is the slope of the line? _____

17. As you move three units to the right on the line, it rises 2 units. What is the slope of the line? _____

18. As a line changes one unit horizontally, it changes $-\frac{2}{5}$ units vertically. What is the slope of the line? _____

19. What are the domain and the range of the function f when $f(x) = 6$?

    domain _____ range _____

Representations Objective L: Graph or interpret graphs of linear equations.

In 20–23, graph the line described.

20. $y = -x + 4$

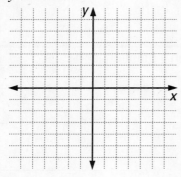

21. slope $= \frac{3}{2}$ and y-intercept $= -3$

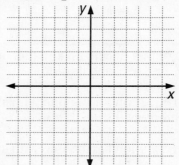

22. $5x + 3y = 12$

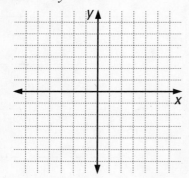

23. y-intercept 2; parallel to $y = \frac{1}{2}x - 20$

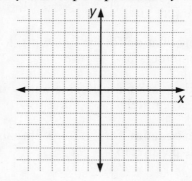

LESSON MASTER  3-3 B

Vocabulary

1. Write an expression that is a *linear combination* of *G* and *H*.

   _____

Uses Objective H: Model situations leading to linear combinations.

2. On a quiz show, 20 points are given for correct answers to regular questions, and 50 points are given for correct answers in the bonus round. Let *R* represent the number of regular questions answered correctly and *B* represent the number of bonus questions answered correctly.

   a. Write an expression that gives the total number of points earned.   _____

   b. Suppose a contestant earned 650 points. Write an equation relating *R*, *B*, and the number of points earned.   _____

   c. Give three different possible solutions to the equation you wrote in Part b.

   _____

   d. If the contestant answered 25 regular questions correctly and earned 650 points, how many bonus questions were answered correctly?   _____

3. Helene bought *S* 60-minute audio tapes at $1.99 each and *L* 90-minute tapes at $2.99 each.

   a. Write an expression that gives the total amount Helene paid for the tapes.   _____

   b. Suppose Helene spent $33.87 and bought 8 90-minute tapes. How many 60-minute tapes did she buy?   _____

4. A chemist mixes *x* ounces of a solution that is 40% acid with *y* ounces of a solution that is 60% acid. The final solution contains 24 ounces of acid.

   a. Write an equation to model this situation. _____

   b. At the right, graph the solutions to the equation in Part a.

   c. Find three pairs of integer values for *x* and *y* that satisfy the equation in Part a.

   _____

   _____

   _____

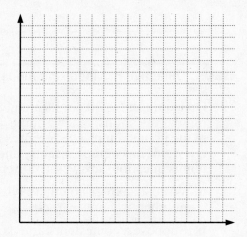

   d. If 10.5 ounces of the 40%-acid solution were used, how much of the 60%-acid is in the final solution? _____

5. Describe a situation that can lead to the expression 8.49*J* + 12.09*K*.

   _____

   _____

   _____

Review Objective C, Lesson 2–4

In 6–13, write the slope of the line containing the given points.

6. (3, 4), (6, -2) _____   **7.** (7, -4), (-1, 0) _____

8. (0, 0), (2, 3) _____   **9.** $(0, \frac{16}{3})$, (1, 4) _____

10. (2, -4.5), (1.5, -4) _____   **11.** (-5, 3), (-5, 2) _____

12. (-1, 8), (6, 8) _____   **13.** (50, 125), (100, 375) _____

LESSON MASTER 3-4 B

Vocabulary

1. Write the *standard form* of a linear equation. _____

2. Describe the *x-intercept* of a graph.

_____

_____

Skills Objective A: Determine the slope and intercepts of a line given its equation

In 3–9, complete the table.

	Equation	Slope	*y*-intercept	*x*-intercept
3.	$3x + 6y = 18$			
4.		0.25	-2.5	
5.	$-5y = 20$			
6.			none	-7
7.	$2x - 9y - 45 = 0$			
8.	$2x = -25$			
9.	$Ax + By = C,$ $A \neq 0, B \neq 0$			

Properties Objective E: Recognize properties of linear functions.

10. Describe the values of the slope of

   a. a horizontal line. _____

   b. a vertical line. _____

   c. an oblique line. _____

_____

▶ **LESSON MASTER 3-4B** *page 2*

In 11–14, determine whether the line with the given equation is *oblique*, *horizontal*, or *vertical*.

11. $y = -9x$ _____

12. $3y = 15$ _____

13. $x - 7y = 10$ _____

14. $-4x = 2$ _____

Representations Objective L: Graph or interpret graphs of linear equations.

15. Graph $x = -3$

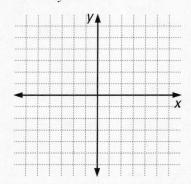

16. Graph $8y = 40$.

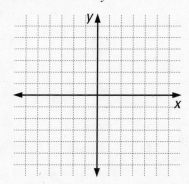

In 17 and 18, use the intercepts to graph the equation.

17. $3x + 5y = -15$

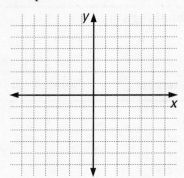

18. $28 = 14x - 7y$

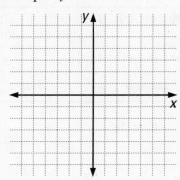

In 19–21, graph a line with the given slope.

19. zero

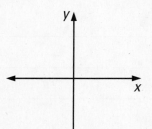

20. undefined

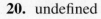

21. negative

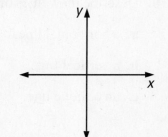

LESSON MASTER  3-5 B

Vocabulary

1. Give the general form of a *point-slope equation* for a line.

   _____

   _____

Skills Objective B: Find an equation for a line given two points on it
or given a point on it and its slope.

**In 2–13, find an equation for the line with the given
information. Write your equation in standard form with
integers for A, B, and C.**

2. slope -1, through (4, -3)   _____

3. slope $\frac{5}{4}$, through (6, 1)   _____

4. through (1, 4) and (-2, -2)   _____

5. through (1, 8) and (9, 8)   _____

6. slope -4, y-intercept 6   _____

7. slope 3, x-intercept -7   _____

8. through (-3, 2) and (-3, 0)   _____

9. slope -3, through (0, 0)   _____

10. x-intercept 2, y-intercept 5   _____

11. through (-4, 1) parallel to $4x + 2y = 7$ _____

12. through (6, 6) with undefined slope.   _____

13. x-intercept 12, parallel to $x - 6y = 10$ _____

Properties Objective E: Recognize properties of linear functions.

---

14. Fill in the three blanks with the correct values. According to
    the Point-Slope Theorem, the line containing (4, -5) with
    slope 2 has equation $y -$ ___?___ $=$ ___?___ $(x-$ ___?___).

    _____   _____   _____

15. *True or false*. The y-axis has a slope of zero.
    Justify your answer.

    _____

    _____

► **LESSON MASTER 3-5B** *page 2*

Uses Objective I: In a real-world context, find an equation for a line
containing two points.

---

16. Card Carriers charges $36 to print 1,200 business cards and
$56 for 2,700 cards. Assume the relationship between the
price and the number of business cards is linear.

   a. Write an equation giving price as a function
of the number of cards printed.   _____

   b. Find the set-up cost (the cost for printing
0 cards).   _____

   c. Find the cost of printing 6,000 cards.   _____

17. Last week, Mr. Chinn sold $20,000 worth of newspaper
advertisements and earned $800. The week before, he sold
$26,000 worth of advertisements and earned $860. Assume
the relationship between Mr. Chinn's weekly earnings and the
value of the advertisements he sells is linear.

   a. Write an equation giving Mr. Chinn's weekly
earnings as a function of the value of the
advertisements he sells.   _____

   b. In this situation, what do the slope and y-intercept mean?

       _____

       _____

   c. If in one week Mr. Chinn sells $30,000 worth
of advertisements, how much will he earn?   _____

Uses Objective K: Model situations leading to piecewise-linear functions.

---

18. Northstreet Disposal Company charges $30 to send out a
truck to pick up debris. For the first 5 cubic yards of rubbish,
the company charges an additional $10 per cubic yard. For
each additional cubic yard, to a maximum of 45 cubic yards,
the company charges $6.

   a. What is the cost to have the following amount of rubbish removed?

     3 cu yd _____   6 cu yd _____

     30 cu yd _____   45 cu yd _____

   b. Write an equation that gives the cost c for picking up y
cubic yards of rubbish for the following values of y.

     $0 \le y \le 5$ _____ $5 \le y \le 45$ _____

LESSON MASTER 3-6 B

Vocabulary

1. a. What is the range of *r*, the *correlation coefficient* for a set of data? _____

b. Suppose *r* = -0.9 for a line fit to a set of data. What does this tell you about the strength of the linear relationship between the variables?

_____

_____

Uses Objective J: Fit lines to data.

2. The following data give the number of city-council members in six cities with various populations.

Population	45,000	16,000	320,000	108,000	61,000	176,000
City-Council Members	8	7	24	19	12	15

a. Draw a scatterplot of the data.

b. Find an equation of the regression line.

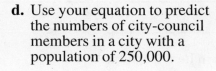

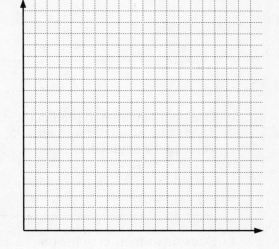

_____

_____

c. Graph the regression line on your scatterplot.

d. Use your equation to predict the numbers of city-council members in a city with a population of 250,000.

_____

e. Interpret the strength of the linear relationship based on the correlation coefficient.

_____

_____

3. The following data give the number of Frostee
Treets sold and the high temperature on 10 different
summer days.

Temperature	88°	71°	84°	98°	95°	88°	80°	72°	77°	85°
Frostee Treets Sold	2,044	1,099	1,941	2,708	2,539	1,886	1,522	503	1,493	1,216

a. Draw a scatterplot of
the data.

b. Find an equation of the
regression line.

_____

_____

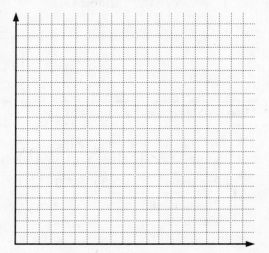

c. Graph the regression line on
your scatterplot.

d. What does the slope in your
equation mean in terms of
this situation?

_____

_____

e. Use your equation to predict the number of Frostee
Treets that would be sold on a 95° day. How close is this
value to the actual data?

_____

_____

f. Does this situation or the one described in Item 2 exhibit
the stronger linear relationship? How do you know this?

_____

_____

_____

4. Use the regression line to determine whether (3.2, 4.08),
(4.5, 4.925), and (6, 5.92) lie on a line. Explain your answer.

_____

LESSON MASTER 3-7 B

Vocabulary

1. Give an example of an *arithmetic sequence*. Then explain why it is an arithmetic sequence.

_____

_____

_____

Skills Objective D: Evaluate or find recursive formulas for arithmetic sequences.

In 2–4, an arithmetic sequence is given.
a. Describe the sequence in words.
b. Write a recursive formula for the sequence.

2. 17, 28, 39, 50, . . .

a. _____ b. _____

_____

_____   _____

3. 80, -160, -400, -640, . . .

a. _____ b. _____

_____

_____   _____

4. $\frac{1}{3}, \frac{2}{3}, 1, \frac{4}{3}, \ldots$

a. _____ b. _____

_____

_____   _____

In 5 and 6, an arithmetic sequence is described.
a. Write the first five terms of the sequence.
b. Write a recursive formula for the sequence.

5. An arithmetic sequence has first term 4 and constant difference 20.

a. _____ b. _____

6. An arithmetic sequence has first term 0.3 and constant difference -0.1.

a. _____ b. _____

▶ **LESSON MASTER 3-7B** *page 2*

Properties Objective F: Recognize properties of arithmetic
sequences.

**In 7 and 8, tell whether or not the sequence could be an
arithmetic sequence. Justify your answer.**

7. 400, 200, 100, 50, . . .

   _____

8. 49, 44, 39, 34, . . .

   _____

Uses Objective G: Model situations involving arithmetic sequences.

---

9. Mrs. Machado contributed $50 to a local charity and pledged
   to donate another $5 every month thereafter.

   a. Write a sequence that shows Mrs. Machado's total
   contributions during the first six months.

   _____

   b. Write a recursive formula for the sequence
   in Part a.

   _____

10. Hector has an empty jar. Every workday he plans
    to add the 30¢ change from his bus fare.

    a. At the start, how much change is in the jar? _____

    b. Write a recursive formula that gives the amount
    of change in the jar after the nth workday.

    _____

11. One afternoon, Matt bought an 85-ounce box of
    dishwasher detergent. Each morning he uses
    3 ounces.

    a. Write a recursive formula for a sequence that
    gives the amount of detergent Matt will have
    left on the nth evening. _____

    b. Find the amount of detergent left on the
    10th evening. _____

LESSON MASTER  3-8 B

Skills Objective D: Evaluate or find explicit formulas for arithmetic sequences.

In 1–4, an arithmetic sequence is given.
a. Find a formula for the nth term.
b. Find a_{25}.

1. -22, -19, -16, -13, . . .

2. $\frac{7}{4}, \frac{9}{4}, \frac{11}{4}, \frac{13}{4}, \ldots$

a. _____

a. _____

b. _____

b. _____

3. 3.2, 4.9, 6.6, 8.3, . . .

4. 75, 25, -25, -75, . . .

a. _____

a. _____

b. _____

b. _____

In 5 and 6, a recursive formula for a sequence is given.
Write an explicit formula for the sequence.

5. $\begin{cases} a_1 = 20 \\ a_n = a_{n-1} + 12, \text{ for } n \geq 2. \end{cases}$ _____

6. $\begin{cases} b_1 = 5.75 \\ b_n = b_{n-1} - 1.25, \text{ for } n \geq 2. \end{cases}$ _____

7. Write a recursive formula for the sequence defined explicitly by $c_n = 45 + (n-1)5$.

_____

8. Write a recursive formula for the sequence defined explicitly by $d_n = 300n + 50$.

_____

In 9 and 10, two terms of an arithmetic sequence are given.
a. Write an explicit formula for the sequence.
b. Write a recursive formula for the sequence.

9. $s_2 = 12$ and $s_8 = 60$

10. $a_5 = 1.6$ and $a_{10} = -0.9$

a. _____

a. _____

b. _____

b. _____

11. Find the 150th term of the arithmetic sequence
$7g, 11g, 15g, 19g, \ldots$ _____

Properties Objective F: Recognize properties of arithmetic
sequences.

In 12–15, determine whether or not the given formula
describes an arithmetic sequence. Justify your answer.

12. $a_n = 9n + 18$

_____

13. $t_n = 3n^2 + 4$

_____

14. $u_n = \frac{1}{2}n - 1$

_____

15. $v_n = n - 30$

_____

Uses Objective G: Model situations involving arithmetic sequences.

16. A wading pool, filled to a depth of 36 inches, drains
at the rate of about 3 inches per hour.

a. Write an explicit formula that gives the
depth of the water after n hours. _____

b. How deep will the water be after 6 hours? _____

17. A vehicle emissions test center tests 320 vehicles
every weekday.

a. Write an explicit formula that gives the
total number of cars tested after n days. _____

b. How many <u>weeks</u> will it take to test
240,000 cars? _____

Name _____

Vocabulary

1. Explain what is meant by the symbol $\lfloor x \rfloor$. Then give an example.

_____

_____

Skills Objective C: Evaluate expressions based on step functions.

In 2–9, evaluate each expression.

2. $\lfloor 15.7 \rfloor$ _____

3. $\lfloor -4.\overline{3} \rfloor$ _____

4. $\lfloor 22 \rfloor$ _____

5. $\lfloor -2.008 \rfloor$ _____

6. $\lfloor 12\frac{3}{4} \rfloor$ _____

7. $7 \cdot \lfloor 6 + 1.6 \rfloor$ _____

8. $\lfloor \sqrt{50} \rfloor$ _____

9. $\lfloor -8 \rfloor$ _____

Uses Objective K: Model situations leading to step functions.

10. Hot dog buns come in packages of 8. Write an equation that shows the number p of complete packages that can be made from b buns. _____

11. *Multiple choice.* A first-grade classroom receives a gross (144) of pencils. There are s students in the classroom. Which of the following represents the number of pencils each student may have? _____

   (a) $\left\lfloor \dfrac{144}{s} \right\rfloor$ (b) $\left\lfloor \dfrac{s}{144} \right\rfloor$ (c) $\dfrac{144}{s}$ (d) $\lfloor 144 \cdot s \rfloor$

12. Student Council is taking part in a clothing drive. They receive 30 passes to the local movie theater for participating in the drive, and for each 50 items of clothing, they receive another 10 passes.

   a. How many passes will the Student Council receive if they collect 736 items of clothing? _____

   b. Let p represent the number of passes Student Council receives for collecting c items of clothing. Write an equation relating p and c. _____

13. The table below gives the cost of a carton of milk at the Milbourne School cafeteria from the years 1965 through 1995. The year reflects the first year that cost was in effect.

a. Find the cost of a carton of milk in each year.

1968 _____   1977 _____   1994 _____

b. Make a graph of the milk costs as a function of the year.

Year	Cost
1965	$.08
1969	$.12
1974	$.18
1977	$.20
1983	$.25
1988	$.30
1992	$.35

Representations   Objective M: Graph or interpret graphs of step functions.

14. The graph at the right shows the cost of renting a chain saw. What would it cost to rent the saw for

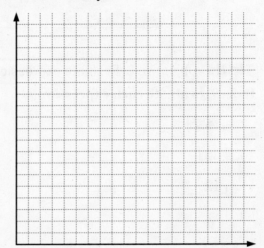

Cost ($)

Number of Hours

a. 3 hours?   _____

b. $5\frac{1}{2}$ hours?   _____

15. a. Graph $f(x) = \lfloor x \rfloor + 1$.

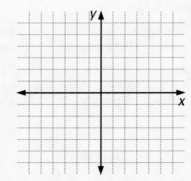

b. Give the domain and the range of the function f.

_____

_____

_____

LESSON MASTER **4-1 B**

Vocabulary

1. A matrix has dimensions $m \times n$. What does this mean? _____

_____

Uses Objective G: Use matrices to store data.

2. In the 1970s, there were 800,368 immigrants to the United States from Europe, 1,588,178 from Asia, and 80,779 from Africa. In the 1980s, there were 705,630 immigrants from Europe, 2,066,455 from Asia, and 192,212 from Africa. Store this information in a 3×2 matrix. _____

3. At Outfits East, 22% of last year's sales were children's clothing, 41% were women's, and 37% were men's. At Outfits West, 17% of the sales were children's clothing, 55% were women's, and 28% were men's. At Outfits North, 33% of the sales were children's clothing, 23% were women's, and 44% were men's. At Outfits South, 14% of last year's sales were children's clothing, 32% were women's, and 54% were men's. Store this information in a 4×3 matrix. _____

4. The matrix at the right gives the subscription figures for *The Metropolitan Sentinel* for a five-year period.

	City	Suburbs
1990	14,662	12,004
1991	15,325	11,867
1992	15,418	12,388
1993	15,790	13,056
1994	17,126	13,540

a. What are the dimensions of this matrix? _____

b. What does the element in row 1 column 2 represent?

_____

c. In what row and column is the entry 13,056? _____

d. How many suburban subscribers were there in 1992? _____

▶ **LESSON MASTER 4-1 B** *page 2*

Representations Objective I: Graph figures described by matrices.

In 5 and 6, draw the polygon described by the matrix.

5. $\begin{bmatrix} 4 & 0 & 5 \\ -2 & -3 & 1 \end{bmatrix}$

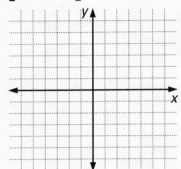

6. $\begin{bmatrix} -4 & -1 & 3 & 2 & -1 \\ 2 & 3 & 2 & -5 & -2 \end{bmatrix}$

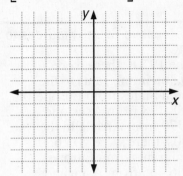

In 7 and 8, write a matrix for the given polygon.

7. *DCBA*

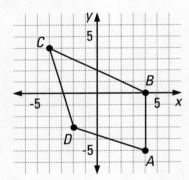

8. *GFEKJH*

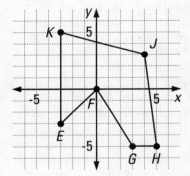

LESSON MASTER 4-2 B

Skills Objective A: Add, subtract, and find scalar multiples of matrices.

In 1 and 2, express as a single matrix.

1. $\begin{bmatrix} 1 & 4 & -6 \\ 2 & -3 & -3 \end{bmatrix} + \begin{bmatrix} 3 & 0 & 6 \\ 4 & -3 & 8 \end{bmatrix}$ _____

2. $\begin{bmatrix} 5 & 2 \\ 2 & -1 \\ 5 & 4 \end{bmatrix} - \begin{bmatrix} -2 & 2 \\ 0 & -1 \\ -5 & 7 \end{bmatrix}$ _____

In 3–8, let $A = \begin{bmatrix} -7 & 2 & 6 \\ 9 & 0 & -2 \\ -5 & 3 & 3 \end{bmatrix}$ and $B = \begin{bmatrix} 4 & -7 & -2 \\ 5 & 5 & 0 \\ -2 & 9 & 6 \end{bmatrix}$. **Calculate.**

3. $3A$ 4. $-4B$ 5. $A + B$

_____   _____   _____

6. $2A + 3B$ 7. $B - A$ 8. $A - 5B$

_____   _____   _____

In 9–11, solve for a and b.

9. $\begin{bmatrix} 3 & a & -2 \\ -2 & 6 & 10 \end{bmatrix} + \begin{bmatrix} 3 & 8 & 0 \\ 1 & -1 & b \end{bmatrix} = \begin{bmatrix} 6 & 11 & -2 \\ -1 & 5 & 5 \end{bmatrix}$ $a =$ _____ $b =$ _____

10. $\begin{bmatrix} 6 & 8 & 0 \\ a & 7 & 13 \end{bmatrix} - \begin{bmatrix} 1 & b & 4 \\ 3 & 7 & 6 \end{bmatrix} = \begin{bmatrix} -5 & 11 & -4 \\ 0 & 0 & 7 \end{bmatrix}$ a _____ $b =$ _____

11. $4\begin{bmatrix} a & 7 \\ 5 & -4 \end{bmatrix} - 3\begin{bmatrix} 4 & b \\ 2 & 0 \end{bmatrix} = \begin{bmatrix} 14 & 31 \\ 14 & -16 \end{bmatrix}$ $a =$ _____ $b =$ _____

Properties Objective D: Recognize properties of matrix addition and scalar multiplication.

12. What addition of matrices

is the same as $4\begin{bmatrix} 2 & 8 \\ 2 & -4 \end{bmatrix}$? _____

13. Suppose A is a 2×3 matrix and B is a matrix added to A.

a. What are the dimensions of $A + B$? _____

b. Must $A + B = B + A$? _____

Uses Objective H: Use matrix addition and scalar multiplication to solve real-world problems.

14. The matrices below show the number of books checked out of the school library during two consecutive weeks.

	Nov. 3–7 Fiction	Non Fiction		Nov. 10–14 Fiction	Non Fiction
Freshmen	476	303		308	352
Sophomores	313	211		366	319
Juniors	416	336		347	288
Seniors	394	510		322	310

a. Subtract the left matrix from the right matrix. Call the difference D. Write D at the right.

b. What is the meaning of the first column of D? _____

_____

_____

c. What is the meaning of the entry in row 4, column 2 of D?

_____

_____

15. The matrix below gives the prices in dollars of school rings in silver. The prices for gold are 6 times those for silver. Give the matrix that represents the prices of gold rings.

	Jade	Onyx
sizes 5-7	22	18
sizes 8-10	26	22
sizes 11+	32	28

LESSON MASTER

4-3
B

Skills Objective B: Multiply matrices.

In 1–8, calculate the product.

1. $[-4 \ 1 \ 0] \begin{bmatrix} 6 \\ 2 \\ -3 \end{bmatrix}$

_____

2. $\begin{bmatrix} -2 & -6 & 0 \\ 7 & 2 & 2 \end{bmatrix} \begin{bmatrix} 5 & 2 \\ 0 & 1 \\ 4 & 8 \end{bmatrix}$

3. $\begin{bmatrix} 9 & -1 & 6 \\ 5 & 3 & 4 \\ 8 & -6 & 3 \end{bmatrix} \begin{bmatrix} 6 & 3 & -2 \\ 8 & 5 & 7 \\ 4 & 2 & 4 \end{bmatrix}$

_____

4. $\begin{bmatrix} -4 & 5 & 0 \\ 0 & 6 & 4 \\ 0 & -7 & 2 \\ 1 & 8 & 1 \end{bmatrix} \begin{bmatrix} 5 & 6 & 6 & 2 \\ 0 & 1 & 0 & 1 \\ 4 & -2 & -6 & 2 \end{bmatrix}$

5. $\begin{bmatrix} 3.8 & 4.8 \\ 3.5 & 0 \\ .6 & 8.1 \end{bmatrix} \begin{bmatrix} 4.1 & -.3 & 2.6 \\ 5.5 & -1.7 & 5.2 \end{bmatrix}$

_____

6. $\begin{bmatrix} 5 & 5 \\ 7 & -3 \end{bmatrix} \begin{bmatrix} 6 & -2 \\ 4 & -8 \end{bmatrix}$

7. $\begin{bmatrix} -5 & -9 \\ 7 & 2 \\ 0 & -4 \end{bmatrix} \begin{bmatrix} 5 & -1 & 2 \\ 0 & 0 & 2 \end{bmatrix}$

_____

8. $[0 \ -4 \ 8] \begin{bmatrix} 2 & 6 & -2 \\ 1 & 1 & 1 \\ 3 & 7 & 4 \end{bmatrix} \begin{bmatrix} 9 & 0 & -1 \\ 3 & 2 & 1 \\ 3 & 4 & 8 \end{bmatrix}$

_____

Properties Objective D: Recognize properties of matrix multiplication.

9. If $\begin{bmatrix} 5 & 6 & 6 & 2 \\ 0 & 1 & 0 & 1 \end{bmatrix} \cdot H = \begin{bmatrix} 38 \\ 8 \end{bmatrix}$, what are the
dimensions of H? _____

10. The product of two matrices A and B exists only
    when the number of ___?___ of A is equal to the
    number of ___?___ of B.   _____ _____

11. Suppose G, H, and M are matrices. If $G \cdot H = M$,
    the product of row i of G and column j of H is
    the element located in row ___?___ and   _____ _____
    column ___?___ of M.

12. **a.** Calculate $\left(\begin{bmatrix} 0 & -4 & 8 \end{bmatrix} \begin{bmatrix} 2 & 6 & -2 \\ 1 & 1 & 1 \\ 3 & 7 & 4 \end{bmatrix} \right) \begin{bmatrix} 9 & 0 & -1 \\ 3 & 2 & 1 \\ 3 & 4 & 8 \end{bmatrix}$. _____

    b. How does your answer compare to your
    answer in Question 8? What does this illustrate? _____

    _____

    _____

Uses Objective H: Use matrix multiplication to solve real-world problems.

13. A band went to a football game in 2 vans, 6 cars, and one bus. There were
    8 band members in each van, 5 in each car, and 38 in the bus. Write V, the
    vehicle matrix, and N, the matrix showing the number of band members in
    each vehicle. Calculate VN. Tell what VN represents.

    $V = $ _____ $N = $ _____ $VN = $ _____

    _____

    _____

14. Music Boosters ordered sweatshirts that cost $12 for small,
    $14 for medium, $17 for large, and $20 for extra large. In
    gray, they ordered 6 S, 8 M, 12 L, and 14 XL. In black, they
    ordered 2 S, 5 M, 10 L, and 15 XL. Write C, the cost matrix
    and N the matrix showing the number ordered. Calculate CN
    and tell what it represents.

    $C = $ _____ $N = $ _____

    $CN = $ _____

    _____

Name _____

Vocabulary

1. What are the *preimage* and *image* under a transformation?

   _____

   _____

   _____

2. If a size change maps (x, y) onto (mx, my), the
   ___?___ is m.   _____

Properties Objective E: Recognize relationships between figures and their size-change images.

3. Suppose $C'D'E'F'$ is the image of quadrilateral $CDEF$ under a size change of magnitude k.

   a. How do the measures of $\angle D$ and $\angle D'$ compare? _____

   b. How do EF and $E'F'$ compare?   _____

4. Under $S_{1/4}$, what is the image of each point?

   a. $(8, -4)$ _____   **b.** $(3, 12)$ _____

   c. $(0, -8)$ _____   **d.** $\left(5, \frac{1}{2}\right)$ _____

Properties Objective F: Relate size changes to matrices and vice versa.

5. Give the matrix for each size transformation.

   a. S_8 _____   **b.** $S_{4/5}$ _____

   c. $S_{.75}$ _____   **d.** $S_{1.5}$ _____

6. What matrix is associated with the size transformation
   that maps $(-12, 6)$ onto $(-4, 2)$?   _____

7. What is the magnitude of the size transformation   _____

   associated with $\begin{bmatrix} 6 & 0 \\ 0 & 6 \end{bmatrix}$?

Representations Objective I: Graph figures and their size-change
images.

8. Graph the polygon $\begin{bmatrix} -1 & 3 & 4 & 1 \\ 2 & 0 & 2 & 4 \end{bmatrix}$
   and its image under S_2.

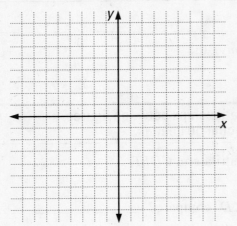

9. Graph the polygon $\begin{bmatrix} 6 & 3 & 3 \\ 0 & -3 & 6 \end{bmatrix}$ and
   and its image under $S_{2/3}$.

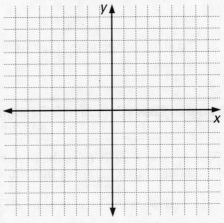

Review Objective B, Lesson 4-3

In 10–13, calculate the product.

10. $\begin{bmatrix} 3 & 1 \\ 3 & -6 \end{bmatrix}\begin{bmatrix} 2 & 1 \\ 0 & -9 \end{bmatrix}$

11. $\begin{bmatrix} -8 & -6 \\ 0 & 3 \end{bmatrix}\begin{bmatrix} 5 & 2 & 5 & 0 \\ 1 & 0 & -4 & 8 \end{bmatrix}$

12. $\begin{bmatrix} 4 & -2 & 2 \\ 8 & 3 & -4 \\ 9 & 0 & -6 \end{bmatrix}\begin{bmatrix} -6 & 5 & 5 \\ 5 & 2 & 1 \\ 1 & -8 & 3 \end{bmatrix}$

13. $\begin{bmatrix} -3 & 4 & 3 \\ 8 & -2 & 4 \\ 0 & -7 & 2 \\ -1 & -6 & 1 \end{bmatrix}\begin{bmatrix} 2 & 1 & -9 & 2 \\ 4 & 7 & -1 & -1 \\ 0 & 0 & 2 & 3 \end{bmatrix}$

LESSON MASTER  4-5 B

Vocabulary

1. Describe what happens to a figure under the scale change $S_{3,1/2}$.

_____

_____

_____

Properties Objective E: Recognize relationships between figures and their scale-change images.

2. *True or false.* A figure and its scale-change image are similar.

_____

In 3–8, $\triangle A'B'C'$ is the image of $\triangle ABC$ under a scale change $S_{.5,4}$.

3. If $A = (4, -2)$, what are the coordinates of A'?

_____

4. If $A' = (3, 12)$, what are the coordinates of A?

_____

5. Is $\triangle ABC$ similar to $\triangle A'B'C'$?

_____

6. Is this scale change a size change?

_____

7. In which direction is $\triangle ABC$ stretched?

_____

8. In which direction is $\triangle ABC$ shrunk?

_____

Properties Objective F: Relate scale-changes to matrices and vice versa.

In 9–11, give the scale change matrix corresponding to each given transformation.

9. $S_{5,2}$

_____

10. a vertical stretch of 2 and a horizontal shrink of $\frac{2}{3}$

_____

11. the transformation that maps $(3, -9)$ onto $(1.5, -3)$

_____

12. $\begin{bmatrix} 5 & 0 \\ 0 & .8 \end{bmatrix}$ is associated with what transformation? _____

13. If $\begin{bmatrix} a & 0 \\ 0 & 4 \end{bmatrix}$ is associated with a size change,

then $a = $ ___?___ . _____

Representations Objective I: Graph figures and their
scale-change images.

14. Graph the polygon $\begin{bmatrix} -3 & 3 & 3 & 1 \\ -6 & 0 & 6 & 4 \end{bmatrix}$ **15.** Graph the polygon $\begin{bmatrix} 4 & 3 & -3 \\ 1 & -3 & 4 \end{bmatrix}$

and its image under $S_{2,2/3}$.

and its image under $\begin{bmatrix} 2 & 0 \\ 0 & 1 \end{bmatrix}$.

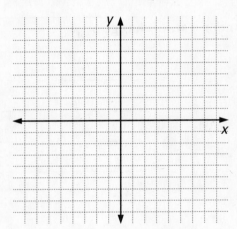
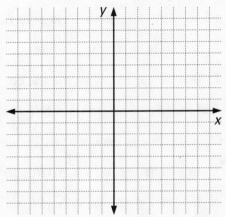

16. Graph the polygon $\begin{bmatrix} -3 & -3 & 0 \\ 0 & 5 & 0 \end{bmatrix}$

and its image under $\begin{bmatrix} \frac{2}{3} & 0 \\ 0 & 2 \end{bmatrix}$

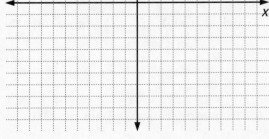

a. What type of triangle is
the preimage?

_____

b. What type of triangle is
the image?

_____

c. Are the image and preimage congruent? _____

d. Are the image and preimage similar?

LESSON MASTER 4-6 B

Questions on SPUR Objectives

Vocabulary

1. Suppose A' is the reflection image of A over line m.

a. If A and A' are distinct points, how are A, A', and m related?

_____

b. When are A and A' the same point?

_____

Properties Objective E: Recognize relationships between figures and their reflection images.

In 2–4, match the matrix with the reflection.

2. $\begin{bmatrix} 0 & 1 \\ 1 & 0 \end{bmatrix}$ _____   **3.** $\begin{bmatrix} -1 & 0 \\ 0 & 1 \end{bmatrix}$ _____   **4.** $\begin{bmatrix} 1 & 0 \\ 0 & -1 \end{bmatrix}$ _____

(a) r_y (b) r_x (c) $r_{y=x}$

5. According to the Matrix Basis Theorem, if a transformation represented by a 2×2 matrix maps $(1, 0)$ onto (x_1, y_1) and $(0, 1)$ onto (x_2, y_2), then what is the matrix for the transformation? _____

Properties Objective F: Relate reflections to matrices and vice versa.

In 6–8, translate the matrix equation into English.

6. $\begin{bmatrix} 0 & 1 \\ 1 & 0 \end{bmatrix}\begin{bmatrix} -3 \\ 8 \end{bmatrix} = \begin{bmatrix} 8 \\ -3 \end{bmatrix}$ The reflection image of the point ___?___ over the line ___?___ is the point ___?___.

_____ _____ _____

7. $\begin{bmatrix} -1 & 0 \\ 0 & 1 \end{bmatrix}\begin{bmatrix} -3 \\ 8 \end{bmatrix} = \begin{bmatrix} 3 \\ 8 \end{bmatrix}$ The reflection image of the point ___?___ over the ___?___ is the point ___?___.

_____ _____ _____

8. $\begin{bmatrix} 1 & 0 \\ 0 & -1 \end{bmatrix}\begin{bmatrix} -3 \\ 8 \end{bmatrix} = \begin{bmatrix} -3 \\ -8 \end{bmatrix}$ The reflection image of the point ___?___ over the ___?___ is the point ___?___.

_____ _____ _____

▶ **LESSON MASTER 4-6 B** *page 2*

9. **a.** Multiply the matrix for r_x by $\begin{bmatrix} 2 & 1 & 6 \\ -3 & 0 & 4 \end{bmatrix}$.

_____

b. Multiply the matrix for r_x by your answer to Part a.

_____

c. Explain what happened.

_____

_____

_____

Representations Objective I: Graph figures and their reflection images.

10. Graph the polygon $\begin{bmatrix} 1 & -1 & -7 & -3 \\ 5 & 7 & 5 & 1 \end{bmatrix}$ and its image under r_y.

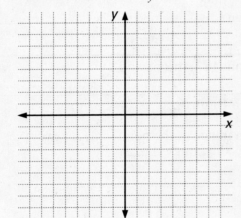

11. Graph the polygon $\begin{bmatrix} 1 & 6 & 5 \\ 1 & 2 & -2 \end{bmatrix}$ and its image under $r_{y=x}$.

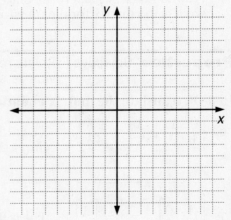

In 12–14, give the coordinates of a point that is its own reflection image under the indicated reflection.

12. r_y _____

13. r_x _____

14. $r_{y=x}$ _____

LESSON MASTER

4-7 B

Vocabulary

1. How do we write in symbols the composite of the transformation T_1 followed by the transformation T_2? What does it mean?

_____

_____

_____

Properties Objective D: Recognize properties of matrix operations.

2. **a.** Write the identity matrix I.

   b. Show that $I \cdot M = M \cdot I$ for all 2×2 matrices M.

   a. _____

   b. _____

3. Name two other properties of 2×2 matrices that are shared by multiplication of real numbers.

_____

_____

Properties Objective F: Relate transformations to matrices and vice versa.

4. Suppose T_1 has matrix $\begin{bmatrix} 4 & 0 \\ 0 & 4 \end{bmatrix}$ and T_2 has matrix $\begin{bmatrix} 1 & 0 \\ 0 & -1 \end{bmatrix}$.

   a. What is the matrix for $T_2 \circ T_1$? _____

   b. Explain what happens to a figure under $T_2 \circ T_1$.

_____

_____

_____

▶ **LESSON MASTER 4-7 B** *page 2*

In 5–10, a point and its image under four composites of
transformations are graphed. **a.** Match the composite to
a graph. **b.** Calculate a matrix for the composite.

5. $r_x \circ r_x$ **6.** $r_x \circ r_y$ **7.** $I \circ r_x$

a. ____ **b.** _____   **a.** ____ **b.** _____   **a.** ____ **b.** _____

8. $S_2 \circ r_y$ **9.** $r_x \circ r_{y=x}$ **10.** $S_2 \circ S_{2.5}$

a. ____ **b.** _____   **a.** ____ **b.** _____   **a.** ____ **b.** _____

i. 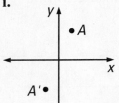   **ii.** 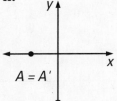   **iii.**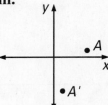

iv. 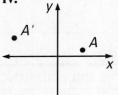   **v.** 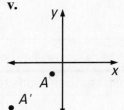   **vi.**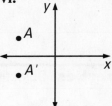

Representations Objective I: Graph figures and their transformation images.

11. Graph the polygon $\begin{bmatrix} 1 & 4 & 4 & 0 \\ -1 & -2 & -5 & -3 \end{bmatrix}$ **12.** Graph the polygon $\begin{bmatrix} -4 & -2 & -4 \\ 2 & 2 & -2 \end{bmatrix}$

and its image under $r_x \circ r_y$.   and its image under $r_{y=x} \circ S_{1/2}$.

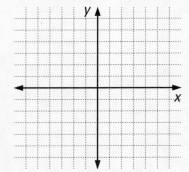

LESSON MASTER

4-8
B

Properties Objective E: Recognize relationships between figures and their rotation images.

In 1–3, match the matrix with the rotation.

1. $\begin{bmatrix} 0 & 1 \\ -1 & 0 \end{bmatrix}$ _____

2. $\begin{bmatrix} 0 & -1 \\ 1 & 0 \end{bmatrix}$ _____

3. $\begin{bmatrix} -1 & 0 \\ 0 & -1 \end{bmatrix}$ _____

(a) R_{180}

(b) R_{270}

(c) R_{90}

Properties Objective F: Relate rotations to matrices and vice versa.

In 4 and 5, a composite of transformations is given. a. Find a matrix for the composite. b. Give a single transformation whose matrix is your answer to Part a.

4. $r_y \circ r_x$

a. _____

b. _____

5. $r_x \circ R_{180}$

a. _____

b. _____

6. Show how to find the matrix for R_{180} from the matrix for R_{90}.

Representations Objective I: Graph figures and their rotation images.

7. **a.** What rotation maps $\triangle FAN$ onto $\triangle F'A'N'$?

_____

b. Give a matrix for the rotation in Part a.

_____

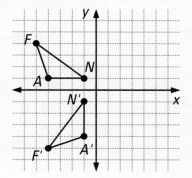

▶ **LESSON MASTER 4-8 B** *page 2*

8. a. What rotation maps $\triangle WAVE$
onto $\triangle W'A'V'E'$?

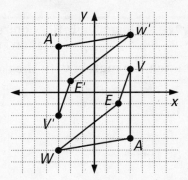

_____

b. Give a matrix for the rotation
in Part a.

_____

9. Graph the polygon $\begin{bmatrix} 0 & -5 & -6 \\ 0 & 1 & -6 \end{bmatrix}$
and its image under R_{90}.

10. Graph the polygon
$\begin{bmatrix} -1 & -3 & 2 & 3 & 2 \\ -1 & 6 & 8 & 3 & 4 \end{bmatrix}$
and its image under R_{180}.

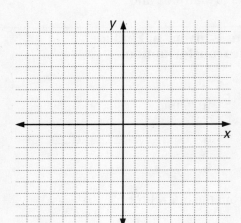

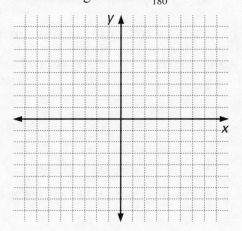

Review Objective B, Lessons 3-2 and 3-5

**In 11–16, write an equation for the line satisfying the
given conditions.**

11. slope -3, through (3, 5)

_____

12. slope 5, through (2, -4)

_____

13. through (2, -3) and (4, 1)

_____

14. through (0, 3) and (2, -1)

_____

15. parallel to $y = 3x$, through (3, 4)

_____

16. parallel to $y = 4x - 9$, through (0, 0)

_____

LESSON MASTER 4-9 B

Skills Objective C: Determine equations of lines perpendicular to given lines.

In 1–8, find an equation for the line that goes through the given point and is perpendicular to the given line.

1. $(4, 3); y = -2x + 6$

2. $(-1, 7); y = -x - 4$

_____

3. $(0, 0); y = \frac{2}{3}x$

4. $(5, 9); y = 3$

_____

5. $(5, 5); x + 4y = 8$

6. $(-3, -1); x = -1$

_____

7. $(0, 6); 2x - 7y = 21$

8. $(.2, .8); y = -.5x$

_____

► **LESSON MASTER 4-9 B** *page 2*

In 9–12, find an equation of the perpendicular bisector of the
line segment with the given endpoints.

9. (4, -2), (6, 6)   **10.** (10, 11), (-4, -3)

_____   _____

11. (0, 0), (3, 3)   **12.** (2, 5), (2, -9)

_____   _____

Properties Objective E: Recognize relationships between figures
and their rotation images.

13. The slope of a line is -4. What is the slope of the
image of this line under R_{90}?   _____

14. The slope of a line is $\frac{8}{5}$. What is the slope of the
image of this line under R_{90}?   _____

15. The slope of a line is $-\frac{1}{3}$. What is the slope of the
image of this line under R_{270}?   _____

16. The equation of a line is $3x + 2y = -30$. What is the
slope of the image of this line under R_{90}?   _____

17. A line contains (0, -2) and (-4, 5). What is the slope
of the image of this line under R_{90}?   _____

18. Let ΔKID have matrix $\begin{bmatrix} 26 & 14 & 70 \\ 38 & -26 & -74 \end{bmatrix}$. Let $\Delta K'I'D' = R_{90}(\Delta KID)$.
Find the slope of the given line.

    a. $\overleftrightarrow{KD}$ _____   **b.** $\overleftrightarrow{K'D'}$ _____

LESSON MASTER

4-10 B

Properties Objective E: Recognize relationships between figures and their translation images.

1. Suppose $A'B'C'D'$ is the image of quadrilateral $ABCD$ under a translation.

   a. Are $ABCD$ and $A'B'C'D'$ congruent? _____

   b. Give two facts about $\overline{AB}$ and $\overline{A'B'}$.

   _____

   _____

2. Under $T_{3,-2}$, what is the image of each point?

   a. $(5, -1)$ _____   **b.** $(-3, 13)$ _____

   c. $(-9, 0)$ _____   **d.** $(1.75, 1.25)$ _____

3. A translation $T_{h,k}$ maps $(-4, 6)$ onto $(-5, 3)$. Find the values of h and k. $h =$ _____ $k =$ _____

Properties Objective F: Relate translations to matrices and vice versa.

4. Fill in the blanks to give a translation of the following matrix addition into English.

$$\begin{bmatrix} -4 & -4 & -4 \\ 5 & 5 & 5 \end{bmatrix} + \begin{bmatrix} 3 & 0 & 1 \\ 2 & -2 & -5 \end{bmatrix} = \begin{bmatrix} -1 & -4 & -3 \\ 7 & 3 & 0 \end{bmatrix}$$

   A triangle with vertices at _____, _____, and _____ is

   translated _____ units _____ and _____ units _____.

   The vertices of the image are at _____, _____, and _____.

5. What matrix is associated with the translation of a triangle under $T_{6,-2}$?

   _____

6. What matrix is the identity matrix for translating pentagons in the plane?

   _____

► **LESSON MASTER 4-10 B** *page 2*

Representations Objective I: Graph figures and their translation images.

7. $\begin{bmatrix} -3 & 0 & 2 & -1 \\ 1 & 0 & 3 & 6 \end{bmatrix}$ represents polygon *ABCD*.

   a. Write the matrix that represents $T_{4,-1}$ for this polygon.

     _____

   b. Apply the matrix that represents $T_{4,-1}$ to the matrix for the polygon. Write the resulting matrix.

     _____

   c. Graph the preimage and image at the right.

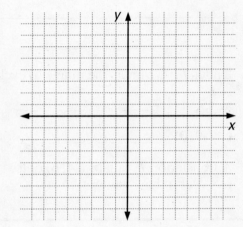

8. $\begin{bmatrix} -1 & 4 & 2 & 0 & -5 \\ -1 & 0 & 3 & 3 & 2 \end{bmatrix}$ represents polygon *PQRST*.

   a. Write the matrix that represents $T_{-3,-2}$ for this polygon.

     _____

   b. Apply the matrix that represents $T_{-3,-2}$ to the matrix for the polygon. Write the resulting matrix.

     _____

   c. Graph the preimage and image at the right.

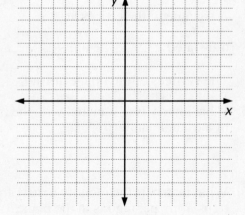

Name _____

LESSON MASTER

5-1 B

Vocabulary

1. **a.** What is the *intersection* of two sets? _____

_____

b. Is intersection the solution set of a
compound sentence using *and* or *or*? _____

2. What is the *union* of two sets? _____

_____

b. Is union the solution set of a compound
sentence using *and* or *or*? _____

Representations Objective H: Solve and graph linear inequalities in one variable.

In 3–10, graph all solutions on the number line.

3. $x \le 8$

4. $u > -6$

5. $n < 0$ and $n \ge -7$

6. $d > -4$ or $d < -8$

7. $-2 \le s \le 3$

8. $7 \ge y > -3$

9. g is from 1 to 6

10. c is between -4 and 4

**In 11 and 12, write an inequality or a compound
sentence that describes the graph.**

11.  _____

12.  _____

▶ **LESSON MASTER 5-1 B** *page 2*

In 13 and 14, solve the inequality and graph its solution set on the number line.

13. $-20 + 6w \leq 40$

$\longleftrightarrow$

14. $13 < y + 3(-4y + 8)$

$\longleftrightarrow$

15. In some hospitals, newborns weighing less than 5 pounds are put on special watch. Graph these weights on the number line.

$\longleftrightarrow$

Representations Objective K: Solve systems of inequalities in one variable by graphing on a number line.

In 16 and 17, graph all solutions on the number line.

16. $\{p:p < 6\} \cap \{p:p > -5\}$

$\longleftrightarrow$

17. $\{y:y < 6\} \cup \{y:y \geq 10\}$

$\longleftrightarrow$

In 18 and 19, write an inequality or a compound sentence that describes the graph.

18. 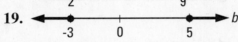 _____

19. _____

Review Objective L, Lesson 3-2

In 20 and 21, graph the line with the given equation.

20. $y = -4x + 2$

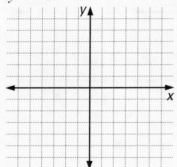

21. $2x - 6y = 12$

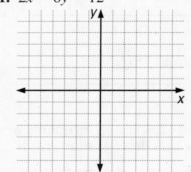

LESSON MASTER 5-2 B

Vocabulary

1. Use the word *intersection* to describe the solution set for a system.

_____

_____

_____

Properties Objective D: Recognize properties of systems of equations.

2. Does the ordered pair (3, -10) solve the system
$\begin{cases} 3x + y = \text{-}1 \\ 2x + 3y = \text{-}17 \end{cases}$? Justify your answer.

_____

_____

3. Does the ordered pair (8, -3) solve the system
$\begin{cases} 4x - 3y = 41 \\ \text{-}x - y = \text{-}5 \end{cases}$? Justify your answer.

_____

_____

4. Use the table at the right to solve
the system $\begin{cases} y = 4x - 9 \\ y = 2x - 6 \end{cases}$.

x	y = 4x − 9	y = 2x − 6
-1	-13	-8
-0.5	-11	-7
0	-9	-6
0.5	-7	-5
1	-5	-4
1.5	-3	-3
2	-1	-2

_____

5. **a.** Write a system that has (-5, 3) as a solution.

_____

b. Show that (-5, 3) is a solution to the system in Part a.

_____

▶ **LESSON MASTER 5-2 B** *page 2*

Representations Objective I: Estimate solutions to systems by graphing.

In 6–9, a system is given. **a.** Graph the system.
b. Tell how many solutions the system has.
c. Estimate any solutions to the nearest tenth.

6. $\begin{cases} 2x + 4y = 6 \\ x + y = \text{-}1 \end{cases}$

7. $\begin{cases} 8x - 4y = 12 \\ y = 2x + 3 \end{cases}$

a.

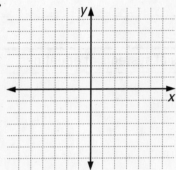

a.

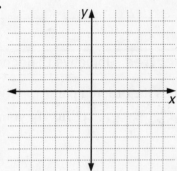

b. _____

b. _____

c. _____

c. _____

8. $\begin{cases} y = \dfrac{4}{x} \\ y = x \end{cases}$

9. $\begin{cases} y = \dfrac{2}{x} \\ y = x^2 \end{cases}$

a.

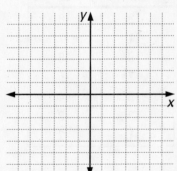

a.

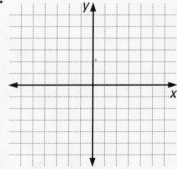

b. _____

b. _____

c. _____

c. _____

LESSON MASTER

5-3 B

Skills Objective A: Solve 2 × 2 and 3 × 3 systems using substitution.

**In 1–8, use substitution to solve the system.
Then check.**

1. $\begin{cases} y = x - 7 \\ y = -2x + 5 \end{cases}$

2. $\begin{cases} y = 3x + 13 \\ y = x + 1 \end{cases}$

3. $\begin{cases} 3m - 2n = 1 \\ 21m - 6n = 11 \end{cases}$

4. $\begin{cases} xy = -4 \\ x = -4y \end{cases}$

5. $\begin{cases} .25x + .1y = 78 \\ 7.5y - 1.5x = 990 \end{cases}$

6. $\begin{cases} 4a + 6b - 3c = -26 \\ b = a + 3 \\ c = -4a \end{cases}$

7. $\begin{cases} xy + z = 10 \\ z = -x + 1 \\ y = x + 1 \end{cases}$

8. $\begin{cases} y = \frac{1}{2}x + 1 \\ x - 2y = -2 \end{cases}$

Properties Objective D: Recognize properties of systems of equations.

9. When you attempt to solve a system of two linear equations, you get the statement "5 = 19."

   a. What does this tell you about the solution?

   _____

   b. Describe the graph. _____

10. When you attempt to solve a different system of two linear equations, you get the statement "8 = 8."

    a. What does this tell you about the solution?

    _____

    b. Describe the graph. _____

Uses Objective F: Use systems of two or three linear equations to solve real-world problems.

11. At Wet Pets, a starter aquarium kit costs $15 plus 60¢ per fish. At Gills and Frills, the same kit is $13 plus 80¢ per fish.

    a. Give an equation for the cost c of f fish at each store.

    W. P. _____   G. and F. _____

    b. For what number of fish is the cost the same at the two stores?   _____

12. A Valentine bouquet of 24 flowers contains pink carnations, red roses, and white mums. There are half as many mums as carnations and 4 more roses than carnations.

    a. Let c be the number of carnations, r the number of roses, and m the number of mums. Write a system of three equations satisfied by c, r, and m in this situation. _____

    b. Solve the system to find how many of each type of flower are in the bouquet.

    C _____,   R _____,   M _____

LESSON MASTER 5-4 B

Skills Objective A: Solve 2 × 2 and 3 × 3 systems using the Linear Combinations Method.

In 1–8, use linear combinations to solve the system. Then check.

1. $\begin{cases} 4x + y = -12 \\ 2x + 2y = -15 \end{cases}$

2. $\begin{cases} 4x + 3y = 2.6 \\ 5x - 2y = 2.1 \end{cases}$

3. $\begin{cases} 2a + b - 5c = -21 \\ a + 2b - 2c = -15 \\ a - 4b + c = 18 \end{cases}$

4. $\begin{cases} 8m - 2n = -16 \\ 2m - .5n = -4 \end{cases}$

5. $\begin{cases} 12x^2 - 5y^2 = 523 \\ 6x^2 + 2y^2 = 482 \end{cases}$

6. $\begin{cases} 4x + 5y = -14 \\ 8x + 10y = -20 \end{cases}$

7. $\begin{cases} \frac{1}{4}x - y = -8 \\ \frac{1}{2}x + 4y = 14 \end{cases}$

8. $\begin{cases} d + 9e - f = 13 \\ 3d + e + 2f = -7 \\ 2d + 2e + 2f = -6 \end{cases}$

▶ **LESSON MASTER 5-4 B** *page 2*

Properties Objective D: Recognize properties of systems of equations.

For 9 and 10, consider the system $\begin{cases} 5x + 15y = -10 \\ x + 3y = k \end{cases}$.

9. For what value(s) of k will the system have
   infinitely many solutions? _____

10. For what value(s) of k will the system
    be inconsistent? _____

Uses Objective F: Use systems of two or three linear equations to solve
real-world problems.

11. Five yards of fabric and three spools of thread cost
    $40.12. Two yards of the same fabric and ten spools
    of the same thread cost $23.88. Find the cost of a
    yard of fabric and the cost of a spool of thread.

    fabric _____   thread _____

12. Two apples and six plums provide 300 calories.
    Three apples and five plums provide 350 calories.
    How many calories are provided by five apples
    and eight plums? _____

Review Objective B, Lesson 4-3

In 13 and 14, calculate the product.

13. $\begin{bmatrix} \frac{3}{4} & 1 \\ 3 & -1 \end{bmatrix} \begin{bmatrix} 8 & 12 \\ 0 & -2 \end{bmatrix}$

14. $\begin{bmatrix} -3 & -1 \\ 2 & 4 \end{bmatrix} \begin{bmatrix} 0 & 2 & -5 & 0 \\ 7 & 1 & -2 & 5 \end{bmatrix}$

_____   _____

LESSON MASTER 5-5 B

Vocabulary

1. What do we call two matrices whose product is the identity matrix?

_____

2. For the matrix $\begin{bmatrix} e & f \\ g & h \end{bmatrix}$, the number ___?___ is the determinant.

_____

Skills Objective B: Find the determinant and the inverse of a square matrix.

**In 3–8, a matrix is given. a. Find its determinant.
b. Find the inverse, if it exists. c. Check your
answer to Part b by multiplying.**

3. $\begin{bmatrix} 3 & -1 \\ 0 & -2 \end{bmatrix}$

a. _____

b. _____

c. _____

4. $\begin{bmatrix} -3 & -6 \\ -2 & 4 \end{bmatrix}$

a. _____

b. _____

c. _____

5. $\begin{bmatrix} \frac{1}{2} & 1 \\ -1 & \frac{1}{2} \end{bmatrix}$

a. _____

b. _____

c. _____

6. $\begin{bmatrix} 0.5 & 1.5 \\ 0.5 & -0.5 \end{bmatrix}$

a. _____

b. _____

c. _____

7. $\begin{bmatrix} 1 & 0 \\ 0 & 1 \end{bmatrix}$

    a. _____

    b. _____

    c. _____

8. $\begin{bmatrix} -1 & 0 \\ 0 & -1 \end{bmatrix}$

    a. _____

    b. _____

    c. _____

9. Show that $\begin{bmatrix} -2 & 1 \\ 2 & -4 \end{bmatrix}$ and $\begin{bmatrix} -1 & -\frac{1}{2} \\ -\frac{1}{4} & 1 \end{bmatrix}$ are *not* inverses of each other.

_____

10. Consider the matrix $\begin{bmatrix} 5 & 4 \\ c & 8 \end{bmatrix}$. For what value(s)

of c does the matrix lack an inverse? _____

**In 11 and 12, a transformation is given. a. Write its matrix.
b. Write the inverse of the matrix in Part a. c. Write the
transformation represented by the matrix in Part b.
d. Describe what the transformation does geometrically.**

11. $S_{.5,3}$

    a. _____   **b.** _____   **c.** _____

    d. _____

_____

_____

12. R_{180}

    a. _____   **b.** _____   **c.** _____

    d. _____

_____

LESSON MASTER 5-6 B

Vocabulary

1. Consider the system $\begin{cases} 3x + y = -1 \\ 4x + 6y = -34 \end{cases}$.

   a. Write the matrix form of the system.

   b. Identify its coefficient matrix.

   c. Identify its constant matrix.

   _____ _____ _____

Skills Objective C: Use matrices to solve systems of two or three linear equations.

In 2–7, use matrices to solve the system. Then check.

2. $\begin{cases} 3x - 4y = 9 \\ 8x - 10y = 20 \end{cases}$

3. $\begin{cases} 4x + 3y = 0 \\ 2x + y = 6 \end{cases}$

4. $\begin{cases} 3a - 4b + 6c = 1 \\ 2a + 4b - 8c = 14 \\ 9a - 10b + 5c = 7 \end{cases}$

5. $\begin{cases} 2g + 7h = 27 \\ 6g + 21h = 81 \end{cases}$

6. $\begin{cases} 4.2g + 5h = 64.1 \\ -5g - 2h = -52.2 \end{cases}$

7. $\begin{cases} 3x + 4y - 7z = -11 \\ 5x - y + z = -36 \\ x + y = -8 \end{cases}$

▶ **LESSON MASTER 5-6 B** *page 2*

Properties Objective D: Recognize properties of systems of equations.

8. What is true of the coefficient matrix of every linear system that has exactly one solution?

_____

Uses Objective F: Use systems of two or three linear equations to solve real-world problems.

9. Half a watermelon and a half pound of cherries cost $3.09.
A whole watermelon and two pounds of cherries cost $8.16.

   a. Write a system of equations that can be used to find the cost of each type of fruit. _____

   b. Use matrices to solve the system and find the cost of each type of fruit.

      watermelon _____ cherries _____

10. For the Summer Rock Festival, there is one price for students, one for adults, and another for senior citizens. The Rueda family bought 3 student tickets and 2 adult tickets for $104. The Cosentinos bought 5 student tickets, 1 adult ticket, and 2 senior tickets for $155. The Cragins bought 2 of each for $126.

   a. Write a system of equations that can be used to find the cost of each ticket. _____

   b. Use matrices to solve the system and find the cost of each ticket.

      students _____ adults _____ seniors _____

Review Objective H, Lesson 5-1

In 11–14, graph on the number line.

11. $e < 2$ and $e > -5$

◀——————————————▶

12. $x \geq 3$ or $x < 0$

◀——————————————▶

13. $\{r: r < 1\} \cap \{r: r > -8\}$

◀——————————————▶

14. $\{k: k < 4\} \cap \{k: k \geq 2\}$

◀——————————————▶

Name

Vocabulary

1. **a.** A line drawn in a plane separates the plane into two distinct regions called ___?___. The line itself is the ___?___.

_____   _____

   b. Draw and label a diagram to illustrate the terms given in your answer to Part a.

Representations Objective J: Graph linear inequalities in two variables.

2. The inequality $ax + by \leq c$ is graphed at the right. Match each point identified on the graph with the sentence it satisfies.

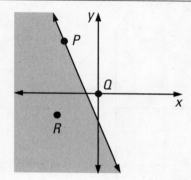

   P _____   (a) $ax + by > c$

   Q _____   (b) $ax + by = c$

   R _____   (c) $ax + by < c$

In 3–6, write an inequality that describes the shaded region.

3.
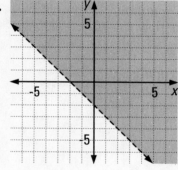

_____

4.
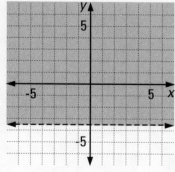

_____

▶ **LESSON MASTER 5-7 B** *page 2*

5.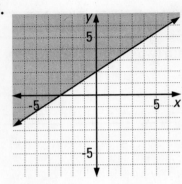

6.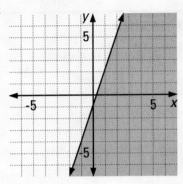

In 7–10, graph the given inequality on the coordinate plane.

7. $y < -1$

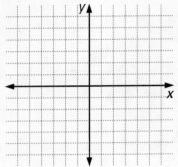

8. $y \geq -2x - 3$

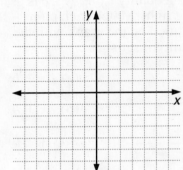

9. $-2x - 3y > 9$

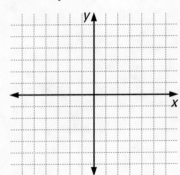

10. $x \geq 2.5$

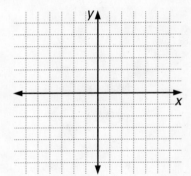

LESSON MASTER

5-8 B

Vocabulary

1. a. What is the *feasible set* for a system of inequalities?

_____

b. What are the *vertices* of a feasible set?

_____

_____

Properties Objective E: Recognize properties of systems of inequalities.

2. A system of inequalities is graphed at the right. Does the given point satisfy the system?

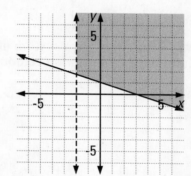

a. (-2, 4) _____ **b.** (0, 0) _____

c. (-2, 1) _____ **d.** (2, 2) _____

e. (0, 3) _____ **f.** (3, 0) _____

Representations Objective K: Solve systems of inequalities by graphing.

In 3 and 4, a system of linear inequalities is given.
a. Graph the feasible region. b. Find the coordinates
of each vertex of the region.

3. $\begin{cases} y > 2x \\ y < -x - 3 \end{cases}$

4. $\begin{cases} x \geq 0 \\ y \leq 3 \\ y < \frac{1}{2}x + 2 \end{cases}$

a.

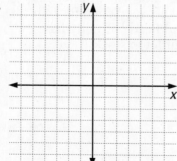

a.

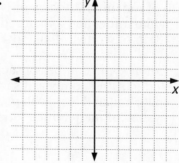

b. _____

b. _____

In 5 and 6, graph the solution set.

5. $\begin{cases} y < x + 1 \\ x + 2y \geq -3 \end{cases}$

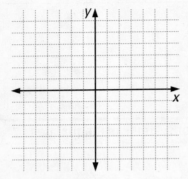

6. $\begin{cases} x \geq -2 \\ y \geq -3 \\ x + y \leq 1 \\ x - 3y \leq 12 \end{cases}$

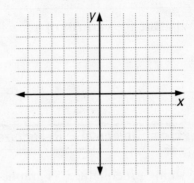

In 7 and 8, write a system of inequalities that describes the shaded region.

7.

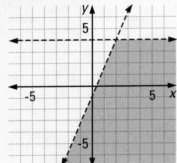

_____

8.

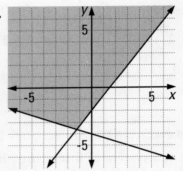

_____

9. A sack of Nutri-Plus parakeet seed contains 8 lb of white millet and 2 lb of red millet. A sack of Ultra-Grow parakeet seed contains 6 lb of white millet and 4 lb of red millet. Seed and Feed currently has 9,000 lb of white millet and 4,000 lb of red millet in stock.

   a. Let n be the number of sacks of Nutri-Plus and u be the number of sacks of Ultra-Grow that Feed and Seed can package. Give a system of inequalities satisfied by n and u.

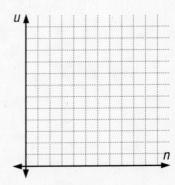

   _____

   b. Graph the feasible set for the system in Part a and label the vertices.

Name _____

LESSON MASTER 5-9 B

Questions on SPUR Objectives

Properties Objective E: Recognize properties of systems of inequalities.

1. *Multiple choice.* List all of the following shaded regions
   that could be the feasible region of a linear-programming
   problem. Explain your answer.

(a)   (b)   (c)   (d)

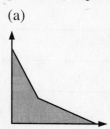 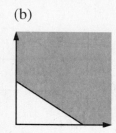 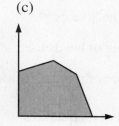 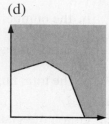

_____

_____

**In 2 and 3, use the graph at the right.
It shows the feasible region of a linear-
programming problem.**

2. Name the points which could be solutions
   to the linear-programming problem.

   _____

3. Find the point in the feasible region
   that minimizes $P = 2.8x + 1.5y$.

   _____

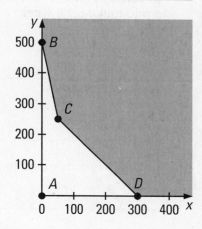

Uses Objective G: Use linear programming to solve real-world problems.

**In 4–8, refer to the following situation: Justine makes
jewelry to sell at a flea market. She can currently make
a pair of earrings with 20 beads in 30 minutes and a
necklace with 30 beads in 30 minutes. She plans to use
no more than 600 beads, work a maximum of 12 hours
(720 minutes), and make at least 5 pairs of earrings
and 5 necklaces. Let e be the number of pairs of earrings
and n be the number of necklaces she can make. The system
of inequalities for this problem is below.**

$$\begin{cases} 20e + 30n \leq 600 \\ 30e + 30n \leq 720 \\ \quad\quad e \geq 5 \\ \quad\quad n \geq 5 \end{cases}$$

▶ **LESSON MASTER 5-9 B** *page 2*

4. Match each inequality in the system with the aspect of the situation.

   (i) $20e + 30n \leq 600$ (ii) $30e + 30n \leq 720$

   (iii) $e \geq 5$ (iv) $n \geq 5$

   a. the number of pairs of earrings   _____

   b. the number of necklaces   _____

   c. the total number of beads used   _____

   d. the total number of minutes worked   _____

5. Graph the system of inequalities and determine the feasible region. Let *e* be the independent variable.

6. Give three possible combinations of earrings and necklaces Justine could make each week.

   _____

   _____

   _____

7. List the vertices of the feasible region.

   _____

8. Justine makes $3.25 profit on each pair of earrings and $5 profit on each necklace. She generally sells every piece of jewelry she makes.

   a. Write an expression for Justine's total profit in terms of *e* and *n*.   _____

   b. Calculate the profits for your answers in Question 6.   _____

   c. How many pairs of earrings and how many necklaces should Justine make to maximize the profit?

   earrings _____   necklaces _____

   d. What is the maximum amount of profit she can make?   _____

LESSON MASTER 5-10 B

Uses Objective G: Use linear programming to solve real-world problems.

In 1–5, refer to the following situation: Mr. Santos needs to borrow at least $50,000, some from a credit union and the rest from a bank. At both institutions, he will repay the amount he borrows after 5 years, but he will need to pay simple interest on the loans for each of the five years. He can borrow no more than $35,000 from the credit union, and he wants the amount borrowed from the bank to be no more than the amount borrowed from the credit union. The credit union charges 11.5% interest and the bank charges 13% interest. Mr. Santos wants to minimize his costs in a single year.

1. Let c be the amount borrowed from the credit union and b be the amount borrowed from the bank. Write a system of three inequalities for this situation. _____

2. Graph the system of inequalities and determine the feasible region. Let c be the independent variable.

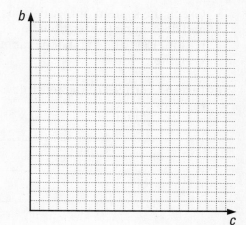

3. List the vertices of the feasible region.

_____

_____

_____

4. Write the expression to be minimized.

_____

5. **a.** According to the Linear-Programming Theorem, how can you find the least expensive plan for Mr. Santos?

_____

_____

b. How much should Mr. Santos borrow from each institution?

credit union _____   bank _____

c. What is the minimum amount of interest Mr. Santos will need to pay in a year? _____

Name _____

In 6–10, refer to the following situation: A convention center designated a maximum of 34,000 square feet of floor space for trade-show exhibits. The space will be divided into two types of areas, wired and unwired zones. Wired zones are for exhibits that require electricity; each occupies 500 sq ft and accommodates 4 exhibits. Unwired zones are for exhibits that do not require electricity; each occupies 850 sq ft and accommodates 6 exhibits. There will be at least 10 of each type of zone, but no more than 40 wired zones. There is not enough space to accommodate all the companies that have applied to exhibit. Linear programming can be used to determine how many wired zones and unwired zones should be used to accommodate as many exhibits as possible.

6. Let *w* be the number of wired zones and *u* be the number of unwired zones. Write a system of inequalities to describe this situation. _____

7. Graph the system of inequalities and determine the feasible region. Let *w* be the independent variable.

8. List the vertices of the feasible region.

   _____

   _____

   _____

   _____

9. Write the expression to be maximized. _____

10. **a.** According to the Linear-Programming Theorem, how can you determine the numbers of wired zones and unwired zones that should be used to accommodate as many exhibits as possible?

    _____

    _____

    b. How many of each type of zone should be planned?

    wired _____   unwired _____

    c. What is the maximum number of exhibits possible? _____

LESSON MASTER

6-1
B

Vocabulary

In 1–3, match the equation or expression with the
English phrase.

1. $ax^2 + bx + c = 0$ _____ (a) the general quadratic expression in the variable x

2. $f{:}x \rightarrow ax^2 + bx + c$ _____ (b) the general quadratic equation in the variable x

3. $ax^2 + bx + c$ _____ (c) the general quadratic function in the variable x

Skills Objective A: Expand squares of binomials.

In 4–15, expand and simplify.

4. $(u + 8)^2$

5. $(v - 4)^2$

6. $(6x + 1)^2$

7. $(a + 3b)^2$

8. $(5g - 4h)^2$

9. $(\frac{1}{4} - b)^2$

10. $(8q - \frac{1}{2})^2$

11. $(9d + 4e)^2$

12. $3(3 + c)^2$

13. $(2x + 1)^2 + (2x - 1)^2$

14. $\frac{3}{4}(6p + 4)^2$

15. $-9(2k - 5)^2 - 2(k + 3)^2$

16. Solve for a: $x^2 + 14x + 49 = (x + a)^2$ _____

17. Solve for e: $x^2 - 40x + 400 = (x + e)^2$ _____

▶ **LESSON MASTER 6-1B** *page 2*

Uses Objective G: Use quadratic equations to solve area problems.

---

18. Refer to the diagram at the right. Give the area of each region in standard form.

    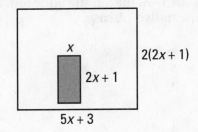

    a. Shaded rectangle _____

    b. Larger rectangle _____

    c. Unshaded region _____

19. Suppose a park district plans to build a rectangular playground 80 m by 60 m with a walkway *w* meters wide around it.

    a. At the right, draw and label a diagram to represent this situation.

    b. Write an expression in standard form for the total area of the playground and walkway.

    _____

    c. Find the total area if *w* = 3. _____

Review Objective C, Lesson 1–5; Objective H, Lesson 5–1

In 20–22, solve.

20. $4m + 12 = 9m + 67$

21. $\dfrac{15}{a} = 4$

22. $0.45u + 0.6(4u) - 3.5(7u - 5.5) = -(20u + 22)$

In 23 and 24, graph on the number line.

23. $y \leq 12$ and $y \geq 0$

24. $e > \text{-}2$ or $e < \text{-}11$

LESSON MASTER 6-2 B

Vocabulary

1. Give an algebraic definition for the *absolute value* of *x*.

   _____

2. Define the term and give an example.

   a. *square root* _____

   _____

   b. *rational number* _____

   _____

   c. *irrational number* _____

   _____

Skills Objective C: Solve quadratic equations.

In 3–8, solve.

3. $w^2 = 144$ _____ 4. $m^2 = 66$ _____

5. $a^2 = 3.61$ _____ 6. $\frac{25}{81} = x^2$ _____

7. $(x + 8)^2 = 0$ _____ 8. $(2r - 6)^2 = 0$ _____

Properties Objective E: Apply the definition of absolute value and the Absolute Value-Square Root Theorem.

In 9–17, evaluate.

9. $|{-55.3}|$ _____ 10. $|711|$ _____ 11. $-|0.8|$ _____

12. $\sqrt{81}$ _____ 13. $\sqrt{(-13)^2}$ _____ 14. $\sqrt{67.2^2}$ _____

15. $\sqrt{(3-8)^2}$ _____ 16. $-\sqrt{(-10)^2}$ _____ 17. $-\sqrt{400}$ _____

18. When does $|x| = -x$? _____

▶ **LESSON MASTER** 6-2 B *page 2*

In 19–22, solve.

19. $|x + 9| = 33$

20. $|c - 5.2| = 3.1$

21. $42 = |3x|$

22. $|\frac{2}{3}p - 8| = 2$

Uses Objective G: use quadratic equations to solve area problems.

23. A square and a circle have the same area.
The square has side 8. To the nearest
hundredth, what is the radius of the circle? _____

Representations Objective J: Graph the absolute-value functions and
interpret the graphs.

In 24 and 25, a function is given. a. Graph the function.
b. Give the domain and the range of the function.

24. $f(x) = -2|x|$

25. $g(x) = |-2x|$

a.

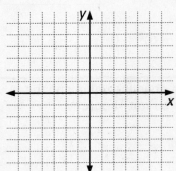

a.

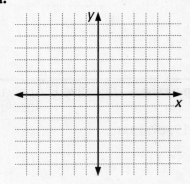

b. _____

_____

b. _____

_____

LESSON MASTER

6-3
B

Questions on SPUR Objectives

Vocabulary

1. Write the general *vertex form* of an equation for a parabola.

_____

2. If a parabola opens down, does it have a
minimum or maximum y-value? _____

Uses Objective I: Use the Graph-Translation Theorem to interpret equations
and graphs.

**In 3–6, a translation is described. a. Give an equation for
the image of the graph of $y = x^2$ under this translation.
b. Name the vertex of the image.**

3. 3 units right, 4 units down

    a. _____

    b. _____

4. 6 units left, 2 units up

    a. _____

    b. _____

5. 7 units left

    a. _____

    b. _____

6. 3 units up

    a. _____

    b. _____

**In 7–10, an equation and a translation are given.
a. Give an equation for the image of the graph of the
equation under the translation. b. Give an equation
for the axis of symmetry.**

7. $y = 4x^2$ $T_{-3,5}$

    a. _____

    b. _____

8. $y = -7x^2$ $T_{6,2}$

    a. _____

    b. _____

9. $y = -\frac{7}{3}x^2$ $T_{-4,-4}$

    a. _____

    b. _____

10. $y = -\frac{1}{2}x^2$ $T_{0,-8}$

    a. _____

    b. _____

▶ **LESSON MASTER 6-3 B** *page 2*

In 11 and 12, assume parabola *P* is a translation image of parabola *Q* at the right.

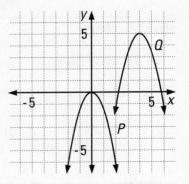

11. What translation maps
parabola *P* onto parabola *Q*? _____

12. Parabola *P* has equation $y = -\frac{3}{2}x^2$.

What is an equation of parabola *Q*?

_____

Representations Objective J: Graph parabolas and interpret the graphs.

In 13–16, an equation for a parabola is given. a. Graph the parabola and show its axis of symmetry. b. Identify its vertex. c. Write an equation for the axis of symmetry.

13. $y = 2(x - 3)^2$

a.

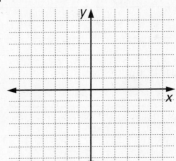

b. _____ c. _____

14. $y - 1 = (x + 4)^2$

a.

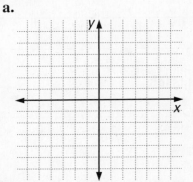

b. _____ c. _____

15. $y + 3 = x^2$

a.

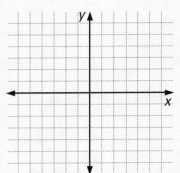

b. _____ c. _____

16. $y - 5 = -2x^2$

a.

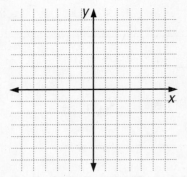

b. _____ c. _____

LESSON MASTER

6-4
B

Skills Objective B: Transform quadratic equations from vertex form to standard form.

In 1–6, write the equation in standard form.

1. $y + 6 = (x - 3)^2$

_____

2. $y - 1 = 2(x - 4)^2$

_____

3. $y = (x + 7)^2$

_____

4. $y = -3(x + 5)^2 + 8$

_____

5. $y + 14 = -x^2$

_____

6. $y - 2 = \frac{2}{3}(x - 9)^2$

_____

Uses Objective G: Use quadratic equations to solve problems dealing with velocity and acceleration.

7. Suppose a ball is thrown upward from a height of 5 feet with an initial velocity of 35 ft/sec.

   a. Write an equation relating the time t and the height h of the ball. _____

   b. Find the height of the ball after 2 seconds. _____

   c. Is the ball still in the air after 3 seconds? Explain.

   _____

   _____

8. Chizuko threw a stone upward at a speed of 10m/sec while standing on a cliff 40 m above the ground.

   a. What was the height of the stone after 3 seconds? _____

   b. Estimate how long it took for the stone to touch the ground. _____

► **LESSON MASTER 6-4 B** *page 2*

9. Kenny is standing on a bridge 22 feet above the water. Suppose he drops a ball over the 3-foot railing.

   a. Write an equation relating the time t (in seconds) and the height h (in feet) of the ball above the water.

   _____

   b. Graph the equation from Part a.

   c. Estimate how long it will take for the ball to hit the water. Explain your reasoning.

   _____

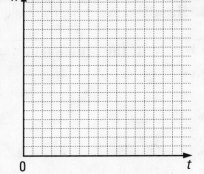

Representations Objective J: Graph quadratic functions and interpret the graphs.

10. Graph $y = x^2 + 2x - 8$.

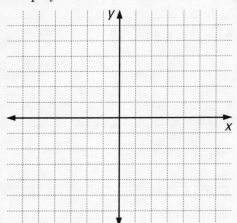

11. Graph $y = -2x^2 + 7x + 5$.

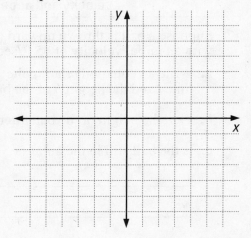

12. The height of a ball thrown upward is shown as a function of time on the graph.

   a. Estimate the initial height of the ball. _____

   b. Approximately when did the ball reach its maximum height? _____

   c. What was the maximum height? _____

   d. When was the ball 8 m high? _____

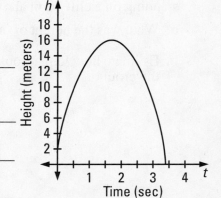

LESSON MASTER **Questions on SPUR Objectives**

Vocabulary

1. **a.** What is a *perfect-square trinomial?*

   _____

   b. Give an example of a perfect-square trinomial. _____

Representations Objective B: Transform quadratic equations from standard form to vertex form.

In 2–7, fill in the blank to make the expression a perfect-square trinomial.

2. $y = x^2 + 8x +$ _____

3. $y = x^2 - 20x +$ _____

4. $y = x^2 + 5x +$ _____

5. $y = x^2 - \frac{2}{3}x +$ _____

6. $y = x^2 - bx +$ _____

7. $y = x^2 + \frac{b}{4}x +$ _____

In 8–17, transform the equation into vertex form.

8. $y = x^2 + 12x + 40$

9. $y = x^2 - 10x + 10$

10. $y = x^2 - 6x - 15$

11. $y = x^2 + 3x + 7$

12. $y = 6x^2 - 18x - 5$

13. $y = -3x^2 + 15x$

► **LESSON MASTER 6-5 B** *page 2*

14. $y = x^2 - 9x + 4$ **15.** $y = x^2 + 18x + 81$

_____   _____

16. $y = \frac{1}{4}x^2 - 3x + 2$ **17.** $8y = 4x^2 + 24x - 6$

_____   _____

In 18–21, find the vertex of the parabola determined by the equation.

18. $y = x^2 - 8x + 13$ **19.** $y = -x^2 - 16x - 68$

_____   _____

20. $y = \frac{1}{2}x^2 - 3x + 8$ **21.** $y = 4x^2 + 16x - 1$

_____   _____

22. *Multiple choice.* The graphs of which equation(s)
    have the same vertex as the graph of $y = x^2 + 14x + 52$?   _____

   (a) $y = x^2 + 14x - 52$ (b) $y = -x^2 - 14x - 46$

   (c) $y = 2x^2 + 28x + 101$ (d) $y = x^2 + 6x + 2$

Review Objective D, Lesson 3-8

In 23–26, an arithmetic sequence is given.
a. Find a formula for the nth term. b. Find a_{20}.

23. 18, 11, 4, -3, -10, -17, . . .   **24.** 109, 129, 149, 169, 189, . . .

   a. _____   a. _____

   b. _____   b. _____

25. 1.55, 2.56, 3.57, 4.58, 5.59, . . .   **26.** $\frac{1}{3}, \frac{4}{3}, \frac{7}{3}, \frac{10}{3}, \ldots$

   a. _____   a. _____

   b. _____   b. _____

LESSON MASTER 6-6 B

Uses Objective H: Fit a quadratic model to data.

1. Lola is studying geodesic domes, glass domes constructed of nearly equilateral connected triangles. She made some models of connected triangles with toothpicks, as pictured below. The side of the first figure is 1 toothpick long, the side of the second figure is 2 toothpicks long, and so on.

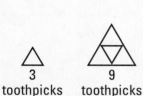

3
toothpicks

9
toothpicks

18
toothpicks

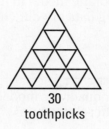

30
toothpicks

a. At the right, draw the next figure with side 5 toothpicks long.

b. How many toothpicks are required?

_____

c. Use a quadratic model to find a formula for $t(s)$, the number of toothpicks in a figure whose side is s toothpicks long.

_____

d. Use your formula to find the number of toothpicks in a figure with side 6 toothpicks long. Then, at the right, draw the figure with side 6 toothpicks long to verify that your formula is correct.

_____

e. How many toothpicks would be required for a figure with a side 50 toothpicks long?

_____

▶ **LESSON MASTER 6-6 B** *page 2*

2. The table below gives the average amount donated to a university alumni fund last year.

Age of Alumnus A	24	30	40	50	60	70
Donation D	$28	$32	$47	$71	$88	$115

a. Draw a scatterplot of the data.

b. Fit a quadratic model to these data using data of your choice.

_____

c. Plot your quadratic model on your scatterplot.

d. Use your model to predict the average amount donated by 80-year-old alumni.

_____

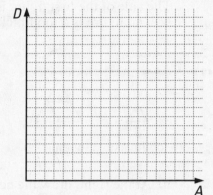

3. The table below gives the prices of a company's color television sets.

Sizes (in.)	5	9	13	19	25	31	35
Price p ($)	$240	$158	$125	$275	$610	$1145	$1690

a. Draw a scatterplot of the data.

b. Fit a quadratic model to these data using the data for the 5-, 19-, and 31-in. televisions.

_____

c. Plot your quadratic model on your scatterplot.

d. Use your model to predict the cost of a 39-inch television.

_____

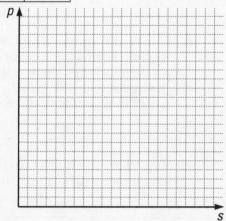

4. In which of Questions 1, 2, and 3 does your quadratic model fit the data exactly?

_____

LESSON MASTER

6-7
B

Vocabulary

1. Write the complete statement of the *Quadratic Formula Theorem.*

Skills Objective C: Solve quadratic equations.

In 2–15, use the Quadratic Formula to solve the equation.

2. $x^2 + 8x + 12 = 0$

3. $n^2 - 6n - 27 = 0$

4. $8c^2 + 2c - 3 = 0$

5. $-3x^2 - 7x + 40 = 0$

6. $x^2 - 16x + 64 = 0$

7. $0 = w(w - 12)$

8. $2v^2 = 3v + 12$

9. $0 = x^2 + 7x + 8$

10. $5x^2 + 6x = 0$

11. $4m^2 - 12m + 9 = 0$

12. $e^2 + 2 = 3e + 11$

13. $(4x + 1)(2x - 3) = 3(x + 4)$

14. $5(a^2 - 7a) = 10$

15. $(x - 11)^2 = (3x + 6)^2$

▶ **LESSON MASTER 6-7 B** *page 2*

16. Consider the parabola with equation $y = 6x^2 - 5x - 4$.

    a. Find its x-intercepts. _____

    b. Find the value(s) of x when $y = 8$. _____

Uses Objective G: Use quadratic equations to solve problems.

17. A square and a rectangle have the same area. The length of the rectangle is 8 less than twice the side of the square. The width of the rectangle is 3 less than the side of the square.

    a. Let x represent the length of the side of the square. Write expressions for the dimensions of the rectangle.

    length _____ width _____

    b. Write an equation that represents the situation. _____

    c. Find the dimensions of the square and rectangle.

    square _____ rectangle _____

18. The path of a ball hit by Giant Dennison is described by the equation $h(x) = -.005x^2 + 2x + 3$. Here, x is the distance (in feet) along the ground of the ball from home plate, and $h(x)$ is the height (in feet) of the ball at that distance.

    a. How high was the ball when Giant hit it? _____

    b. Stretch Hanson caught the ball at the same height at which Giant hit it. How far from the plate was Stretch when he caught the ball? _____

    c. How high was the ball when it was 300 feet from the plate? _____

    d. How far from the plate was the ball when it was 75 feet high? _____

19. A model rocket is launched straight up at an initial velocity of 150 ft/sec. The launch pad is 1 foot off the ground.

    a. When will the rocket be 300 ft high? _____

    b. Will the rocket ever reach a height of 500 ft? Why or why not?

    _____

    _____

    c. When will the rocket hit the ground? _____

LESSON MASTER

6-8
B

Questions on SPUR Objectives

Vocabulary

1. What are *imaginary numbers*?

_____

2. **a.** What symbol is used to designate the
imaginary unit?   _____

   b. What is the value of the imaginary unit?   _____

Skills Objective C: Solve quadratic equations.

In 3–12, solve.

3. $x^2 = -900$

4. $y^2 = -14$

5. $a^2 + 8 = -28$

6. $b^2 - 12 = -13$

7. $5d^2 = -20$

8. $-8g^2 = 24$

9. $3h^2 + 17 = -130$

10. $x^2 + 3x + 8 = 0$

11. $(k - 1)^2 + 20 = 5$

12. $(m + 5)(m - 5) = -31$

Name _____

Skills Objective D: Perform operations with complex numbers.

13. Show that $4i$ is a square root of -16.

_____

14. Show that $i\sqrt{13}$ is a square root of -13.

_____

In 15–36, simplify.

15. $\sqrt{-11}$ _____

16. $\sqrt{-100}$ _____

17. $\sqrt{-8}$ _____

18. $\sqrt{-75}$ _____

19. $\sqrt{-1296}$ _____

20. $\sqrt{-288}$ _____

21. $8i^2$ _____

22. $-5i^2$ _____

23. $6i + 9i$ _____

24. $10i - 16i$ _____

25. $(7i)(3i)$ _____

26. $(6i)^2$ _____

27. $\sqrt{-16} + \sqrt{-4}$ _____

28. $\sqrt{-81} - \sqrt{-64}$ _____

29. $\sqrt{-25}\,\sqrt{-100}$ _____

30. $\sqrt{-49}\,\sqrt{-49}$ _____

31. $\sqrt{-5}\,\sqrt{-10}$ _____

32. $\sqrt{-100}\,\sqrt{100}$ _____

33. $(i\sqrt{3})^2$ _____

34. $2i(3i + 9i)$ _____

35. $\dfrac{\sqrt{-36}}{\sqrt{-81}}$ _____

36. $\dfrac{12i}{3i}$ _____

Review Multiplying binomials, previous course

In 37–40, multiply and simplify.

37. $(x + 6)(x + 2)$

38. $(m - 5)(m + 10)$

_____

39. $(2n + 1)(3n - 6)$

40. $(b - 8c)(4b - 3c)$

_____

LESSON MASTER 6-9 B

Vocabulary

1. Give a complete definition for *complex number*. Be sure to identify the real part and the imaginary part.

_____

_____

_____

In 2–6, name the real part and the imaginary part of the number.

	Real Part	Imaginary Part
2. $7 + 3i$	_____	_____
3. $-4 + i$	_____	_____
4. $6i$	_____	_____
5. $\sqrt{15} - 2i$	_____	_____
6. 24	_____	_____

7. Give the complex conjugate of the number $a + bi$. _____

In 8 and 9, give the complex conjugate of the number.

8. $2 + 9i$ _____

9. $\sqrt{5} - i$ _____

Skills Objective D: Perform operations with complex numbers.

In 10–19, rewrite the expression in $a + bi$ form.

10. $\dfrac{8 + 4i}{4}$ _____

11. $\dfrac{9 - 24i}{3i}$ _____

12. $-7i$ _____

13. 18π _____

14. $\sqrt{-16}$ _____

15. $-\sqrt{3}$ _____

16. $\dfrac{2 - i}{3 + 5i}$ _____

17. $\dfrac{4 + i}{6 - i}$ _____

18. $\dfrac{7}{-2 + 2i}$ _____

19. $\dfrac{12i}{10 + 3i}$ _____

► **LESSON MASTER 6-9 B** *page 2*

In 20–31, perform the operations and write the answer in $a + bi$ form.

20. $(12 + 3i) - (2 + 6i)$

21. $(7 + i)(3 - 4i)$

22. $(8 - i)(8 + i)$

23. $(4 - 3i) + (10 + 2i)$

24. $5(6 - 4i)$

25. $7i(1 + 5i)$

26. $(3 + 9i)(3 - 9i)$

27. $(5 - 2i)(1 - 3i)$

28. $(4 - i)^2$

29. $(7i + 2)^2$

30. $(\sqrt{3} + i)^2$

31. $(\sqrt{3} + i\sqrt{3})^2$

In 32–37, suppose $p = 4 + i$ and $q = -3 - 2i$. Evaluate and write the answer in $a + bi$ form.

32. $2p - iq$

33. pq

34. q^2

35. iq

36. $p^2 + 2p - 3$

37. $(ip)^2 - (iq)^2$

LESSON MASTER  6-10 B

Vocabulary

1. Consider the quadratic equation $ax^2 + bx + c = 0$.

   a. Give the *discriminant*.

   _____

   b. What does the discriminant determine?

   _____

   _____

2. What are the *roots* of an equation?

   _____

Skills Objective C: Solve quadratic equations.

In 3–6, solve.

3. $2x^2 - x + 15 = 0$

4. $2h^2 - h - 15 = 0$

5. $(3m + 1)^2 - 5 = 0$

6. $16x^2 - 72x + 81 = 0$

Properties Objective F: Use the discriminant of a quadratic equation to determine the nature of the solutions to the equation.

In 7–9, suppose D is the discriminant for a quadratic equation. Tell how many roots there are to the equation and tell whether they are *real* or *not real*.

7. $D = 0$ _____ _____

8. $D > 0$ _____ _____

9. $D < 0$ _____ _____

10. Consider the equation $ax^2 + bx + c$. Complete the following statement: If a, b, and c are ___?___ and $b^2 - 4ac$ is ___?___, then the solutions to the equation are rational numbers.

   _____ _____

▶ **LESSON MASTER 6-10 B** *page 2*

In 11–14, a quadratic equation is given. **a.** Calculate
its discriminant. **b.** Give the numbers of real solutions.
c. Tell whether the real solutions are *rational* or *irrational*.

11. $x^2 - 3x + 6 = 0$ **12.** $2x^2 - x - 40 = 0$

    a. _____   **a.** _____

    b. _____   **b.** _____

    c. _____   **c.** _____

13. $e^2 - 8e + 16 = 0$ **14.** $5x^2 - 6x - 11 = 0$

    a. _____   **a.** _____

    b. _____   **b.** _____

    c. _____   **c.** _____

In 15–20, give the number of real solutions.

15. $m^2 - 5m + 7 = 0$ _____   **16.** $3x^2 - x - 10 = 0$ _____

17. $8w^2 = 3w$ _____   **18.** $5x^2 - 10x = 5$ _____

19. $9 + 7x = 3 - 4x^2$ _____   **20.** $5d^2 + 144 = 0$ _____

Representations   Objective K: Use the discriminant of a quadratic equation
to determine the number of *x*-intercepts of
the graph.

In 21–24, give the number of *x*-intercepts of the graph
of the equation.

21. $y = 9x^2 - 30x + 25$ _____   **22.** $y = -x^2 - 5x - 8$ _____

23. $y + 13x = 14x^2 + 3$ _____   **24.** $y = 2(x^2 - 2x) - 7$ _____

In 25–27, suppose *D* is the discriminant for a quadratic
equation. Sketch a possible graph of the equation.

25. $D = 0$ **26.** $D > 0$ **27.** $D < 0$

 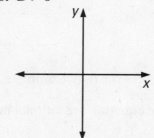 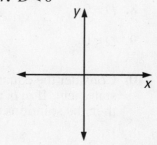

Name _____

Vocabulary

1. Consider the expression 6^4. Identify

   a. the base. _____ **b.** the exponent. _____ **c.** the power. _____

2. Complete each equation to express the given power function.

   a. squaring function: $f(x) =$ _____

   b. cubing function: $f(x) =$ _____

   c. 8th power function: $f(x) =$ _____

   d. identity function: $f(x) =$ _____

   e. nth-power function: $f(x) =$ _____, where n is _____

Uses Objective F: Solve real-world problems which can be modeled by expressions with nth powers.

---

3. Consider a 10-question *true-false* test.

   a. Doreen has a 90% probability of answering each question correctly. What is the probability that Doreen will answer all 10 questions correctly? _____

   b. Mel has an 80% probability of answering each question correctly. What is the probability that Mel will answer all 10 questions correctly? _____

   c. Suppose someone decides to randomly guess at each answer. What is the probability that all 10 questions will be answered correctly? _____

4. Mrs. Montoyo has a computer golf game. She has a 60% chance of shooting par or better on each hole.

   a. What is the probability that Mrs. Montoyo will shoot par or better on each of the first 5 holes? _____

   b. What is the probability that Mrs. Montoyo will shoot par or better on each of the holes in a 9-hole course? _____

   c. What is the probability that Mrs. Montoyo will shoot par or better on each of the holes in an 18-hole course? _____

▶ **LESSON MASTER 7-1 B** *page 2*

Representations Objective I: Graph *n*th power functions.

In 5–8, consider the following graphs. For what values of *n*,
if any, could the graph represent a power function, $y = x^n$? If
the graph cannot represent a power function, tell why.

5.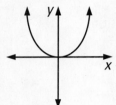

_____

6.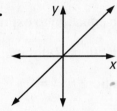

_____

7.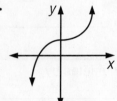

_____

8.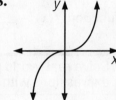

_____

9. The point (-3, -243) is on the graph of a power function.

   a. Is the function an even or odd power function? _____

   b. Does the graph have a minimum or a maximum
   value? If so, what is its value? _____

   c. Write an equation for the function. _____

10. **a.** On the same coordinate grid, sketch
    graphs of $f(x) = x^2$ and $g(x) = x^4$.

    b. For what values(s) of *x* is $g(x) = f(x)$?

    _____

    c. For what values(s) of *x* is $g(x) > f(x)$?

    _____

    _____

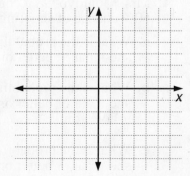

LESSON MASTER 7-2 B

Skills Objective A: Evaluate b^n when $b > 0$ and n is a rational number.
Objective B: Simplify expressions using properties of exponents.

In 1–20, simplify.

1. $x^4 \cdot x^8$ _____

2. $(r^5)^3$ _____

3. $(3d^3)^4$ _____

4. $5m^2 \cdot 2m^6$ _____

5. $7y \cdot 2y^9$ _____

6. $(-4g)^2$ _____

7. $-(2r^3)^6$ _____

8. $(x^2)^8(2x^4)^3$ _____

9. $\dfrac{c^6}{c^2}$ _____

10. $\dfrac{u^{17}}{u^0}$ _____

11. $\dfrac{12c^5}{4c^2}$ _____

12. $\dfrac{d^4 \cdot a^2}{a \cdot a^3}$ _____

13. $\left(\dfrac{w}{3}\right)^5$ _____

14. $\left(\dfrac{12}{n}\right)^2\left(\dfrac{n}{2}\right)^4$ _____

15. $\dfrac{(-5k^4)^4}{5^2k^{15}}$ _____

16. $\left(\dfrac{m}{n}\right)^8\left(\dfrac{n}{m}\right)^8$ _____

17. $4xy^4z^2 \cdot 3x^6y^9z^2$ _____

18. $a^2b^5c^8 \cdot b^4c^3d$ _____

19. $\dfrac{s^3 \cdot s^{10} \cdot u^8}{s \cdot s^{12} \cdot u}$ _____

20. $(\pi r^3)(3r)^2$ _____

In 21–31, evaluate and write in standard form.

21. $(-4)^4$ _____

22. $(-18)^0$ _____

23. $(-3)^7$ _____

24. $(6^2)^3$ _____

25. $4^3 \cdot 5^3$ _____

26. $\dfrac{8^5}{8^3}$ _____

27. $8.9 \cdot 10^5$ _____

28. $511 \cdot 10^0$ _____

29. $\dfrac{325 \cdot 10^9}{25 \cdot 10^6}$ _____

30. $\dfrac{1.2 \cdot 10^{12}}{1.6 \cdot 10^{12}}$ _____

31. $(6.3 \cdot 10^3)(9.4 \cdot 10^7)$ _____

▶ **LESSON MASTER 7-2 B** *page 2*

Properties Objective E: Recognize properties of *n*th powers.

In 32–37, match the equation with the property it illustrates.

32. $(u^4)^5 = u^{20}$ _____   (a) Quotient of Powers Postulate

33. $\dfrac{e^{12}}{e^4} = e^8$ _____   (b) Power of a Product Postulate

34. $\left(\dfrac{c}{v}\right)^4 = \dfrac{c^4}{v^4}$ _____   (c) Power of a Power Postulate

35. $r^0 = 1$,
    for $r \neq 0$ _____   (d) Product of Powers Postulate

36. $(3b^6)^2 = 9b^{12}$ _____   (e) Zero Exponent Theorem

37. $g^3 \cdot g^8 = g^{11}$ _____   (f) Power of a Quotient Postulate

Uses Objective F: Solve real-world problems which can be modeled by expressions with *n*th powers.

38. A Merit Driver Citation is given to everyone who answers correctly all the questions in Parts I and II of the driving test. Each part has 7 questions. Suppose a person estimates that the probability of correctly answering a question in Part I is *j* and the probability of correctly answering a question in Part II is *k*. Assuming the questions are independent, what is the probability that this person will earn a Merit Driver Citation? _____

39. The diameter of Saturn is about $1.2 \cdot 10^5$ km. Estimate Saturn's volume. _____

In 40–44, find the average number of people per square mile.

	State	Land Area (sq. mi)	Population (1992)	People per Sq.Mi
40.	Michigan	$5.8 \cdot 10^4$	$9.4 \cdot 10^6$	
41.	Idaho	$8.3 \cdot 10^4$	$1 \cdot 10^6$	
42.	Texas	$2.6 \cdot 10^6$	$17.7 \cdot 10^6$	
43.	New Jersey	$7.4 \cdot 10^3$	$7.79 \cdot 10^6$	
44.	Alaska	$5.7 \cdot 10^5$	$.59 \cdot 10^6$	

LESSON MASTER 7-3 B

Skills Objective A: Evaluate b^n when $b > 0$ and n is a negative integer.
Objective B: Simplify expressions using the Negative-Exponent Theorem.

In 1–21, write as a decimal or a simple fraction.

1. 8^{-3} _____

2. 6^{-1} _____

3. $\left(\frac{5}{6}\right)^{-1}$ _____

4. $\left(\frac{3}{2}\right)^{-3}$ _____

5. $(-5)^{-2}$ _____

6. $-(-3)^{-4}$ _____

7. $3^{-2} \cdot 3^{-1}$ _____

8. $7^{-5} \cdot 7^3$ _____

9. $4^{-6} \cdot 4^6$ _____

10. $9 \cdot 7^{-4}$ _____

11. $-\left(\frac{1}{7}\right)^{-3}$ _____

12. $\frac{8^4}{8^7}$ _____

13. $\frac{5^{-2}}{5^3}$ _____

14. $\frac{7^2}{7^{-2}}$ _____

15. $\frac{12}{12^3}$ _____

16. $\frac{9^{-4} \cdot 13^{-2}}{9 \cdot 13^{-3}}$ _____

17. 10^{-7} _____

18. $1.4 \cdot 10^{-3}$ _____

19. $\frac{6 \cdot 10^4}{1.5 \cdot 10^8}$ _____

20. $(8 \cdot 10^{-2})(22 \cdot 10^{-4})$ _____

21. $\frac{2 \cdot 10^{-4}}{5 \cdot 10^2}$ _____

In 22–31, simplify and write the result using only positive exponents.

22. $x^8 \cdot x^{-6}$ _____

23. $m^{-7} \cdot m^4$ _____

24. $c^{-5} \cdot c^{-2}$ _____

25. $(5b)^{-3}$ _____

26. $\frac{e^{-5}}{e}$ _____

27. $\frac{s^{-8}}{s^{-2}}$ _____

28. $(3c^{-2})^{-4}$ _____

29. $(5^{-2} \cdot y^2)^2 (2xy^4)^{-3}$ _____

30. $\left(\frac{4r^5}{3r^6}\right)^{-1}$ _____

31. $\left(\frac{5x}{10y}\right)^{-3}\left(\frac{2y}{15x^2}\right)$ _____

▶ **LESSON MASTER 7-3 B** *page 2*

32. Show why b^n and b^{-n} are reciprocals.

_____

_____

33. In the expression b^n, for what value(s) of n must b be a nonzero number?

_____

_____

Uses Objective F: Solve real-world problems which can be modeled by expressions with negative-integer exponents.

In 34–36, meanings are given for several prefixes used in the metric system. a. Write the number using negative exponents. b. Write the number as a decimal. c. Write the number as a simple fraction.

34. micro: one millionth

a. _____ b. _____ c. _____

35. nano: one billionth

a. _____ b. _____ c. _____

36. pico: one trillionth

a. _____ b. _____ c. _____

37. The cost C of operating an electrical appliance is one-thousandth of the product of W, the number of watts; t, the time in hours; and k, the cost per kilowatt-hour.

a. Write a formula for C using positive exponents. _____

b. Write a formula for C using negative exponents. _____

38. 1 foot$^2 \approx 2.2957 \cdot 10^{-5}$ acres, and 1 acre $= 1.5625 \cdot 10^{-3}$ miles^2. So 1 square foot $\approx$ ___?___ square miles. Fill in the blank with a number in scientific notation. _____

LESSON MASTER

7-4 B

Vocabulary

1. The original amount of money placed in an investment is called the ___?___. _____

2. If a savings account earns *compound interest*, what does this mean?

   _____

   _____

3. The annual rate of interest earned after all the compounding has taken effect is called the ___?___. _____

Uses Objective G: Apply the compound-interest formula.

4. Write the General Compound-Interest Formula and explain what each variable represents.

   _____

   _____

   _____

   _____

5. Norio had invested $800 in a savings account that paid 4.2% interest compounded annually. How much money was in the account after 4 years, if he left the money untouched? _____

6. Mrs. Rubino has put $2,500 in a 5-year CD (certificate of deposit) that pays 7.4% compounded quarterly. How much will the CD be worth when it matures? _____

7. When their daughter was 2 years old, the Nashans paid $7,000 for a 15-year college bond for her. The bond pays 7.1% compounded monthly. Their banker told them that if the money is left alone, it will triple in value. Is the banker right? _____

▶ **LESSON MASTER 7-4 B** *page 2*

8. Nancy has $4,000 in a savings account that pays
   3.9% interest compound semi-annually. Suppose
   the money is left untouched for 10 years.

   a. How much money is in the account after
   the first five years?   _____

   b. How much money is in the account
   after 10 years?   _____

   c. Does the account earn more interest during the first five
   years or the second five years? Explain why this is so.

   _____

   _____

9. Blanca invested $1,800 in an account that pays 4.4%
   compounded daily (365 days a year). If she leaves
   the money alone, how much will be in the account
   after 2.5 years?   _____

10. Find the effective annual yield on an account that pays
    6% compounded quarterly.   _____

Review Objective F, Lesson 3–8

**In 11–14, determine whether or not the given formula
describes an arithmetic sequence. Justify your answer.**

11. $a_n = 4n + 15$ _____

12. $a_n = 2n^2 + 5$ _____

13. $a_n = \frac{1}{3}n$ _____

14. $a_n = \frac{1}{n}$ _____

LESSON MASTER 7-5 B

Vocabulary

1. What is another name for *geometric sequence*?

_____

_____

Skills Objective C: Describe geometric sequences explicitly and recursively.

In 2–11, give the first five terms of the geometric
sequence described.

2. constant ratio 4, first term 1 _____

3. constant ratio .3, first term 8 _____

4. constant ratio $\frac{5}{4}$, first term 20 _____

5. constant ratio -5, first term -5 _____

6. first term 6, second term 18 _____

7. fourth term 20, fifth term 5 _____

8. $g_n = 10(3)^{n-1}$, for integers $n \geq 1$ _____

9. $g_n = 2(-.1)^{n-1}$, for integers $n \geq 1$ _____

10. $\begin{cases} g_1 = \frac{1}{2} \\ g_n = 6g_{n-1} \end{cases}$, for integers $n \geq 2$ _____

11. $\begin{cases} g_1 = 10 \\ g_n = -g_{n-1} \end{cases}$, for integers $n \geq 2$ _____

In 12–15, a sequence is given. a. Is the sequence
geometric? b. If yes, give its constant ratio.

12. 7, 21, 63, 189, . . .

  a. _____

  b. _____

13. 8, 16, 24, 32, . . .

  a. _____

  b. _____

14. $\frac{3}{2}, -\frac{3}{4}, \frac{3}{8}, -\frac{3}{16}, \cdots$

  a. _____

  b. _____

15. $\frac{9}{5}, \frac{13}{5}, \frac{17}{5}, \frac{21}{5}, \cdots$

  a. _____

  b. _____

▶ **LESSON MASTER 7-5 B** *page 2*

In 16–19, the first four terms of a geometric sequence are given. a. Give a recursive formula for the sequence. b. Give an explicit formula for the sequence.

16. 8, 88, 968, 10,648, . . .

17. 12, -36, 108, -324, . . .

a. _____

a. _____

b. _____

b. _____

18. $\frac{3}{4}, \frac{3}{16}, \frac{3}{64}, \frac{3}{256}, \ldots$

19. -2.5, 3.5, -4.9, 6.86, . . .

a. _____

a. _____

b. _____

b. _____

In 20–22, find the tenth term of the geometric sequence described.

20. first term 20, constant ratio .9 _____

21. $g_n = 7(-2)^{n-1}$, for integers $n \geq 1$ _____

22. $\begin{cases} g_1 = 4^2 \\ g_n = \frac{3}{2}g_{n-1} \end{cases}$, for integers $n \geq 2$ _____

Uses Objective H: Solve real-world problems involving geometric sequences.

23. A ball is dropped from a height of 2 m and rises to 60% of its previous height each time it bounces. Find the height the ball reaches after its eighth bounce. _____

24. The population in Manrose County approximately doubled every decade from 1920 through 1970. If there were 1,650 residents in 1920, about how many were there in 1970? _____

25. A sheet of a certain type of glass allows 90% of the light to pass through. How much light will pass through a triple thickness of this glass? _____

LESSON MASTER 7-6 B

Vocabulary

1. If u is an nth root of h, what equation relates the three variables? _____

Skills Objective A: Evaluate b^n when $b > 0$ and n is a rational number.

Objective B: Simplify expressions or solve equations with exponents of the form $\frac{1}{n}$.

Objective D: Solve equations of the form $x^n = b$, where n is a rational number.

In 2–9, write as a decimal or a simple fraction.

2. $81^{\frac{1}{2}}$ _____

3. $(-125)^{\frac{1}{3}}$ _____

4. $-16^{\frac{1}{4}}$ _____

5. $1.44^{\frac{1}{2}}$ _____

6. $1^{\frac{1}{8}}$ _____

7. $\left(\frac{8}{27}\right)^{\frac{1}{3}}$ _____

8. $(-32)^{\frac{1}{5}}$ _____

9. $343^{\frac{1}{3}}$ _____

In 10–15, use a calculator to approximate to the nearest thousandth.

10. $5^{\frac{1}{2}}$ _____

11. $22^{\frac{1}{3}}$ _____

12. $10^{\frac{1}{4}}$ _____

13. $2^{\frac{1}{10}}$ _____

14. $262{,}144^{\frac{1}{6}}$ _____

15. $(-.5)^{\frac{1}{9}}$ _____

In 16–23, solve.

16. $c^{\frac{1}{2}} = 5$ _____

17. $p^{\frac{1}{4}} = 20$ _____

18. $g^{\frac{1}{3}} = -6$ _____

19. $n^{\frac{1}{7}} = .2$ _____

20. $5m^{\frac{1}{2}} = 10$ _____

21. $-10r^{\frac{1}{3}} = 40$ _____

22. $b^{\frac{1}{4}} - 4 = 4$ _____

23. $\frac{2}{3}\left(x^{\frac{1}{2}}\right) + 9 = 15$ _____

In 24–27, an equation is given. a. Give the exact
real solution(s). b. Approximate the solution(s) to
the nearest thousandth.

24. $d^3 = 14$

    a. _____

    b. _____

25. $w^2 = 218$

    a. _____

    b. _____

26. $m^5 + 9 = 6$

    a. _____

    b. _____

27. $2v^{10} = 24$

    a. _____

    b. _____

Properties Objective E: Recognize properties of *n*th roots.

In 28–30, show that the given number is an
8th root of 390,625.

28. 5 _____

29. -5 _____

30. 5*i* _____

In 31–34, use the Number of Real Roots Theorem
to determine the number of real roots possible.

31. 4th root(s) of 20 _____

32. 5th root(s) of 18 _____

33. 6th root(s) of -12 _____

34. 9th root(s) of -7 _____

Uses Objective F: Solve real-world problems which can be modeled by
expressions with *n*th roots.

35. The volume of a cube is 20 cubic feet.

    a. What is the exact length of an edge of the cube? _____

    b. What is the length of an edge of the cube to the
       nearest hundredth? _____

36. Some bacteria double every 20 minutes. What
is the ratio of the number of bacteria one minute to
the number of bacteria the previous minute? _____

LESSON MASTER **7-7** **B**

Vocabulary

1. Write as a power of m.

    a. the 8th power of the cube root of m _____

    b. the 7th power of the 5th power m _____

Skills Objective A: Evaluate b^n when $b > 0$ and n is a rational number.
Objective B: Simplify expressions or solve equations using the Rational-Exponent Theorem.
Objective D: Solve equations of the form $x^n = b$, where n is a rational number.

In 2–11, write as a decimal or simple fraction.

2. $27^{\frac{4}{3}}$ _____   3. $64^{\frac{7}{6}}$ _____

4. $64^{\frac{5}{3}}$ _____   5. $1^{\frac{7}{8}}$ _____

6. $100^{1.5}$ _____   7. $.36^{2.5}$ _____

8. $32^{\frac{4}{5}} \cdot 32^{\frac{2}{5}}$ _____   9. $.008^{\frac{7}{3}}$ _____

10. $\left(\frac{64}{9}\right)^{\frac{3}{2}}$ _____   11. $\frac{2}{5} \cdot \left(\frac{8}{125}\right)^{\frac{2}{3}}$ _____

In 12–17, use a calculator to approximate to the nearest hundredth.

12. $100^{\frac{3}{4}}$ _____   13. $8^{\frac{7}{6}}$ _____

14. $7.51^{\frac{8}{3}}$ _____   15. $45^{.3}$ _____

16. $64{,}078^{1.2}$ _____   17. $.006^{\frac{5}{12}}$ _____

In 18–25, simplify.

18. $a^{\frac{3}{4}} \cdot a^{\frac{1}{2}}$ _____   19. $m^{3.6} \cdot m^{1.8}$ _____

20. $u^{\frac{2}{3}} \cdot u^{\frac{6}{5}}$ _____   21. $k^{\frac{4}{5}} \cdot k$ _____

22. $\left(r^{\frac{5}{8}}\right)^3$ _____   23. $\left(f^{\frac{3}{2}} g^{\frac{1}{4}}\right)^{\frac{2}{3}}$ _____

24. $(64y^3)^{\frac{7}{6}}$ _____   25. $(16e^{\frac{4}{3}})^{\frac{3}{4}}$ _____

▶ **LESSON MASTER 7-7 B** *page 2*

In 26–31, solve. If the solution is not an integer, round to the nearest hundredth.

26. $n^{\frac{3}{2}} = 27$ _____

27. $v^{\frac{5}{4}} = 32$ _____

28. $2g^{\frac{2}{3}} = 98$ _____

29. $a^{\frac{6}{7}} = 24$ _____

30. $m^{1.5} = .064$ _____

31. $\dfrac{d^{\frac{2}{5}}}{6} + 2 = 8$ _____

Properties Objective E: Recognize properties of rational powers.

32. Consider the expression $x^{\frac{m}{n}}$. The Rational Exponent Theorem applies to which values of

   a. x? _____   **b.** m and n? _____

Uses Objective F: Solve real-world problems which can be modeled by expressions with rational powers.

In 33–35, recall from Lesson 7-6 that the ratio of the frequencies of consecutive keys on a piano is the 12th root of 2, or $2^{\frac{1}{12}}$. The frequency of the A below middle C is tuned to 220 hertz. The frequency F of a note n notes above A can be found by using the following formula: $F = 220 \cdot 2^{\frac{n}{12}}$. Find the frequency of the note.

33. E above middle C (7 notes above A) _____

34. F♯ above middle C (9 notes above A) _____

35. A above middle C (12 notes above A) _____

In 36 and 37, use Kepler's formula $d = 1.82r^{\frac{3}{2}}$ which gives the average distance d (in million of miles) of the sun from a planet with period of revolution r (in days).

36. Venus orbits the sun every 224.7 days. Find the distance from the sun to Venus to the nearest million miles. _____

37. Jupiter is about 484 million miles from the sun. Estimate Jupiter's period of revolution in *years*. _____

LESSON MASTER 7-8 B

Skills Objective A: Evaluate b^n when $b > 0$ and n is a rational number.
Objective B: Simplify expressions or solve equations using properties of exponents.
Objective D: Solve equations of the form $x^n = b$, where n is a negative rational number.

In 1–8, write as a decimal or a simple fraction.

1. $64^{-\frac{4}{3}}$ _____

2. $100^{-\frac{3}{2}}$ _____

3. $625^{-\frac{1}{4}}$ _____

4. $81^{-.75}$ _____

5. $\left(\frac{25}{49}\right)^{-\frac{5}{2}}$ _____

6. $\left(\frac{1}{27}\right)^{-\frac{1}{3}}$ _____

7. $6 \cdot 32^{-\frac{4}{5}}$ _____

8. $9.3 \cdot 10,000^{-\frac{1}{2}}$ _____

In 9–14, use a calculator to approximate to the nearest thousandth.

9. $40^{-\frac{3}{5}}$ _____

10. $5^{-\frac{4}{3}}$ _____

11. $1.21^{-\frac{1}{2}}$ _____

12. $24^{-.8}$ _____

13. $12 \cdot 3.8^{-\frac{2}{3}}$ _____

14. $7.5 \cdot 16^{-2.2}$ _____

In 15–22, simplify. Use only positive exponents in your answer.

15. $\left(\frac{a}{b}\right)^{-\frac{1}{2}}$ _____

16. $\left(\frac{1}{h}\right)^{-\frac{3}{4}}$ _____

17. $e^{-\frac{2}{3}}$ _____

18. $(r^3)^{-\frac{3}{8}}$ _____

19. $v^{-\frac{1}{2}} \cdot w^3$ _____

20. $(x^{-\frac{3}{2}} y^{\frac{1}{4}})^{-2}$ _____

21. $\dfrac{a^{-\frac{4}{5}}}{a^{\frac{6}{5}}}$ _____

22. $\dfrac{-20xy^{-\frac{1}{2}}}{4x^3 y^{-\frac{3}{4}}}$ _____

In 23–28, solve. If the solution is not an integer, round to the nearest hundredth.

23. $m^{-\frac{3}{2}} = 64$ _____

24. $a^{-\frac{1}{4}} = .7$ _____

25. $y^{-.8} = 16$ _____

26. $c^{-\frac{5}{3}} = 10$ _____

27. $u^{-4} = 318$ _____

28. $9p^{-\frac{1}{3}} = 45$ _____

▶ **LESSON MASTER 7-8 B** *page 2*

Properties Objective E: Recognize properties of negative rational exponents.

29. *Multiple choice.* List the expression(s) below
    that are equivalent to $a^{-\frac{p}{q}}$.   _____

    (a) $\dfrac{1}{a^{\frac{p}{q}}}$
    (b) $(a^{-p})^q$
    (c) $(a^{-1})^{\frac{p}{q}}$

    (d) $\left(\dfrac{1}{a}\right)^{\frac{q}{p}}$
    (e) $((a^{-1})^p)^{\frac{1}{q}}$
    (f) $\left(\dfrac{1}{a}\right)^{\frac{p}{q}}$

Uses Objective F: Solve real-world problems which can be modeled by
expressions with *n*th powers or *n*th roots.

30. Carbon 14 dating is used to estimate the age of a fossil less than
    50,000 years old. When an organism dies, the Carbon 14, or ^{14}C,
    in the organism decomposes at a constant rate. The amount of
    ^{14}C is reduced to half in about 5750 years. The amount of ^{14}C is
    reduced to the fraction $2^{-\frac{x}{5750}}$ after x years.

    Approximately what fraction of a living organism's ^{14}C is left
    after the given time period? Express the answer as a percent.

    a. 2,875 years   _____   **b.** 11,500 years _____

    c. 25,000 years   _____   **d.** 50,000 years _____

Review Objective I, Lesson 4-7

31. Graph the polygon $\begin{bmatrix} 2 & 5 & 3 & 0 \\ 1 & -1 & -4 & -3 \end{bmatrix}$
    and its image under $r_y \circ r_x$.

32. Graph the polygon $\begin{bmatrix} -3 & -1 & -3 \\ 2 & 2 & -1 \end{bmatrix}$
    and its image under $r_{x=y} \circ S_2$.

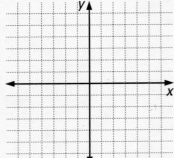
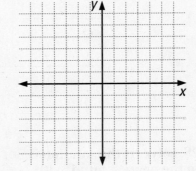

LESSON MASTER 8-1 B

Vocabulary

1. Define the *composite* $g \circ f$ of two functions f and g.

_____

_____

_____

Skills Objective A: Find values and rules for composites of functions.

In 2–11, let $f(x) = -2x^2$ and $g(x) = 6x + 1$.

2. Evaluate $f(g(2))$. _____

3. Evaluate $g(f(2))$. _____

4. Evaluate $f(g(-3))$. _____

5. Evaluate $f \circ g(-3)$. _____

6. Evaluate $f(f(0))$. _____

7. Evaluate $g(g(0))$. _____

8. Evaluate $f(g(0))$. _____

9. Evaluate $g(f(0))$. _____

10. Find an expression for $f(g(x))$. _____

11. Find an expression for $g(f(x))$. _____

In 12–21, $r(n) = \dfrac{1}{2n}$ and $s(n) = -4n - 8$.

12. Evaluate $r(s(1))$. _____

13. Evaluate $s(r(1))$. _____

14. Evaluate $r(r(3))$. _____

15. Evaluate $s(s(-2))$. _____

16. Find an expression for $r(s(n))$. _____

17. Find an expression for $s(r(n))$. _____

18. State the restrictions, if any, on the domain of $r \circ s$. _____

19. State the restrictions, if any, on the domain of $s \circ r$. _____

20. State the restrictions, if any, on the domain of $r \circ r$. _____

21. State the restrictions, if any, on the domain of $s \circ s$. _____

▶ **LESSON MASTER 8-1 B** *page 2*

In 22 and 23, rules for functions *g* and *h* are given.
Does $g \circ h = h \circ g$? **Justify your answer.**

22. $g: m \to m - 9$ $h: m \to m + 9$

_____

_____

23. $g(n) = 3n + 5$ $h(n) = 3n - 5$

_____

_____

In 24–26, suppose $p(x) = x^2$ and $q(x) = x^4$. **Write an expression for**

24. $p \circ q(x)$.   **25.** $q \circ p(x)$.   **26.** $p(x) \cdot q(x)$.

_____   _____   _____

Review Objective L, Lessons 3-2 and 3-4

In 27–30, graph the equation.

27. $y = 2x - 5$

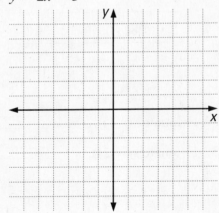

28. $6y = 24$

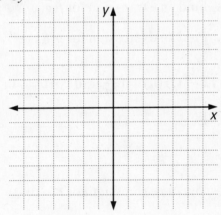

29. $3x + 4y = -12$

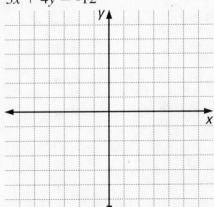

30. $y = -x$

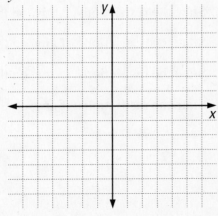

LESSON MASTER 8-2 B

Vocabulary

1. How is the *inverse* of a relation obtained?

   _____

   _____

Skills Objective B: Find the inverse of a relation.

In 2–7, a function is defined. a. Describe the inverse of the function. b. Tell if the inverse is a function.

2. $f(x) = \{(2, 8), (6, -1), (-4, 4), (0, -1)\}$

   a. _____

   b. _____

3. $y = 5x$

   a. _____

   b. _____

4. $y = 9x - 2$

   a. _____

   b. _____

5. $y = x^2 + 5x + 4$

   a. _____

   b. _____

6. $y = |x| + 1$

   a. _____

   b. _____

7. $y = -x^3$

   a. _____

   b. _____

Properties Objective F: Apply properties of inverse relations and functions.

8. Complete the following: According to the Horizontal-Line Test for Inverses, if no horizontal line intersects the graph of a function f in more than one point, then ___?___ .

   _____

9. How are the domain and range of a function g related to the domain and range of the inverse of g?

   _____

   _____

   _____

10. How is the graph of a function related to the graph
of its inverse?

_____

_____

Representations Objective I: Make and interpret graphs of inverses of
relations.

11. Identify all of the graphs which represent a function
whose inverse is also a function. _____

(a) 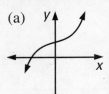   (b) 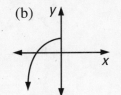   (c) 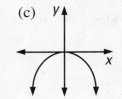   (d)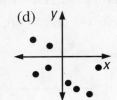

12. The graph of a function is shown on the
grid at the right.

   a. On the same grid, sketch the graph
of the inverse of the function.

   b. Is the inverse also a function?
Why or why not?

_____

_____

_____

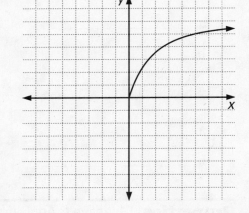

13. **a.** At the right, graph the inverse of
the function with equation $y = -2x^2$.

   b. Is the inverse also a function?
Why or why not?

_____

_____

_____

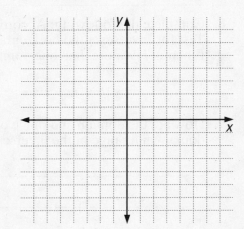

LESSON MASTER

8-3
B

Skills Objective B: Find the inverse of a relation.

In 1–10, write an equation for the inverse in $f(x)$ notation.

1. $h(x) = 8x$

2. $f(x) = x + 9$

_____

3. $g(t) = 2t - 7$

4. $f(a) = -4a + 3$

_____

5. $h(x) = \dfrac{7}{x}$

6. $g(x) = \dfrac{x - 5}{2}$

_____

7. $f(z) = -5(z + 10)$

8. $m(x) = \frac{1}{2}x^2$, when $x \geq 0$

_____

9. $f(x) = x^7$, when $x \geq 0$

10. $g(x) = x^{\frac{1}{8}}$, when $x \geq 0$

_____

Properties Objective F: Apply properties of inverse relations and functions.

11. Consider the function f defined by $f(x) = -5x + 12$.

    a. Write a rule for $f^{-1}(x)$. _____

    b. Find $f \circ f^{-1}(x)$. _____

    c. Find $f^{-1} \circ f(x)$. _____

In 12–15, two functions f and g are defined over the domain $x \geq 0$. a. Find $f(g(x))$. b. Find $g(f(x))$. c. Tell if f and g are inverses and explain why or why not.

12. $f(x) = x + 4$ and $g(x) = \frac{1}{4}x$

    a. _____

    b. _____

    c. _____

13. $f(x) = x^{\frac{4}{7}}$ and $g(x) = x^{\frac{7}{4}}$

    a. _____

    b. _____

    c. _____

▶ **LESSON MASTER 8-3 B** *page 2*

14. $f(x) = -x$ and $g(x) = -x$

   a. _____

   b. _____

   c. _____

      _____

15. $f(x) = x^1$ and $g(x) = x^{-1}$

   a. _____

   b. _____

   c. _____

      _____

Representations Objective I: Make and interpret graphs of inverses of relations.

---

16. Consider the function $g: x \to x^2 - 1$, when $x \geq 0$.

   a. Graph g at the right.

   b. Write a formula for g^{-1}.

   _____

   c. Graph g^{-1} at the right.

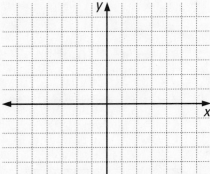

   d. Describe how the graphs of g and g^{-1} are related.

   _____

   _____

   e. Explain why, if the domain of g is taken as the set of real numbers, the inverse of g is not a function.

   _____

   _____

17. *Multiple choice.* A function h is graphed at the right. Which of the following domains for h gives a function whose inverse is also a function?

   _____

   (a) $\{x: 1 \leq x \leq 6\}$

   (b) $\{x: x \leq 7\}$

   (c) $\{x: -5 \leq x \leq 5\}$

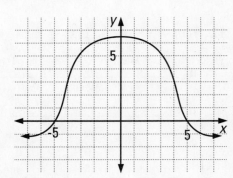

LESSON MASTER

8-4
B

Vocabulary

1. Complete the following definition.

When m is ___?___ and n is ___?___, $\sqrt[n]{m} = $ ___?___.

_____ _____ _____

Skills Objective C: Evaluate radicals.
Objective D: Rewrite or simplify expressions with radicals.

In 2–7, evaluate.

2. $\sqrt[3]{512}$ _____

3. $\sqrt{169}$ _____

4. $\sqrt[4]{10,000}$ _____

5. $\sqrt[3]{.008}$ _____

6. $\sqrt[6]{\dfrac{64}{729}}$ _____

7. $\sqrt[4]{50,625}$ _____

In 8–11, approximate to the nearest hundredth.

8. $\sqrt[5]{10}$ _____

9. $\sqrt[8]{8}$ _____

10. $\sqrt[4]{716,448}$ _____

11. $\sqrt[3]{0.00029}$ _____

In 12–15, rewrite using a single radical. Assume that the variables represent nonnegative real numbers.

12. $\sqrt{\sqrt{\sqrt{u}}}$ _____

13. $\sqrt{\sqrt{45y}}$ _____

14. $\sqrt{\sqrt{\sqrt{e^3m}}}$ _____

15. $\sqrt[5]{\sqrt[4]{y}}$ _____

In 16–19, write without a radical sign and simplify. Assume that the variables represent nonnegative real numbers.

16. $\sqrt{r^5}$ _____

17. $\sqrt[6]{y^4}$ _____

18. $\sqrt[4]{a^4}$ _____

19. $\sqrt[3]{u^{15}}$ _____

▶ **LESSON MASTER 8-4 B** *page 2*

Properties Objective G: Apply properties of radicals and *n*th-root functions.

20. Consider the statement $\sqrt[6]{m^6} = m$.

   a. For which values of *m* is the statement true? _____

   b. If the statement is not true for all real numbers, give a counterexample to justify that.

   _____

21. Suppose $r \geq 0$ and *a* and *b* are integers such that $a \geq 1$ and

   $b \geq 2$. Write two other expressions equivalent to $\sqrt[b]{r^a}$.

   _____

Uses Objective H: Solve real-world problems which can be modeled by equations with radicals.

22. The frequency *F* of a note that is *n* notes above a note with frequency *f* can be found by using the following formula: $F = f \cdot 2^{\frac{n}{12}}$.

   a. Write this formula using radical notation. _____

   b. Suppose you want to know the frequency *F* of a note 5 notes above the note with frequency *f*. Write a formula for *F* using radical notation. _____

23. Suppose the probability of spinning a B six times in a row is *p*. Use radical notation to give the probability of spinning a B on a single spin. _____

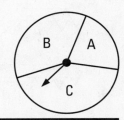

Review Objective B, Lesson 7-2

In 24–27, simplify.

24. $d^4 \cdot d^8$ _____   25. $(-4e^5)^2$ _____

26. $\dfrac{18a^4}{9a}$ _____   27. $\left(\dfrac{m}{4}\right)^3$ _____

LESSON MASTER

8-5 B

Questions on SPUR Objectives

Vocabulary

1. Explain how to find the *geometric mean* of a set of
   n positive numbers.

   _____

   _____

Skills Objective D: Rewrite or simplify expressions with radicals.

**In 2–4, *multiple choice*. Identify the expression that is *not*
equivalent to the given expression.**

2. $\sqrt[3]{96}$ _____

   (a) $\sqrt[3]{48} \cdot \sqrt[3]{2}$ (b) $\sqrt[3]{12} \cdot \sqrt[3]{8}$ (c) $8\sqrt[3]{12}$

   (d) $2\sqrt[3]{12}$ (e) $\sqrt[3]{16} \cdot \sqrt[3]{6}$ (f) $\sqrt[3]{4} \cdot \sqrt[3]{24}$

3. $\sqrt[4]{5} \cdot \sqrt[4]{250}$ _____

   (a) $\sqrt[4]{5} \cdot \sqrt[4]{125} \cdot \sqrt[4]{2}$ (b) $2\sqrt[4]{5}$ (c) $\sqrt[4]{5^4} \cdot \sqrt[4]{2}$

   (d) $\sqrt[4]{1250}$ (e) $\sqrt[4]{25} \cdot \sqrt[4]{50}$ (f) $5\sqrt[4]{2}$

4. $\sqrt[6]{128y^{14}}$ _____

   (a) $\sqrt[6]{128} \cdot \sqrt[6]{y^{12}} \cdot \sqrt[6]{y^2}$ (b) $\sqrt[6]{2^6 \cdot 2 \cdot y^6 \cdot y^6 \cdot y^2}$ (c) $\sqrt[6]{2^7} \cdot \sqrt[6]{y^{14}}$

   (d) $64y^{12} \cdot \sqrt[6]{2y^2}$ (e) $\sqrt[6]{128} \cdot \sqrt[6]{y^{14}}$ (f) $2y^2\sqrt[6]{2y^2}$

In 5–14, simplify. Assume that the variables are nonnegative.

5. $\sqrt[3]{250}$ _____

6. $\sqrt[4]{48}$ _____

7. $\sqrt[4]{50,000x^7}$ _____

8. $\sqrt[3]{27x^6y^4}$ _____

9. $\sqrt[6]{x^{12}y^6}$ _____

10. $\sqrt[4]{81m^5}$ _____

11. $\sqrt[4]{5} \cdot \sqrt[4]{125}$ _____

12. $\sqrt[3]{9} \cdot \sqrt[3]{48}$ _____

13. $\sqrt[3]{2u^7} \cdot \sqrt[3]{4u^2}$ _____

14. $\sqrt[5]{3^3x} \cdot \sqrt[5]{3^4x^8}$ _____

15. Find the geometric mean of the following set
of numbers. Round to the nearest hundredth.

18, 27, 84, 33.6, 4   _____

16. The chart at the right gives
the period of revolution for
the nine planets in our solar
system. Find the geometric
mean of these periods.

Planet	Period of Revolution (years)
Mercury	0.24
Venus	0.62
Earth	1
Mars	1.88
Jupiter	11.86
Saturn	29.46
Uranus	84
Neptune	165
Pluto	248

_____

Properties Objective G: Apply properties of radicals and *n*th-root functions.

17. Prove that if $x \geq 0$, $\sqrt[6]{x} = \sqrt[12]{x^2}$.

_____

_____

18. Prove that if $y \geq 0$, $\sqrt[5]{y} \cdot \sqrt[3]{y} = \sqrt[15]{y^8}$.

_____

_____

In 19 and 20, write the expression using a single radical sign.

19. $\sqrt[3]{r} \cdot \sqrt[4]{r}$ _____   **20.** $\sqrt[6]{a} \cdot \sqrt[5]{b}$ _____

LESSON MASTER

8-6 B

Vocabulary

1. Complete the following: When we *rationalize* the denominator of a fraction, we rewrite the fraction in an equivalent form so that ___?___.

   _____

   _____

2. What is the *conjugate* of the expression $m + \sqrt{n}$? _____

Skills Objective D: Rewrite or simplify expressions with radicals.

In 3–18, rationalize the denominator. Assume variables under the radical sign are positive.

3. $\dfrac{1}{\sqrt{3}}$ _____

4. $\dfrac{2}{\sqrt{7}}$ _____

5. $\dfrac{6}{\sqrt{6}}$ _____

6. $\dfrac{5}{2\sqrt{10}}$ _____

7. $\dfrac{4}{\sqrt{x}}$ _____

8. $\dfrac{1}{\sqrt{x^3}}$ _____

9. $\dfrac{5a}{\sqrt{a}}$ _____

10. $\dfrac{3e}{\sqrt{e^7}}$ _____

11. $\dfrac{8n}{\sqrt{6n^5}}$ _____

12. $\dfrac{9}{c\sqrt{c}}$ _____

13. $\dfrac{7}{3+\sqrt{2}}$ _____

14. $\dfrac{4}{8-\sqrt{5}}$ _____

15. $\dfrac{x}{\sqrt{x}+1}$ _____

16. $\dfrac{4}{6-\sqrt{r}}$ _____

17. $\dfrac{5+\sqrt{3}}{5-\sqrt{3}}$ _____

18. $\dfrac{6}{\sqrt{10}-\sqrt{7}}$ _____

In 19 and 20, write the expression in radical form with a rational denominator. Assume that the variables are positive.

19. $5^{\frac{3}{2}} \cdot a^{-\frac{1}{2}}$ _____

20. $b^{-\frac{7}{2}}c$ _____

► **LESSON MASTER 8-6 B** *page 2*

21. Show that $(\sqrt{50} - 7)$ is 14 less than its reciprocal.

_____

_____

In 22–24, use the triangle at the right. Write the ratio with a rationalized denominator.

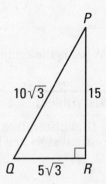

22. $\dfrac{PR}{QR}$ _____

23. $\dfrac{PR}{QP}$ _____

24. $\dfrac{QR}{QP}$ _____

In 25 and 26, use the square at the right. Write the ratio with a rationalized denominator.

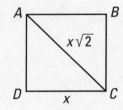

25. $\dfrac{CD}{AC}$ _____

26. $\dfrac{AC}{CD}$ _____

In 27 and 28, rationalize the numerator.

27. $\dfrac{2 - \sqrt{5}}{3}$ _____   **28.** $\dfrac{6 + 4\sqrt{2}}{9}$ _____

Review Objective A, Lesson 7-2

In 29–37, evaluate and write in standard form.

29. $(-5)^2$ _____   **30.** $(15)^3$ _____

31. $(-1)^{19}$ _____   **32.** $(-12)^2$ _____

33. $2^3 \cdot 7^3$ _____   **34.** $6^3 \cdot 6^2$ _____

35. $1.9 \cdot 10^5$ _____   **36.** $44{,}066 \cdot 10^0$ _____

37. $(9.1 \cdot 10^2)(3.4 \cdot 10^3)$ _____

LESSON MASTER

8-7
B

Vocabulary

1. Complete the following: When x is negative and n is ___?___, $\sqrt[n]{x}$ stands for the real nth root of x. _____

Skills Objective C: Evaluate radicals.

2. Calculate $(-7)^n$ for all integer values of n from -4 to 4.

_____ _____ _____ _____ _____

_____ _____ _____ _____

In 3–8, *multiple choice*. Tell which of the following describes the expression.

(a) defined, real positive number   (b) defined, real negative number

(c) defined, nonreal number   (d) not defined

3. $\sqrt[3]{-20}$ _____   4. $\sqrt{-18}$ _____

5. $\sqrt{12}$ _____   6. $\sqrt[6]{-64}$ _____

7. $\sqrt[4]{5}$ _____   8. $\sqrt[11]{-9}$ _____

In 9–16, write as a decimal or a simple fraction.

9. $\sqrt[3]{-64}$ _____   10. $\sqrt[9]{-1}$ _____

11. $\sqrt[5]{100,000}$ _____   12. $\sqrt[5]{3125}$ _____

13. $\sqrt[3]{-27} \cdot \sqrt[3]{-64}$ _____   14. $\sqrt[7]{-1} + \sqrt[7]{-128}$ _____

15. $\sqrt[9]{-2^{18}}$ _____   16. $\sqrt[9]{(-2)^{18}}$ _____

▶ **LESSON MASTER 8-7 B** *page 2*

Properties Objective G: Apply properties of radicals and *n*th-root functions.

In 17-20, for what values of *n* is the expression defined?

17. $\sqrt[8]{n}$ _____

18. $\sqrt[9]{n}$ _____

19. $n^{\frac{4}{5}}$ _____

20. $\sqrt[n]{-18}$ _____

21. If a is negative, is $a^3 = \sqrt{a^6}$? Why or why not?

_____

_____

Representations Objective I: Make and interpret graphs of inverses of relations.

22. **a.** Sketch the graph of $y = x^4$ for $-8 \le x \le 8$.

b. Sketch the graph of $y = \sqrt[4]{x}$ for $-8 \le x \le 8$.

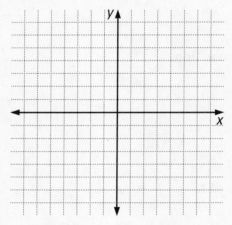
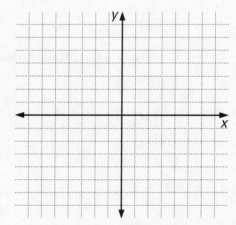

c. Is $y = \sqrt[4]{x}$ the inverse of $y = x^4$? Why or why not?

_____

_____

_____

LESSON MASTER

8-8 B

Vocabulary

1. Suppose Equation A implies Equation B.
   If a solution to Equation B is *not* a solution to
   Equation A, the solution is called ___?___ .   _____

Skills Objective E: Solve equations with radicals.

In 2–11, find all real solutions.

2. $\sqrt[4]{a} = 4$ 3. $\sqrt[5]{w} = -3$

4. $8\sqrt[5]{x} = -4$ 5. $\frac{8}{5} \cdot \sqrt[6]{m} = 8$

6. $18 - \sqrt[4]{u} = 9$ 7. $5\sqrt[3]{y} - 2 = {}^-\sqrt[3]{y}$

8. $\sqrt[4]{r + 3} = -5$ 9. $\sqrt{2m - 6} = 18$

10. $22 + \sqrt[7]{c + 2} = 21$ 11. $8 + \sqrt[6]{2b} = 3$

▶ **LESSON MASTER 8-8 B** *page 2*

Uses Objective H: Solve real-world problems which can be modeled by equations
with radicals.

12. Find two points on the line $y = 4$ that are 5 units
away from the point (2, 3).   _____

13. Find two points on the line $x = -5$ that are 6 units
away from the point (3, 0).   _____

14. Janet made a wooden-cube lamp table and veneered
it with $\frac{1}{8}$-inch-thick walnut. The finished cube has
volume of about 3725 cubic inches. What was the
approximate length of an edge of the cube before
it was veneered?   _____

15. The equation $d = 1.82 \sqrt[3]{r^2}$ approximates the average
distance (in millions of miles) of a planet from the
sun where r is the number of days in the planet's
revolution. Venus is an average distance of
108.2 million miles from the sun. Find the number
of days in Venus's revolution.   _____

Review Objective G, Lesson 7-4

16. Mr. Machado invested $7,500 in a 5-year CD
(certificate of deposit) that paid 6.8% compounded
quarterly. If he leaves the money alone, how much
will the CD be worth when it matures?   _____

17. Dana invested $2,600 in an account that pays 5.4%
compounded daily (365 days a year). If she leaves
the money alone, how much will be in the account
after 3.5 years?   _____

LESSON MASTER 9-1 B

Vocabulary

1. Write the general equation for an *exponential function* and give the restrictions, if any, for each variable.

   _____

   _____

Properties
Objective D: Recognize properties of exponential functions.

In 2 and 3, an equation for a function is given. a. Give the domain of the function. b. Give the range of the function.

2. $f(x) = 9^x$

   a. _____

   b. _____

3. $f(x) = 3(1.05)^x$

   a. _____

   b. _____

Uses
Objective F: Apply exponential-growth models.

4. The population N of a certain strain of bacteria grows according to the equation $N = 200 \cdot 2^{1.4t}$, where t is the time in hours.

   a. How many bacteria were there at the beginning of the experiment? _____

   b. After how many hours will the number of bacteria double? _____

   c. Estimate the number of bacteria in 10 hours. _____

   d. Estimate the number of bacteria 2 hours before the experiment began. _____

5. In 1994, the number of weekly passes sold by Tri-Cities Transit was 98,481 and was growing at a rate of about 3.8% per year. At this rate, estimate the number of passes sold in each year.

   a. 1997 _____

   b. 1985 _____

6. Of the American cities with populations over 100,000, Mesa, Arizona, had the fastest growing population for the decade from 1980 to 1990. In 1980, its population was 152,404. In 1990, it was 288,091. Assume that the growth rate continues.

   a. By what percent did the population of Mesa increase in the decade from 1980 to 1990? Round to the nearest percent. _____

   b. What was the growth rate for the decade? _____

   c. Let $P(x)$ = the population x decades after 1980. Find a formula for $P(x)$. _____

   d. Estimate the population of Mesa in 2010. _____

   e. Use the function $P(x)$ from part **c** to:

      (i) estimate the year during which the population was 200,000. _____

      (ii) estimate the year during which the population will reach a half million. _____

Representations Objective I: Graph exponential functions.

7. *Multiple choice.* Which equation has a graph that is an exponential curve? _____

   (a) $y = 4x$ (b) $y = x^4$ (c) $y = 4^x$ (d) $y = \dfrac{x}{4}$

8. At the right, sketch a graph that could represent exponential growth.

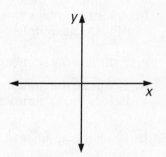

9. Locate at least five points on the graph of $y = .25 \cdot 3^x$ on the grid at the right.

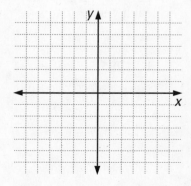

LESSON MASTER

9-2
B

Vocabulary

1. What is true of the growth factor in situations of *exponential decay*?

   _____

2. What is *depreciation*?

   _____

   _____

Properties Objective D: Recognize properties of exponential functions.

In 3 and 4, an equation for a function is given. a. Give the domain of the function. b. Give the range of the function.

3. $f(x) = 0.9^x$ 4. $f(x) = 1.5(.08)^x$

   a. _____   a. _____

   b. _____   b. _____

5. Give the equations of all asymptotes of the graph
   defined by $f(x) = 3(.44)^x$.   _____

6. *Multiple choice.* The reflection image over the
   y-axis of an exponential-decay curve is
   which of the following?   _____

   (a) same exponential-decay curve   (b) different exponential-decay curve

   (c) exponential-growth curve   (d) none of these

7. Consider the exponential function with equation $y = ab^x$.
   Give an equation for its x-intercept and y-intercept.

   _____   _____

Uses Objective F: Apply exponential-decay models.

8. Suppose a new car bought in 1988 for $14,675 depreciates
   15% each year.

   a. Find an equation that gives the car's value
      x years after 1988.   _____

   b. Predict the car's value in 1995.   _____

► **LESSON MASTER 9-2 B** *page 2*

9. Consider the equation $L = .87^x$, which gives the percent of
   light that will pass through x thicknesses of a certain type of
   tinted glass. (L = lumens per square meter)

   a. What percent of light will pass through a
   single thickness? _____

   b. What percent of light will pass through
   four thicknesses? _____

   c. What percent of light will pass through a
   half-thickness of the glass? _____

   d. Suppose a source emits light with an intensity
   of 1400 lumens per square meter. What is the
   intensity of the light passing through six
   thicknesses of the glass? _____

10. Radium-226 (^{226}Ra) has a half-life of 1620 years.

   a. Determine an equation for the percent of
   ^{226}Ra remaining in the original sample after
   x half-life periods. _____

   b. If you start with 4 g of ^{226}Ra, how much will
   remain after 5 half-life periods? _____

   c. How many years equal 5 half-life periods
   of ^{226}Ra? _____

Representations Objective I: Graph exponential functions.

11. At the right, sketch a graph that could
    represent exponential decay.

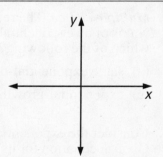

12. Locate at least five points on the graph
    of $y = .6^x$ on the grid at the right.

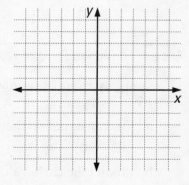

LESSON MASTER 9-3 B

Vocabulary

1. Consider the number e.

   a. After whom was it named? _____

   b. Give its value to the nearest millionth. _____

   c. Fill in the blank: As n increases, the sequence
   of numbers ___?___ approaches e. _____

Properties Objective D: Recognize properties of exponential functions.

In 2 and 3, an equation for a function is given. a. Give the domain of the function. b. Give the range of the function.

2. $f(x) = e^{2x}$

   a. _____

   b. _____

3. $g(x) = 3e^{-4x}$

   a. _____

   b. _____

In 4–9, *multiple choice*. Which situation is described by the function?

    (a) constant increase   **(b) constant decrease**

    (c) exponential growth   **(d) exponential decay**

4. $f(x) = e^{-3x}$ _____

5. $g(x) = 5ex$ _____

6. $h(x) = -2ex + 1$ _____

7. $u(x) = 4e^x$ _____

8. $v(x) = e^{8x}$ _____

9. $w(x) = e^{0.5x}$ _____

Uses Objective F: Apply exponential-growth and exponential-decay models.

10. Suppose an initial amount of $20,000 grows at the
    rate of 13% per year. Use function notation to
    describe this continuous-change model. _____

11. Suppose $1800 is invested at an annual interest rate of 7%
    compounded continuously, and the money is left untouched.

    a. How much is in the account after 5 years? _____

    b How much is in the account after 10 years? _____

    c. Find the effective annual yield on the account. _____

12. A machine depreciates so that its value after t years is given by $N(t) = N_0e^{-.18t}$.

    a. What is the annual rate of depreciation of the machine?   _____

    b. If after 5 years the machine is worth \$16,000, what was its original value?   _____

13. Suppose the accident rate in Julian County is continually decreasing at an annual rate of 3%.

    a. If there were 5,706 accidents this year, write a function to give the number of accidents in t years.   _____

    b. Estimate the number of accidents in 10 years.   _____

14. The amount L of Radium-226 (^{226}Ra) remaining after t years decreases according to the formula $L = Be^{-0.000428t}$. If 500 micrograms of ^{226}Ra are left after 8,000 years, how many micrograms were present initially?   _____

Representations Objective I: Graph exponential functions.

15. At the right is a graph of the function $N(t) = N_0e^{-rt}$. Is r positive or negative?

    _____

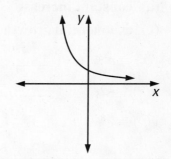

16. **a.** Draw the graphs of $y = e^{.3x}$ and $y = e^{-.3x}$ on the grid at the right.

    b. How are the graphs related?

    _____

    _____

    _____

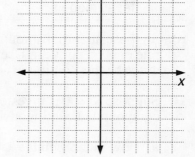

LESSON MASTER

9-4
B

Vocabulary

1. Suppose the decade growth factor for a population is D and the annual growth factor is A. Write an equation that relates D and A.

Uses Objective G: Fit an exponential model to data.

2. *Multiple choice.* For which set of data below is an exponential model most appropriate? Explain why. _____

(a)

x	0	1	2	3	4	5
y	5	40	320	2560	20,480	163,840

(b)

x	0	1	2	3	4	5
y	5	20	800	4000	20,000	120,000

(c)

x	0	1	2	3	4	5
y	5	15	60	300	1800	12,600

3. An experiment began with 200 of a certain type of bacteria. The bacteria grew exponentially, and 4 hours later there were 18,000.

   a. Fit an exponential model to these data. _____

   b. After 12 hours, how many bacteria will be present? _____

4. In a horticultural experiment, the monthly growth of a plant was monitored. The results of the experiment are in the table below.

Month	1	2	3	4	5	6
Growth (cm)	5.2	4.2	3.5	2.7	2.2	1.8

a. Draw a scatterplot of these data at the right.

b. Let *G* be the amount of growth and *m* the number of months. Fit an exponential model to these data.

_____

_____

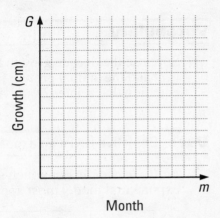

5. The table at the right gives the population in Kuever County for the years 1870 through 1950.

Year	Population	Decade Growth Factor
1870	8,320	
1880	11,823	1.421
1890	16,848	1.425
1900	24,042	1.427
1910	34,188	1.422
1920	48,923	1.431
1930	69,666	1.424
1940	76,911	1.104
1950	98,831	1.285

a. For which years is it appropriate to fit the data to an exponential model? Explain your reasoning.

_____

_____

b. Calculate the annual growth factor between 1890 and 1900.

_____

c. Find an exponential model for the population of Kuever County for the years given in your answer in Part a.

_____

Review Objective B, Lesson 8-2

In 6–11, find the inverse of the function described.

6. $f(x) = \{(7, 2), (-9, 0), (-1, 2), (5, 5)\}$ **7.** $y = -8x$

_____   _____

8. $y = 7x + 4$ **9.** $y = x^2 - 7x + 6$

_____   _____

10. $y = |x|$ **11.** $y = -4x^2$

_____   _____

LESSON MASTER 9-5 B

Vocabulary

1. a. Write the following sentence as an equation.
    y is the logarithm of x to the base 10.   _____

    b. Complete the following definition.
    y is the logarithm of x to the base 10 if and
    only if __?__ .   _____

2. What are *common logarithms*?

    _____

    _____

Skills   Objective A: Determine values of common logarithms.

**In 3–12, write the number as a decimal. Do not use
a calculator.**

3. $\log 10{,}000$ _____

4. $\log (0.001)$ _____

5. $\log 10^{18}$ _____

6. $\log 10$ _____

7. $\log \frac{1}{1{,}000{,}000}$ _____

8. $\log (1 \text{ trillion})$ _____

9. $\log 10^{.35}$ _____

10. $\log \sqrt[6]{10}$ _____

11. $\log 10^{\frac{5}{4}}$ _____

12. $\log \sqrt[4]{10^6}$ _____

**In 13–18, use a calculator. Give the logarithm to the
nearest thousandth.**

13. $\log 7$ _____

14. $\log 316$ _____

15. $\log 6.31$ _____

16. $\log 298{,}055$ _____

17. $\log 0.000069$ _____

18. $\log (29 \text{ million})$ _____

Skills   Objective C: Solve common-logarithmic equations.

**In 19–24, solve. Round solutions to the nearest
ten-thousandth.**

19. $\log x = 3$ _____

20. $\log y = -4$ _____

21. $\log z = 0$ _____

22. $\log w = 2.9$ _____

23. $\log a = \frac{1}{3}$ _____

24. $\log b = -3.55$ _____

Properties Objective E: Identify and apply properties of common
logarithms.

25. What are the domain and the range of the common
logarithm function?

domain _____   range _____

26. What is the logarithm of 1? Justify your answer.

_____

27. Use the definition of logarithm of x to the base 10 to explain
why the log (-100) does not exist.

_____

28. *True or false.* The common logarithm of a number is an
exponent. Justify your answer.

_____

_____

29. The inverse of the function with equation $y = \log x$ is $y =$ ___?___. _____

Representations Objective J: Graph common-logarithmic curves.

30. a. Complete the table of
values at the right. Round
to the nearest tenth.

x	.5	1	2	5	10	20
$y = \log x$						

b. Plot the points from
Part a on the grid.

c. Join the points with a
smooth curve. What is
this curve called?

_____

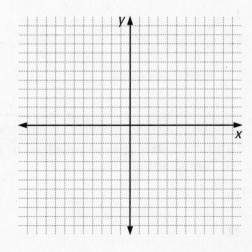

LESSON MASTER

9-6 B

Vocabulary

1. **a.** How are the units spaced on a *linear scale*?

   _____

   _____

   b. How are the units spaced on a *logarithmic scale*?

   _____

   _____

Skills Objective B: Use logarithms to solve exponential equations.
Objective C: Solve logarithmic equations.

In 2–5, use the formula $D = 10 \log \left(\frac{N}{10^{-12}} \right)$, which gives
the measure in D decibels (dB) for a sound with intensity
N given in w/m².

2. Find the relative intensity in decibels of a sound
   with intensity $3.16 \cdot 10^{-4}$ w/m². _____

3. Find the intensity, in w/m², of a sound having a
   relative intensity of 95 dB. _____

4. Find the relative intensity in decibels of air
   conditioning in which the sound intensity is
   10^{-6} w/m². _____

5. Find the intensity, in w/m², of a freight train
   having a relative intensity of 75 dB. _____

In 6–11, use the formula $pH = -\log H^+$ to find the pH
of a solution in which H^+ is the concentration of
hydrogen ions (in moles/liter).

6. What is the pH of a solution that has a concentration
   of hydrogen ions of 10^{-9} moles/liter? _____

7. What is the concentration of hydrogen ions in a
   solution with a pH of 5? _____

8. What is the pH of a solution that has a concentration
   of hydrogen ions of $5.62 \cdot 10^{-6}$ moles/liter? _____

9. What is the concentration of hydrogen ions in a
   solution with a pH of 2.5? Express your answer
   in scientific notation.   _____

10. What is the concentration of hydrogen ions in a
    sample of stream water with a pH of 7.8?
    Express your answer in scientific notation.   _____

11. A soil sample from a desert has a concentration
    of hydrogen ions of $3.16 \cdot 10^{-10}$ moles/liter. What
    is the pH?   _____

Uses Objective H: Apply logarithmic scales (pH, decibel), models,
         and formulas.

Use the formulas given in Exercises 6–11.

12. When exposed to noise levels of 80 dB for several
    hours, a person's hearing may be affected for half a
    day. However, even a single, short exposure to
    noises of 160 dB may cause physical damage
    inside the ear. This noise that damages the ear is
    how many times as intense as the noise that
    only temporarily affects hearing?   _____

13. The noise from a riveting machine measures
    100 dB. The noise in a busy office measures 65 dB.
    How many times as intense is the noise from the
    machine as the noise from the office?   _____

14. The noise level in a classroom measures 55 dB.
    If the noise level in the gym is 3 times as intense,
    how many decibels would it be?   _____

15. The pH of rainwater is 5.6. Atmospheric pollutants
    have caused acid rain, which in some regions has a
    pH of 4.6. How many times as great is the
    concentration of hydrogen ions in acid rain as in
    the normal rainwater?   _____

16. A solution has a pH of 9.5. What would be the
    pH of a solution that has twice the concentration
    of hydrogen ions?   _____

17. A soil sample from garden *A* has a pH of 6.2. A
    sample from garden *B* has a pH of 6.8. The soil
    in garden *B* is how many times as alkaline as the
    soil in garden *A*?   _____

LESSON MASTER

9-7
B

Vocabulary

1. Give a complete definition of *logarithm of m to the base b*.

_____

_____

_____

Skills Objective A: Determine values of logarithms.

In 2–17, write the number as a decimal.

2. $\log_5 125$ _____

3. $\log_6 36$ _____

4. $\log_2 128$ _____

5. $\log_9 9$ _____

6. $\log_8 \frac{1}{8}$ _____

7. $\log_4 \frac{1}{64}$ _____

8. $\log_9 3$ _____

9. $\log_{81} 3$ _____

10. $\log_{14} 1$ _____

11. $\log_2 2^{21}$ _____

12. $\log_6 \sqrt{6}$ _____

13. $\log_7 7^{\frac{4}{3}}$ _____

14. $\log_{100} .000001$ _____

15. $\log_{12} \sqrt[4]{12^5}$ _____

16. $\log_5 (5^3)^2$ _____

17. $\log_6 36^4$ _____

Skills Objective C: Solve logarithmic equations.

In 18–29, solve. Round solutions to the nearest hundredth.

18. $\log_4 a = 7$ _____

19. $\log_6 b = \frac{3}{5}$ _____

20. $\log_{12} c = 0$ _____

21. $\log_d \frac{1}{625} = -4$ _____

22. $\log_y 28 = \log_5 28$ _____

23. $\log_x 10 = \frac{1}{3}$ _____

24. $\log_z 7 = 2.35$ _____

25. $\log_m 22 = \frac{2}{3}$ _____

26. $\log_g 13 = 1$ _____

27. $\log_n 100 = 4.25$ _____

28. $\log_r 53 = .5$ _____

29. $\log_{15} w = -.08$ _____

▶ **LESSON MASTER 9-7 B** *page 2*

Properties Objective E: Identify and apply properties of logarithms.

30. Write the equivalent logarithmic form for $p^r = s$. _____

In 31–34, write in exponential form.

31. $\log_4 16{,}384 = 7$ _____ **32.** $\log_{16} 64 = \frac{3}{2}$ _____

33. $\log_8 2.55 \approx .45$ _____ **34.** $\log_9 \frac{1}{729} = -3$ _____

In 35–38, write in logarithmic form.

35. $12^4 = 20{,}736$ _____ **36.** $25^{3.5} = 78{,}125$ _____

37. $14^{\frac{1}{2}} \approx 3.74$ _____ **38.** $.2^{-5} = 3125$ _____

Representations Objective J: Graph logarithmic curves.

39. Locate at least 5 points on the graph of the equation $y = \log_4 x$.

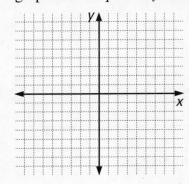

40. The graph below has equation $y = \log_b x$. Find b.

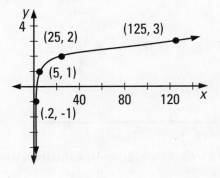

_____

41. Consider the graph of the equation $y = 8^x$. The reflection image of this graph over the line $x = y$ results in a graph described by what equation? _____

Review Objective B, Lessons 7-2, 7-3, 7-6, 7-7, 7-8

In 42–47, simplify.

42. $a^4 \cdot a^3$ _____ **43.** $(m^6)^5$ _____ **44.** $\dfrac{u^{10}}{u^7}$ _____

45. $\left(\dfrac{x^{12}}{y^{15}}\right)^{\frac{1}{3}}$ _____ **46.** $(r^6)^{\frac{1}{2}}$ _____ **47.** $\sqrt[6]{w^{18}}$ _____

LESSON MASTER

9-8
B

Skills Objective C: Solve logarithmic equations.

In 1–10, solve.

1. $\log x = 5 \log 4$

2. $\log_5 u = \frac{1}{3} \log_5 64$

3. $\log m = \log 2 + \log 14$

4. $\log 28 - \log 7 = \log y$

5. $\log p = \log 6 + 3 \log 5$

6. $\log_4 h = \frac{1}{2} \log_4 49 - \log_4 3$

7. $\log 6 + \log 10 = \log (5a)$

8. $4 \log x = \log 32 - \log 2$

9. $\frac{-1}{2} \log n = \log 1 - 2 \log 9$

10. $\log_8 \left(\frac{x}{2}\right) = 2 \log_8 5 + 3 \log_8 2$

Properties Objective E: Identify and apply properties of logarithms.

In 11–18, write the number as a decimal.

11. $\log_{18} 18^{20}$ _____

12. $\log_{12} 3 + \log_{12} 4$ _____

13. $4 \log_3 9$ _____

14. $\log_6 72 - \log_6 2$ _____

15. $\log_{25} 7 - \log_{25} 35$ _____

16. $\frac{1}{5} \log_8 32{,}768$ _____

17. $7 \log_3 3 - 8 \log_3 3$ _____

18. $\log \sqrt[8]{100}$ _____

▶ **LESSON MASTER 9-8 B** *page 2*

In 19–24, name the general property illustrated.

19. $\log\left(\frac{24}{5}\right) = \log 24 - \log 5$

_____

20. $\log_{16} 16^{-9} = -9$

_____

21. $\log 4 + \log 12 = \log 48$

_____

22. $6 \log_8 7 = \log_8 7^6$

_____

23. $\log\left(\frac{2}{3} \cdot 28\right) = \log \frac{2}{3} + \log 28$

_____

24. $\log \sqrt[4]{18^3} = \frac{3}{4} \log 18$

_____

_____

Review Objective F, Lesson 9-3

25. Write the formula for continuously compounded interest and
    tell what each variable represents.

_____

_____

_____

26. Suppose $3200 is invested at an annual interest rate of 8.2%
    compounded continuously, and the money is left untouched.

    a. How much is in the account after 3 years? _____

    b. How much is in the account after 10 years? _____

Name _____

Vocabulary

1. Complete the following: Logarithms to the base
   ___?___ are called *natural logarithms*.   _____

Skills Objective A: Determine values of natural logarithms.

In 2–5, write the number as a decimal. Do not use a calculator.

2. $\ln e^{14}$ _____

3. $\ln e^{\frac{4}{3}}$ _____

4. $5 \ln e^2$ _____

5. $\ln e^{-3}$ _____

In 6–11, give the logarithm to the nearest hundredth.

6. $\ln 8$ _____

7. $\ln 0.44$ _____

8. $\ln 5{,}068$ _____

9. $\ln .05$ _____

10. $\ln 1$ _____

11. $\ln (-9)$ _____

Properties Objective E: Identify and apply properties of natural logarithms.

In 12–15, write in exponential form.

12. $\ln 42 \approx 3.738$ _____

13. $\ln 0.2 \approx -1.609$ _____

14. $\ln 2.4 \approx .875$ _____

15. $\ln 3{,}000 \approx 8.006$ _____

In 16–19, write in logarithmic form.

16. $e^7 \approx 1097$ _____

17. $e^{1.5} \approx 4.482$ _____

18. $e^{-\frac{1}{2}} \approx .607$ _____

19. $e^{\frac{7}{4}} \approx 5.755$ _____

In 21–23, identify the property that justifies the equation.

20. $\ln e^{10} = 10$ _____

21. $\ln 12 - \ln 2 = \ln 6$ _____

22. $50 \ln 6 = \ln 6^{50}$ _____

23. $\ln 15 = \ln 3 + \log 5$ _____

Uses Objective H: Apply logarithmic models and formulas.

24. Suppose an account pays an annual interest rate r compounded continuously. The formula $t = \dfrac{\ln g}{r}$ can be used to determine the number of years t for the investment to grow to g times what it was, assuming that the money is left untouched.

  a. How long will it take an investment to double if the account pays

   (i) 5% compounded continuously? _____

   (ii) 7% compounded continuously? _____

   (iii) 10% compounded continuously? _____

  b. If $8,000 is invested at 8% compounded continuously, in how many years will the account be worth $12,000? _____

  c. What annual rate of interest compounded continuously would be necessary for an account to triple in

   (i) 20 years? _____   (ii) 15 years? _____

   (iii) 10 years? _____   (iv) 5 years? _____

Representations Objective J: Graph natural-logarithmic curves.

25. a. Complete the table of values at the right. Round to the nearest tenth.

x	.5	1	2	5	10	20
$y = \ln x$						

  b. Plot the points from Part a on the grid.

  c. Join the points with a smooth curve.

  d. Draw the reflection image of your graph over the line $y = x$. What equation describes the reflection image?

  _____

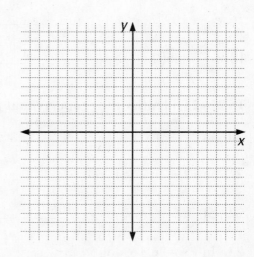

LESSON MASTER 9-10 B

Skills Objective B: Use logarithms to solve exponential equations.

In 1–12, solve. Round solutions to the nearest hundredth.

1. $64^x = 4096$

2. $625^x = 125$

3. $12^u = 400$

4. $6^a = 3$

5. $10^c = 2.77$

6. $196^{w+1} = 537{,}824$

7. $e^x = 24$

8. $5e^n = 33$

9. $(0.8)^y = e^2$

10. $6.5 \cdot 10^8 = e^n$

11. $11^{6y-3} = 80$

12. $2^r = 0.0053$

Uses Objective F: Apply exponential-growth and exponential-decay models.

In 13–15, assume the money is left untouched in the account.

13. Jacob's college savings are invested in a bond that pays an annual interest of 6.2% compounded continuously. How long will it take the money to triple?

_____

14. Marta invested $5,000 in an account that pays an annual interest of 8.1% compounded continuously. In how many years will there be $8,000 in the account?

_____

15. At what rate of interest, compounded continuously, would you have to invest your money for it to double in 8 years?

_____

16. The equation $p = 100(0.5)^{\frac{x}{5730}}$ gives the percent p of Carbon 14 (^{14}C) remaining after an organism has been decomposing for x years. How many years will it take for there to be the given percent of ^{14}C remaining?

   a. 50% (Recall, this is called the *half-life*.)

_____

   b. 75%

_____

   c. 30%

_____

17. The intensity L_t of light transmitted through a certain type of tinted glass t mm thick can be found with the formula $L_t = L_0 10^{-.034t}$, where L_0 is the intensity before entering the glass. How thick should the glass be in order to block 30% of the light?

_____

18. In 1995, the profits for Uptown Manufacturing were $763,000 and growing at a rate of about 4.5% annually. Assuming that profits continue to grow at this rate, during what year will the profits reach one million dollars?

_____

LESSON MASTER 10-1 B

Vocabulary

1. Refer to the diagram at the right. Fill in the blank.

   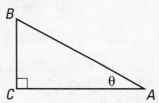

   a. The *leg adjacent* to θ is _____.

   b. The *leg opposite* θ is _____.

   c. The *hypotenuse* is _____.

2. Fill in the blank with the name of a trigonometric ratio.

   a. the _____ of $\theta = \dfrac{\text{length of leg opposite } \theta}{\text{length of leg adjacent to } \theta}$

   b. the _____ of $\theta = \dfrac{\text{length of leg opposite } \theta}{\text{length of hypotenuse}}$

   c. the _____ of $\theta = \dfrac{\text{length of leg adjacent to } \theta}{\text{length of hypotenuse}}$

Skills Objective A: Approximate values of trigonometric functions using a calculator.

In 3–5, approximate each trigonometric value to the nearest thousandth.

3. Refer to the triangle at the right.

   a. sin θ _____

   b. cos θ _____

   c. tan θ _____

4. Refer to the triangle at the right.

   a. sin *D* _____   **b.** cos *D* _____

   c. sin *E* _____   **d.** cos *E* _____

   e. tan *D* _____   **f.** tan *E* _____

   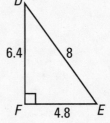

▶ **LESSON MASTER 10-1 B** *page 2*

5. a. Measure the length of each side of the triangle at the right. Then estimate the trigonometric value.

   i. sin R ii. cos R iii. tan R

   _____   _____   _____

b. Measure ∠R in the triangle at the right. Then use that measure to find each trigonometric value.

   i. sin R ii. cos R iii. tan R

   _____   _____   _____

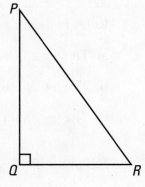

6. Refer to the regular octagon at the right. Suppose the length of each side is 12 cm. Find the length of $\overline{BD}$.

   _____

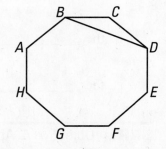

Uses Objective F: Solve real-world problems using the trigonometry of right triangles.

---

7. A ship sails 64 kilometers on a bearing of 20°. How far east of its original position is the ship? _____

8. Dennis sights the top of a rocket at 54° when he stands 65 ft away. He is 5 ft tall. About how tall is the rocket?

   _____

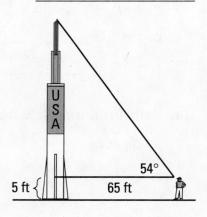

9. A straight water slide makes a 40° angle with the surface of the water. If the slide is 11.5 meters high, how long is it? _____

LESSON MASTER 10-2 B

Vocabulary

Refer to the diagram at the right. Complete the sentence with the appropriate phrase.

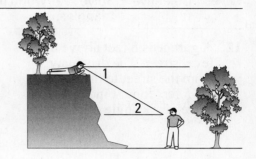

1. a. ∠1 is called a(n)

_____.

b. ∠2 is called a(n)

_____.

c. In geometry, ∠1 and ∠2 are called _____.

d. How are the measures of ∠1 and ∠2 related?

_____

_____

Skills Objective C: Determine the measure of an angle given its sine, cosine, or tangent.

In 2–5, find the measure of the acute angle θ to the nearest degree.

2. $\sin \theta = .42$ _____

3. $\cos \theta = \frac{1}{2}$ _____

4. $\tan \theta = 9.5$ _____

5. $\sin \theta = \frac{\sqrt{3}}{2}$ _____

In 6–9, evaluate the functions to the nearest tenth.

6. $\cos^{-1} .951$ _____

7. $\tan^{-1} .067$ _____

8. $\sin^{-1} .966$ _____

9. $\cos^{-1} \frac{5}{13}$ _____

In 10 and 11, refer to the diagram at the right. Find the measure to the nearest degree.

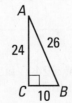

10. $m\angle A$ _____

11. $m\angle B$ _____

▶ **LESSON MASTER 10-2 B** *page 2*

Uses Objective F: Solve real-world problems using the trigonometry of right triangles.

---

12. A garage is 8 feet above the level street. The driveway from the street to the garage is 45 feet long. Find the driveway's angle of incline.

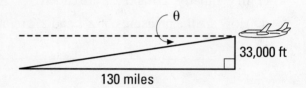

45 feet   8 ft

_____

13. A plane flying at 33,000 ft is 130 miles from the airport when it begins to descend. If the angle of descent is constant, find this angle.

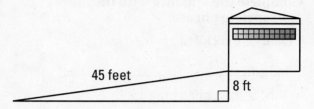

θ   33,000 ft   130 miles

_____

14. If a tower 18 meters high casts a shadow 9.5 meters long, what is the angle of elevation of the sun?

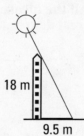

18 m   9.5 m

_____

15. A person on top of a building finds there is a 38° angle of depression to the head of an assistant who is 170 cm tall. If the assistant is 10 meters from the building, how tall is the building?

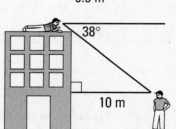

38°   10 m

_____

16. The base of a 24-ft ladder is placed 8 ft from a building.

a. What angle does the ladder make with the level ground?

_____

b. How high above the ground is the top of the ladder?

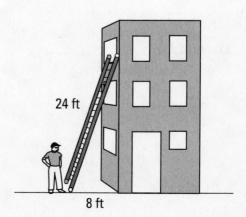

24 ft   8 ft

_____

Name _____

Skills Objective B: Find exact values of trigonometric functions of multiples of 30° or 45°.

In 1–9, give the exact value.

1. cos 60° _____   2. sin 60° _____   3. tan 60° _____

4. cos 45° _____   5. sin 45° _____   6. tan 45° _____

7. cos 30° _____   8. sin 30° _____   9. tan 30° _____

In 10–13, find the trigonometric value and the indicated length. Give the exact answer.

10.
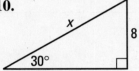

    a. sin 30° _____

    b. x _____

11.
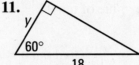

    a. cos 60° _____

    b. y _____

12.

    a. cos 45° _____

    b. a _____

13.
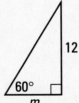

    a. tan 60° _____

    b. m _____

Properties Objective E: Identify and use definitions and theorems relating sines, cosines, and tangents.

In 14–21, fill in the blank with the measure of an acute angle.

14. sin 74° = cos _____

15. cos 19° = sin _____

16. sin 45° = cos _____

17. cos 7° = sin (90 − _____)

18. $\dfrac{\sin 23°}{\cos 23°}$ = tan _____

19. tan 68° = $\dfrac{\sin \underline{\hspace{1cm}}}{\cos 68°}$

20. (sin 88°)^2 + (cos _____)^2 = 1

21. (sin _____)^2 + (cos 14°)^2 = 1

▶ **LESSON MASTER 10-3 B** *page 2*

In 22–26, assume the angle is acute.

22. If $\cos x = 0.49$, then what is the value of $\sin x$? _____

23. If $\sin y = \dfrac{\sqrt{5}}{3}$, then what is the value of $\cos y$? _____

24. If $\sin z \approx .515$, and $\cos z \approx .857$, what is the value of $\tan z$? _____

25. Suppose $\sin \theta = \dfrac{\sqrt{6}}{5}$.

    a. What is the value of $\cos \theta$? _____

    b. What is the value of $\tan \theta$? _____

26. Suppose $\cos \theta = \dfrac{\sqrt{10}}{10}$ and $\tan \theta = 3$, what is the value of $\sin \theta$? _____

In 27–29, verify the property for the triangle at the right.

27. $(\sin \theta)^2 + (\cos \theta)^2 = 1$

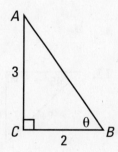

28. $\sin (90° - \theta) = \cos \theta$

29. $\tan \theta = \dfrac{\sin \theta}{\cos \theta}$

LESSON MASTER 10-4 B

Vocabulary

1. What is the *unit circle?*

_____

_____

2. Let (x, y) be image of $(1, 0)$ under R_θ. What is the relationship between (x, y) and the sine and cosine of θ?

_____

_____

Skills Objective B: Find exact values of trigonometric functions of multiples of 30° or 45°.

3. Explain how to find the exact value of cos 390° without using a calculator.

_____

_____

4. Explain how to find the exact value of sin -300° without using a calculator.

_____

_____

In 5–20, give the exact value. Do not use a calculator.

5. cos 360° _____

6. sin 180° _____

7. cos 270° _____

8. cos (-180°) _____

9. sin (-90°) _____

10. cos (-90°) _____

11. cos 720° _____

12. sin (-270°) _____

13. cos 540° _____

14. sin 540° _____

15. sin (-330)° _____

16. sin 450° _____

17. cos (-450)° _____

18. sin 405° _____

19. sin 3600° _____

20. sin (-300)° _____

▶ **LESSON MASTER 10-4 B** *page 2*

Representations Objective I: Use the properties of a unit circle to find trigonometric values.

In 21–26, to the nearest thousandth, find the coordinates of the image of the point (1, 0) under the given rotation.

21. $R_{65°}$ _____   **22.** $R_{10°}$ _____

23. $R_{378°}$ _____   **24.** $R_{400°}$ _____

25. $R_{-325°}$ _____   **26.** $R_{-700°}$ _____

In 27–29, use the diagram of a unit circle at the right.

27. Find $\cos θ$. _____

28. Find $\sin θ$. _____

29. Find $θ$ to the nearest degree. _____

(.559, .829)

In 30–37, refer to the diagram at the right. Give the letter that could stand for the function value.

30. $\cos 180°$ _____

31. $\sin 270°$ _____

32. $\sin 28°$ _____

33. $\cos 82°$ _____

34. $\sin (-270°)$ _____   **35.** $\cos 388°$ _____

36. $\cos 450°$ _____   **37.** $\sin (-278°)$ _____

Review Objective F, Lesson 10-1

38. A loading-dock ramp makes a 20° angle with the ground. If the dock is 2.5 meters high, how long is the ramp? _____

39. A person sights the top of the San Jacinto Monument at an angle of 85° when standing 50 feet from the base of the monument. If the person is 6 feet tall, about how high is the monument? _____

40. A rock dropped 182 ft from the top of the Leaning Tower of Pisa lands at a point 14 ft from the base of the tower. What angle does the tower make with the ground? _____

LESSON MASTER

10-5
B

Skills Objective A: Approximate values of trigonometric functions using a calculator.

In 1–12, use a calculator to evaluate. Round the value to the nearest thousandth.

1. $\cos 98°$ _____

2. $\sin 159°$ _____

3. $\cos 280°$ _____

4. $\cos 195°$ _____

5. $\sin 250°$ _____

6. $\sin 348°$ _____

7. $\cos 410°$ _____

8. $\sin (-200°)$ _____

9. $\sin (-25)°$ _____

10. $\cos 915°$ _____

11. $\sin (-1300)°$ _____

12. $\cos (-640.5°)$ _____

Skills Objective B: Find exact values of trigonometric functions of multiples of 30° or 45°.

In 13–18, *true or false*. Do not use a calculator.

13. $\sin 390° = \sin{-30°}$ _____

14. $\cos 540° = \cos 180°$ _____

15. $\sin{-300°} = \sin 60°$ _____

16. $\cos 210° = \cos 30°$ _____

17. $\sin 240° = -\sin 60°$ _____

18. $\cos 300° = -\cos 60°$ _____

In 19–34, give the exact value.

19. $\sin 150°$ _____

20. $\cos 225°$ _____

21. $\cos 240°$ _____

22. $\sin 300°$ _____

23. $\sin 135°$ _____

24. $\cos 315°$ _____

25. $\sin 480°$ _____

26. $\cos 570°$ _____

27. $\cos 585°$ _____

28. $\sin (-45°)$ _____

29. $\cos (-60°)$ _____

30. $\sin (-210°)$ _____

31. $\cos (-150)°$ _____

32. $\cos (-810°)$ _____

33. $\sin (-3000)°$ _____

34. $\cos (-585°)$ _____

▶ **LESSON MASTER 10-5 B** *page 2*

Representations Objective I: Use the properties of a unit circle to find trigonometric values.

In 35–42, for the indicated point, tell if the value for sin θ or cos θ is *positive, negative,* or *neither*.

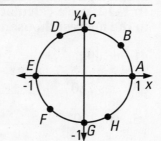

35. *A,* cos θ _____

36. *B,* sin θ _____

37. *C,* sin θ _____

38. *D,* cos θ _____

39. *E,* cos θ _____

40. *F,* cos θ _____

41. *G,* cos θ _____

42. *H,* sin θ _____

In 43–45, refer to the unit circle at the right. Use a calculator to find the coordinates of the point to the nearest thousandth.

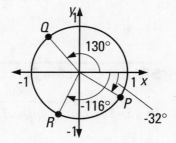

43. *P* _____

44. *Q* _____

45. *R* _____

In 46–49, give the letter in the diagram at the right that could represent the given value.

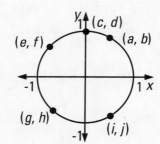

46. sin 138° _____

47. sin (-270°) _____

48. cos (-68°) _____

49. cos 228° _____

In 50–55, use the graph of the unit circle at the right to find the value.

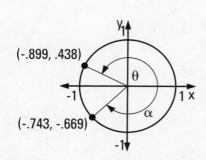

50. sin θ _____

51. cos θ _____

52. cos α _____

53. sin α _____

54. θ _____

55. α _____

LESSON MASTER 10-6 B

Uses Objective G: Solve real-world problems using the Laws of Cosines.

1. Ship *A* sights Ship *B* at a distance of 6.4 km, and Ship *A* sights Ship *C* at a distance of 7.7 km. The angle between the two sightings is 80°.

   a. In the space below, draw and label a diagram to represent this situation.

   b. How far apart are Ship *B* and Ship *C*? _____

2. Refer to the drawing at the right. At what angle θ should a 36-inch-wide door be opened so that distance *a* is at least 15 inches?

   _____

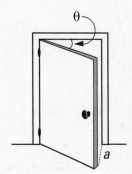

3. Refer to the drawing at the right. Maxine is designing a tent. If the two sides meet at a 40° angle, find *w*, the width of the tent along the ground.

   _____

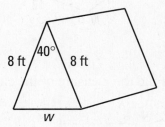

8 ft /40° 8 ft

w

4. Refer to the diagram at the right. If two planes leave Berlin, one flying toward London and the other flying toward Paris, by approximately what angle θ do their headings differ?

   _____

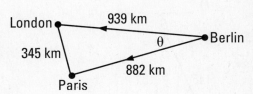

London• 939 km •Berlin
345 km θ
882 km
Paris

Representations Objective H: Find missing parts of a triangle using the
Law of Cosines.

5. Find *AB*. _____

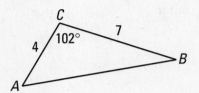

6. Find *DE*. _____

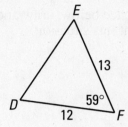

7. Find m∠*G*. _____

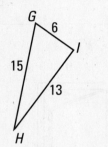

8. Find *KJ*. _____

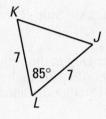

9. Find *MN*. _____

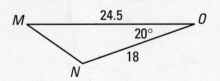

10. Find *PR*. _____

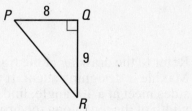

11. Find the measure of the angle.

∠*S* _____   ∠*T* _____

∠*U* _____

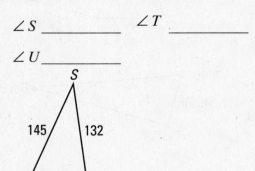

12. Find *n*. _____

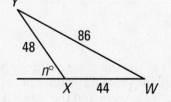

LESSON MASTER  10-7 B

Vocabulary

1. Define *triangulation*.

_____

_____

_____

Uses Objective G: Solve real-world problems usng the Law of Sines.

2. A bridge is to be built across a canyon from point *A* to point *B*. A surveyor drew the diagram at the right based on measurements taken at the site. Find the length of the bridge.

   _____

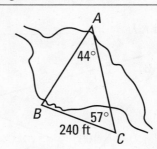

3. In the drawing at the right, *PS* is the height of a mountain. Find the given measure.

   a. m ∠*QRP* _____

   b. m ∠*RPQ* _____

   c. *PR* _____

   d. *PS* _____

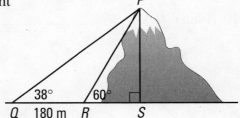

4. As shown at the right, a ship heading due west had to detour around an oil spill. At point *U*, the ship steered 45° off course, and sailed until it cleared the spill. Then at point *V* it turned back toward its original course and intersected it at a 36° angle at point *W*. If the original route from *U* to *W* is 32 km long, how many additional kilometers did the ship have to sail?

   _____

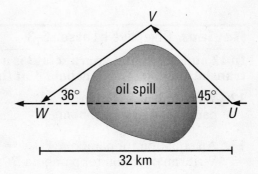

5. Fire stations *X* and *Y* are 45 mi apart. The ranger at station *X* sees a fire at point *Z* such that m ∠ *YXZ* = 30°. The ranger at station *Y* sees the fire such that m ∠ *XYZ* = 70°. How far is the fire from each station?

   X _____   *Y* _____

Representations Objective H: Find missing parts of a triangle using the Law of Sines.

6. Find *BC*. _____

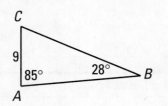

7. Find *DE*. _____

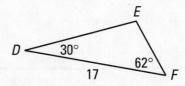

8. Find *KJ*. _____

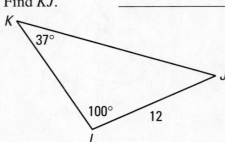

9. Find *NO*. _____

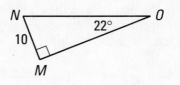

10. Find *GH*. _____

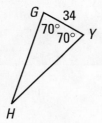

11. Find *TU*. _____

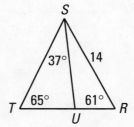

Review Objective I: Lesson 6–3

In 12 and 13, assume parabola B is a translation image of parabola A at the right.

12. What translation maps parabola *A* onto parabola *B*? _____

13. An equation for parabola *A* is $y = x^2$. Write an equation for parabola *B*.

_____

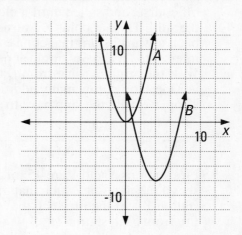

LESSON MASTER 10-8 B

Vocabulary

1. Define *sine wave*.

_____

_____

_____

In 2 and 3, complete the definition.

2. If the graph of a function can be mapped onto itself under a horizontal translation of positive magnitude, then we call this type of function a ___?___.

_____

3. Situations that lead to sine waves are called ___?___.

_____

Representations   Objective J: Identify properties of the sine and cosine functions using their graphs.

4. Consider $R_\theta(0,1)$.

   a. What is the first coordinate of the image? _____

   b. What is the second coordinate of the image? _____

5. On the grid at the right, graph the function $f(x) = \sin x$ for $-360° \le x \le 360°$.

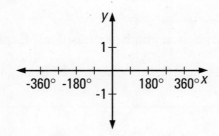

6. On the grid at the right, graph the function $f(x) = \cos x$ for $-360° \le x \le 360°$.

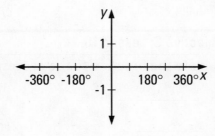

7. Give the domain and the range of the sine function.

   domain _____   range _____

8. Give the domain and the range of the cosine function.

   domain _____   range _____

9. What is the *y*-intercept of

   a. the sine graph? _____   **b.** the cosine graph? _____

10. Give the least 4 nonnegative *x*-intercepts of

    a. the sine function.   _____

    b. the cosine function.   _____

11. Give the period of

    a. the sine function. _____   **b.** the cosine function. _____

12. Refer to the graph at
    the right.

    a. Does this function
    seem to be periodic?
    If so, what is
    its period?

    _____

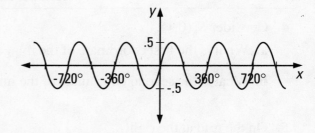

    b. Is the function graphed sinusoidal? Explain your reasoning.

    _____

    _____

    c. What equation might describe the graph?   _____

Review Objective C: Lesson 10-2

In 13–16, evaluate the function to the nearest tenth.

13. $\cos^{-1} .844$ _____   14. $\tan^{-1} .093$ _____

15. $\sin^{-1} .331$ _____   16. $\cos^{-1} \frac{7}{25}$ _____

LESSON MASTER 10-9 B

Skills Objective C: Determine the measure of an angle given its sine or cosine.

In 1–4, solve for all θ between 0° and 180°. Give θ to the nearest degree.

1. sin θ = .788 _____

2. sin θ = .358 _____

3. sin θ = -.995 _____

4. sin θ = .988 _____

In 5 and 6, give the exact values for all x between 0° and 180°.

5. $\sin x = \dfrac{\sqrt{3}}{2}$ _____

6. sin x = 1 _____

7. Suppose sin θ = .891. Find θ to the nearest degree if

   a. θ is acute. _____

   b. θ is obtuse. _____

Properties Objective E: Identify and use theorems relating sines and cosines.

8. *Multiple choice.* If sin 34° = n, then ___?___ _____
   - (a) sin 34° = 180 − n
   - (b) sin 56° = n
   - (c) sin 146° = 180 − n
   - (d) sin 146° = n

9. *Multiple choice.* If sin 34° = n, then ___?___ _____
   - (a) cos 34° = 180 -n
   - (b) cos 56° = n
   - (c) cos 146° = n
   - (d) cos 56° = -n

10. If θ is between 0° and 180°, how many solutions does the equation have?

    a. cos θ = .58 _____

    b. sin θ = .58 _____

11. If sin θ = 0.8 and 0° < θ < 180°, give all possible values for cos θ. _____

12. If sin θ = 0.23 and θ is obtuse, find cos θ to the nearest thousandth. _____

▶ **LESSON MASTER 10-9 B** *page 2*

Uses Objective G: Solve real-world problems using the Law of Sines or the Law of Cosines.

---

13. In a state park, camp headquarters are 6 km from the ranger's station, and the ranger's station is 4.5 km from the park entrance. The line from the camp headquarters to the entrance forms a 48° angle with the line joining camp headquarters and the ranger's station.

   a. At what angle does the line joining the entrance and the camp headquarters meet the line joining the entrance and the ranger's station? (Hint: There are two possibilities.) _____

   b. Find the distance from camp headquarters to the entrance. (Give both possibilities.) _____

Representations Objective H: Find missing parts of a triangle using the Law of Sines or the Law of Cosines.

**In 14–16, a triangle is described. a. Solve the triangle.
b. Sketch the triangle. Give all possibilities.**

14. $\triangle ABC$, with m$\angle B = 40°$, $AC = 6$, and $AB = 8$

15. $\triangle RST$, with m$\angle R = 102°$, $RS = 10$, and $ST = 18$

16. $\triangle XYZ$, with m$\angle X = 72°$, $XZ = 7.3$, and $YZ = 7$

LESSON MASTER

10-10
B

Vocabulary

1. Define *radian*.

_____

_____

Skills Objective A: Approximate values of trigonometric functions using a calculator.

In 2–9, approximate to the nearest thousandth.

2. $\sin\left(\frac{5\pi}{9}\right)$ _____

3. $\tan\left(\frac{\pi}{8}\right)$ _____

4. $\cos\left(\frac{\pi}{12}\right)$ _____

5. $\sin\left(-\frac{4\pi}{15}\right)$ _____

6. $\tan(-2.3\pi)$ _____

7. $\cos(4.6\pi)$ _____

8. $\sin 3$ _____

9. $\tan -5$ _____

Skills Objective B: Find exact values of trigonometric functions of radian equivalents of multiples of 30° or 45°.

In 10–23, give the exact value.

10. $\cos\left(\frac{\pi}{6}\right)$ _____

11. $\sin\left(\frac{\pi}{4}\right)$ _____

12. $\cos\left(\frac{\pi}{2}\right)$ _____

13. $\sin\left(-\frac{3\pi}{4}\right)$ _____

14. $\tan\left(-\frac{\pi}{4}\right)$ _____

15. $\cos 0$ _____

16. $\sin\left(-\frac{\pi}{3}\right)$ _____

17. $\tan\left(\frac{5\pi}{6}\right)$ _____

18. $\sin 3\pi$ _____

19. $\cos 12\pi$ _____

20. $\sin\left(-\frac{3\pi}{2}\right)$ _____

21. $\cos -4.5\pi$ _____

22. $\cos\left(\frac{19\pi}{6}\right)$ _____

23. $\sin\left(-\frac{23\pi}{3}\right)$ _____

▶ **LESSON MASTER 10-10 B** *page 2*

Skills Objective D: Convert angle measures from radians to degrees or degrees to radians.

In 24–35, convert to radians.

24. 135° _____

25. -180° _____

26. 36° _____

27. -90° _____

28. 45° _____

29. 720° _____

30. 1° _____

31. 60° _____

32. -30° _____

33. -540° _____

34. 225° _____

35. 660° _____

In 36–47, convert to degrees.

36. $\frac{\pi}{8}$ _____

37. 3π _____

38. -4π _____

39. $\frac{\pi}{2}$ _____

40. $\frac{5\pi}{6}$ _____

41. 1.5π _____

42. 9.46 _____

43. $\frac{11\pi}{12}$ _____

44. $\frac{8\pi}{3}$ _____

45. 6 _____

46. $-\frac{\pi}{4}$ _____

47. $\frac{7\pi}{8}$ _____

Representations Objective I: Use the properties of a unit circle to find trigonometric values.

In 48–55, refer to the diagram at the right. Give the letter that could represent the given function value.

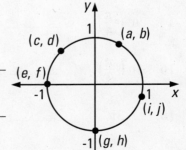

48. $\cos \pi$ _____

49. $\sin \frac{3\pi}{2}$ _____

50. $\sin \frac{\pi}{3}$ _____

51. $\sin 3\pi$ _____

52. $\cos \frac{3\pi}{4}$ _____

53. $\cos -\frac{\pi}{12}$ _____

54. $\sin -\frac{5\pi}{4}$ _____

55. $\sin 2.75\pi$ _____

LESSON MASTER

11-1
B

Vocabulary

1. Give an example of a *polynomial in x* written in standard form.

_____

_____

Properties Objective E: Use technical vocabulary to describe polynomials.

In 2–7, a polynomial is given. a. Write the polynomial in standard form. b. Give the degree of the polynomial. c. Name the leading coefficient. d. Give the number of terms.

2. $9v^2 + 7v^3$

a. _____

b. _____

c. _____

d. _____

3. $8m^2 + 4 - 6m$

a. _____

b. _____

c. _____

d. _____

4. $c^5 - 2c^3 - c^2 - 5$

a. _____

b. _____

c. _____

d. _____

5. $12 - 6p$

a. _____

b. _____

c. _____

d. _____

6. $-14r^7 + 6r^{19} - r^3 - r + 4r^{10}$

a. _____

b. _____

c. _____

d. _____

7. $12e^4$

a. _____

b. _____

c. _____

d. _____

Uses Objective H: Use polynomials to model real-world situations.

8. For five years, Mr. Volaskis invested $1600 per year in a retirement account paying $r\%$ compounded annually. No additional money was added or withdrawn.

   a. Write a polynomial expression to give the total amount in his account at the end of the fifth year.

   _____

   b. Determine how much is in his account if it earned 4.8% each year.

   _____

9. A parents' organization saved the fun-fair profits in a special fund for new playground equipment. The money was left untouched and earned $r\%$ interest compounded annually. The table shows the deposits.

   a. Write a polynomial expression for the amount in the account after the 6/94 deposit.

Date	Deposit
6/89	$ 800
6/90	1150
6/91	1200
6/92	750
6/93	1130
6/94	980

   _____

   b. Evaluate how much was in the account after 6/94, if $r = 3.7\%$.

   _____

Representations Objective J: Graph polynomial functions.

In 10 and 11, a polynomial function is given. a. Evaluate $f(-2)$, $f(0)$, and $f(1)$. b. Sketch the graph of the polynomial function on the given window.

10. $f(x) = -4x^4 + 12x^2 - 3x + 20$

    a. _____

    b.

11. $P(x) = x^5 + 4.5x - 7$

    a. _____

    b.

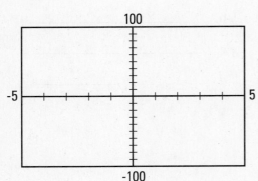

LESSON MASTER 11-2 B

Skills Objective A: Use the Extended Distributive Property to multiply polynomials.

In 1–8, expand and write in standard form.

1. $(x^3 + 6)(x - 3)$

_____

2. $(2 + 4n^4)^2$

_____

3. $(e + 9)(e + 4)(e - 9)$

_____

4. $(5x + 3)^2(2x - 8)$

_____

5. $(-y^2 + 6)(y^4 + 2y^2 - 3)$

_____

6. $b(6b - 5)(2b^3 + 1)$

_____

7. $(2u + 1)(3u - 4)(-u^2 + 1)$

_____

8. $(g^2 - 2g + 2)(g^2 + 2g - 4)$

_____

In 9–12, multiply and simplify.

9. $(x + 3y)(2x - 2xy + y)$

_____

10. $(4w + 3)(-2w - 5x + 7)$

_____

11. $(r + s)(r + 5s)(r - 3s)$

_____

12. $(a + b + c)(a - b + c)$

_____

Properties Objective E: Use technical vocabulary to describe polynomials.

13. Give an example of each.

   a. monomial _____

   b. binomial _____

   c. trinomial _____

In 14 and 15, give the degree of the polynomial.

14. $12a^2b^4 + 3ab^3 + b^2$

_____

15. $-9m^7n - 4m^4n^3 + m^2n^2 - 16$

_____

Uses Objective I: Use polynomials to describe geometric situations.

**In 16 and 17, consider the largest of the rectangles in
the diagram. a. Give its dimensions. b. Find its area.**

16.

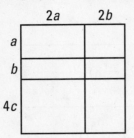

17.

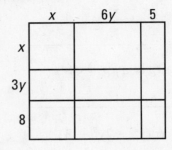

a. 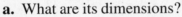   a. _____

b. _____   b. _____

18. Refer to the largest rectangular solid
to the right.

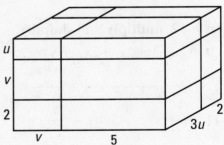

    a. What are its dimensions?

    _____

    b. What is its volume?

    c. What is its surface area?

_____

19. An open box is folded from a sheet
of tag board 55 cm by 70 cm, after
removing squares of side x from
each corner.

    a. At the right, sketch a diagram of
this situation.

    b. Write a formula for the volume $V(x)$
of the box.

    _____

    c. Write a formula for the surface $S(x)$
area of the box.

    _____

LESSON MASTER

11-3
B

Vocabulary

1. For real numbers a, b, and c, if $ax^2 + bx + c = 0$,
   then what is the quantity $b^2 - 4ac$ called? _____

2. **a.** What does it mean if we say a polynomial is *prime*
   over the set of polynomials with rational coefficients?

   _____

   _____

   _____

   b. What does it mean if we say a polynomial is *prime* over
   the set of polynomials with real coefficients?

   _____

   _____

   _____

Skills Objective B: Factor polynomials using common-monomial factoring, perfect-square patterns, or patterns for the difference of squares.

In 3–7, fill in the blanks.

3. $6g^2h - 15gh^2 = 3gh\,(\underline{\hspace{2cm}} - \underline{\hspace{2cm}})$

4. $16x^3y + 20x^2 = \underline{\hspace{2cm}}(4xy + 5)$

5. $a^3b^4c^7 - a^2b^2c^5 + a^2b^2c^4 = a^2b^2c^4\,(\underline{\hspace{2cm}} - \underline{\hspace{2cm}} + \underline{\hspace{2cm}})$

6. $-18x^3y^2z^2 + 14x^2y^2 - 30y^2z = \underline{\hspace{2cm}}(9x^3z^2 - 7x^2 + 15z)$

7. $4(a + 2b) - (a + 2b)^2 = (a + 2b)(\underline{\hspace{2cm}} - \underline{\hspace{2cm}})$

**In 8–15, *multiple choice*. Which of the following describes
the polynomial?**

    (a) perfect square   **(b) difference of squares**

    (c) sum of squares   **(d) none of the above**

8. $a^2 - 81$ _____

9. $c^2 + 14c + 49$ _____

10. $r^2 + 144$ _____

11. $2m^2 + 8m + 16$ _____

12. $36x^2 - 60x + 25$ _____

13. $49 - 9u^2$ _____

14. $x^6 - 1$ _____

15. $25e^2 + 10e + 4$ _____

▶ **LESSON MASTER 11-3 B** *page 2*

In 16–23, factor over the set of polynomials with rational coefficients, if possible. If this is not possible, write *prime*.

16. $8a^2 - 2a - 3$

_____

17. $m^2 + 2m + 6$

_____

18. $x^2 - 100$

_____

19. $4n^3 + 20n^2 - 24n$

_____

20. $a^2b^4c^2 - 81d^2$

_____

21. $49g^2 + 42g + 9$

_____

22. $4e^2 - ef - 3f^2$

_____

23. $9x^3 - 30x^2 + 25x$

_____

24. a. Write $r^4 - 1$ as the product of two binomials.   _____

   b. Write $r^4 - 1$ as the product of three binomials.   _____

25. Factor $4x^2 - 5$ over the set of real numbers.   _____

26. Factor $4y^2 + 1$ over the set of complex numbers.   _____

Review Objective K, Lesson 6-10

In 27–29, suppose D **is the discriminant for a quadratic function** $f(x) = ax^2 + bx + c$. **Tell if** $D = 0, D > 0,$ **or** $D < 0$ **for the graph of** $f(x)$.

27.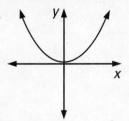

_____

28.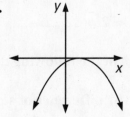

_____

29.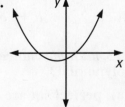

_____

In 30–33, give the number of x**-intercepts of the graph of the parabola.**

30. $y = 16x^2 - 24x + 9$ _____

31. $y = -x^2 - 5x - 12$ _____

32. $y = 3x^2 - 10x + 8$ _____

33. $y + 3 = 8x^2 - 10x$ _____

LESSON MASTER 11-4 B

Representations Objective K: Estimate zeros of functions of polynomials using tables or graphs.

In 1 and 2, the graph of a polynomial function is shown.
a. Give the minimum number of x-intercepts.
b. Estimate the value of each x-intercept.

1.

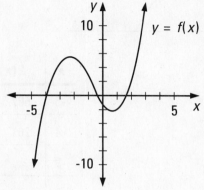

a. _____

b. _____

2.

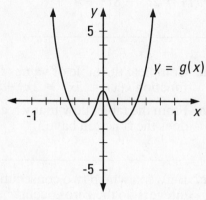

a. _____

b. _____

In 3 and 4, the graph of a polynomial function is shown.
a.   Give the minimum number of x-intercepts.
b.   Give the minimum number of solutions to the equation $h(x) = 60$. Between which pair of consecutive integers does each solution occur?
c.   Give the minimum number of solutions to the equation $h(x) = -20$. Between which pair of consecutive integers does each solution occur?

3.

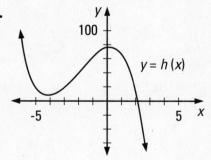

a. _____

b. _____

c. _____

4.

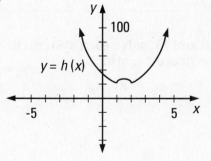

a. _____

b. _____

c. _____

▶ **LESSON MASTER 11-4 B** *page 2*

In 5–8, estimate the real zeros of the function described to the nearest tenth.

5. $f(x) = x^3 + 2x^2 - 4x - 1$

_____

6. $g(x) = -3x^5 + 6x^4 + 2x^3 - 3x^2 + 8x - 5$

_____

7. $h(t) = 2t^4 - 8t^2 + 4$

_____

8. $P(n) = n^6 - 4n^5 + 3n^2$

_____

9. a. Complete the table of values for the function $k(x) = .5x^4 - 2x^3 + 5$

b. From the table, how many real zeros does the function have?

_____

c. Between which two consecutive integers do the zeros occur?

_____

d. How could you use a graph to justify your answers in Parts **b** and **c**?

_____

_____

_____

e. Use technology to find each zero to the nearest tenth.

_____

x	$k(x)$
-5	567.5
-4	261
-3	
-2	
-1	
0	
1	
2	
3	-8.5
4	
5	

In 10 and 11, solve each system. Round solutions to the nearest tenth.

10. $\begin{cases} y = -x^3 + 5x + 2 \\ y = 5 \end{cases}$

11. $\begin{cases} y = .5x^4 - 3x^2 \\ y = 2x - 3 \end{cases}$

LESSON MASTER

11-5
B

Skills Objective C: Find zeros of polynomial functions by factoring.

In 1–9, find the exact zeros of the polynomial function described.

1. $f(x) = (x + 1)(x - 3)(3x + 2)$ _____

2. $g(x) = 4x(2x + 9)$ _____

3. $h(a) = a^2 - 10a + 25$ _____

4. $d(x) = x^2 - 64$ _____

5. $j(x) = x^3 + 18x^2 + 81x$ _____

6. $e(n) = 15n^3 - 45n^2 - 60n$ _____

7. $g(x) = x^4 - 36x^2$ _____

8. $h(a) = 4a^3 - 4a$ _____

9. $d(x) = 18x^3 + 57x^2 - 21x$ _____

Skills Objective D: Determine an equation for a polynomial function from data points.

In 10–13, write equations for three different polynomial functions with the given zeros.

10. 0, -5, and 3 _____

_____

11. 0, 9, and -9 _____

_____

12. $\frac{3}{2}, \frac{5}{4}$, and -2 _____

_____

13. -3, 0, 3.5, and 7 _____

_____

▶ **LESSON MASTER 11-5 B** *page 2*

Properties Objective F: Apply the Zero-Product Theorem and the Factor
Theorem.

---

14. Consider the two polynomial functions with equations
$f(x) = 3x(x + 4)(2x - 1)$ and $g(x) = x^2(x + 4)(2x - 1)$. What
do the graphs of the two equations have in common?

_____

15. Suppose $f(x) = (x + a)(x + b)(x - 2c)$.
What are the zeros of the function f?   _____

16. The graph of a polynomial function contains the points
$(a, 0)$, $(b, 0)$, $(0, c)$, (d, e), and $(f, 0)$. Give as many factors
of the polynomial as you can.

_____

17. The graph of a polynomial equation does not cross
the x-axis. Can the polynomial be factored? Explain
your reasoning.

_____

_____

Representations Objective J: Graph polynomial functions.

---

18. At the right is the graph of a fourth-
degree polynomial with leading
coefficient 1 and integer zeros.

    a. Name the zeros.

    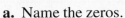

    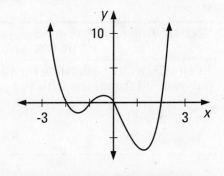

    b. Write an equation for the function.

    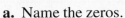

Representations Objective K: Estimate zeros of functions of polynomials
using graphs.

---

19. Consider the polynomial
equation $y = x^3 - 2x^2 - 3x$.

    a. Sketch a graph of the
    polynomial.

    b. Use the graph to factor the polynomial.

    _____

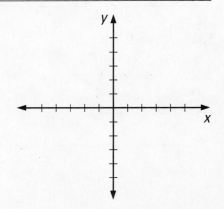

LESSON MASTER

11-6
B

Skills Objective B: Factor polynomials
Objective C: Find zeros of polynomial functions by factoring.

In 1–9, a polynomial is given. a. Factor the polynomial over the set of *complex* numbers. b. Check your answers by multiplying the factors.

1. $x^2 + 4x - 357$ **a.** _____

   b. _____

2. $10z^2 + 51z + 27$ **a.** _____

   b. _____

3. $y^2 - 3$ **a.** _____

   b. _____

4. $n^2 + 4n + 7$ **a.** _____

   b. _____

5. $6m^3 - 17m^2 + 5m$ **a.** _____

   b. _____

6. $2a + 3a^2 - 10$ **a.** _____

   b. _____

7. $c^3 - 17c$ **a.** _____

   b. _____

8. $16g^2 + 8\sqrt{5}g + 5$ **a.** _____

   b. _____

9. $8d^3 - 2d^2 - 3d$ **a.** _____

   b. _____

▶ **LESSON MASTER 11-6 B** *page 2*

In 10–13, an equation is given. **a.** Find all real solutions.
b. Check your answer by graphing.

10. $0 = x^2 - 17$ 　　　　　　　　　**11.** $24x^2 + 53x - 7 = 0$

　a. _____ 　**a.** _____

　b. 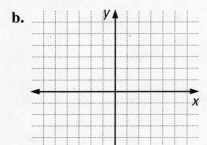 　**b.**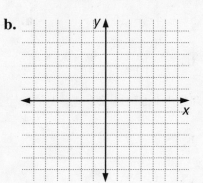

12. $x^2 + x + 4 = 0$ 　　　　　　　**13.** $5x^3 - 19x^2 - 30x = 0$

　a. _____ 　**a.** _____

　b. 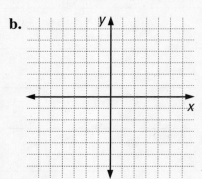 　**b.**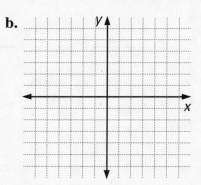

In 14 and 15, an equation is given. **a.** Solve. **b.** Check the
solution by substituting into the original equation.

14. $m^2 + 10 = 0$ 　　　　　　　　**15.** $2k^3 - 13k^2 + 20k = 0$

　a. _____ 　**a.** _____

　b. 　　　　　　　　　　　　　　　　　**b.**

LESSON MASTER **11-7** **B**

Properties Objective G: Apply the Rational Zero Theorem.

1. Suppose $8m^6$ is the first term of a polynomial function written in standard form and 7 is the last term. Let $\frac{p}{q}$ be a rational number in lowest terms and let $\frac{p}{q}$ be a zero of the polynomial function.

   a. Fill in each blank with a number: p is a factor of ___?___ and q is a factor of ___?___ .   _____

   b. Give three possible values for $\frac{p}{q}$.   _____

In 2–5, use the Rational Zero Theorem to factor the polynomial.

2. $x^3 - 2x^2 - 21x - 18$

   _____

3. $6y^3 - 13y^2 + y + 2$

   _____

4. $15z^3 - 22z^2 - 5z$

   _____

5. $9a^5 - 30a^4 - 81a^3 + 30a^2$

   _____

In 6–13, a polynomial is given. a. Use the Rational Zero Theorem to list all possible rational zeros of the given polynomial. b. Find all rational zeros.

6. $f(x) = 2x^3 - x^2 - 2x + 1$

   a. _____

   b. _____

7. $g(x) = 125x^3 - 1$

   a. _____

   b. _____

8. $q(x) = 3x^2 + 2x + 8$

   a. _____

   b. _____

9. $h(x) = 10x^2 - 11x + 3$

   a. _____

   b. _____

10. $f(x) = x^5 - 12x^4 + 36x^3 - x^2 + 12x - 36$

    a. _____

    b. _____

11. $t(x) = 8x^5 - 32x^4 + x^2 - 4$

    a. _____

    b. _____

12. $t(x) = 2x^6 + 6x^5 + 3x + 21$

    a. _____

    b. _____

13. $s(x) = x^6 + 4x^5 - x - 4$

    a. _____

    b. _____

▶ **LESSON MASTER 11-7 B** *page 2*

Representations Objective J: Graph polynomial functions.

14. Consider $g(x) = -3x^5 + 20x^2 - 8$.

   a. Use the Rational Zero
   Theorem to list all possible
   rational zeros.

   _____

   _____

   b. Graph the polynomial
   function at the right.

   c. Use Parts **a** and **b** to find all
   rational zeros.

   _____

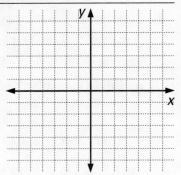

15. Consider $h(x) = 4x^6 + 6x^2 + 5$.

   a. Use the Rational Zero
   Theorem to list all possible
   rational zeros.

   _____

   b. Graph the polynomial
   function at the right.

   c. Use Parts **a** and **b** to find all
   rational zeros.

   _____

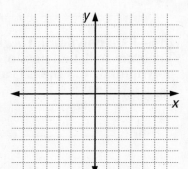

Review Objective C, Lessons 6-7 and 6-8

In 16–19, find all solutions.

16. $2x^2 + 9x - 1 = 0$ 17. $4n^2 - 6n - 7 = 0$

18. $6m^2 + 7m = 5$ 19. $4a - 10 = 3a^2$

LESSON MASTER 11-8 B

Vocabulary

1. Suppose r is a *root* of a polynomial function and has *multiplicity 3*. What does this mean?

_____

_____

2. Give an example of a polynomial function in factored form that has

  a. 5 as a double root.   _____

  b. 3 as a root with mutiplicity 4.   _____

Properties Objective F: Apply the Fundamental Theorem of Algebra.

3. State the Fundamental Theorem of Algebra.

_____

_____

_____

4. Consider the equation $8x^4 - i\sqrt{2}\,x^2 + 3 + 2i = 0$.

  a. What is the minimum number of complex roots of the equation?   _____

  b. What is the maximum number of different roots of the equation?   _____

5. Consider the equation $(2x - 1)^5(x^2 - 5)(x^2 + 4) = 0$.

  a. What is the minimum number of complex roots of the equation?   _____

  b. What is the maximum number of roots of the equation?   _____

  c. Find all the rational roots and state the multiplicity of each.

_____

▶ **LESSON MASTER 11-8 B** *page 2*

    d. Find all the irrational roots and the multiplicity of each.

    _____

    e. Find all the nonreal roots and the multiplicity of each.

    _____

    f. Without graphing, tell how many times the equation
    crosses the *x*-axis. Explain your reasoning.

    _____

    _____

Culture Objective L: Be familiar with the history of the solving of polynomial
                equations.

---

  6. Match each name with his contribution towards solving all
     polynomial equations.

    a. Évariste Galois   _____ In the 16th century, discovered how
                                         to solve any quartic equation

    b. Niccolo Tartaglia   _____ In the 18th century, proved the
                                         Fundamental Theorem of Algebra

    c. Omar Khayyam
                               _____ In the 16th century, discovered how
    d. Karl Friedrich Gauss   to solve some types of cubic
                                           equations exactly

    e. Ludovico Ferrari   _____ In 1799, provided most of the proof
                                         that a general quintic equation cannot
    f. Niels Abel   be solved by formulas

                              _____ In 1824, completed the proof that a
    g. Scipione Del Ferro   general quintic equation cannot be
                                         solved by formulas

    h. Paolo Ruffini
                               _____ In 1535, discovered a method for
                                         solving all cubic equations exactly

                              _____ In the 12th century, showed how
                                         to solve many cubic equations

                              _____ In 19th century, described a method
                                         for determining which polynomial
                                         equations of degree 5 or more can
                                         be solved using formulas

LESSON MASTER 11-9 B

Skills Objective D: Determine an equation for a polynomial function from data points.

In 1–7, a set of ordered pairs or a sequence is given.
a. Determine whether the given values can be described by a polynomial function of degree 5 or less.
b. If so, give its degree.

1.

x	1	2	3	4	5	6	7	8
y	6	13	32	69	130	221	348	517

a. _____ b. _____

2.

x	5	6	7	8	9	10	11	12
y	-27,500	-8896	27,228	91,072	196,196	360,000	604,204	955,328

a. _____ b. _____

3.

x	-4	-3	-2	-1	0	1	2	3
y	1407	1539	1674	1814	1960	2113	2271	2440

a. _____ b. _____

4.

x	-18	-12	-6	0	6	12	18	24
y	-304	-124	-16	20	-16	-124	-304	-556

a. _____ b. _____

5.

x	0	5	10	15	20	25	30	35
y	0	-5	-80	-405	-1280	-3125	-6480	-12,005

a. _____ b. _____

6. the sequence in which $a_1 = 7$
and $a_n = a_{n-1} + 4$

a. _____ b. _____

7. the sequence in which $a_1 = 3$
and $a_n = 4a_{n-1} - 2$

a. _____ b. _____

Name _____

8. Can the method of finite differences be used with this
set of data? Explain why or why not.

x	0	4	12	24	40	60	84	112
y	23	34	45	56	67	78	89	100

_____

_____

9. Suppose there is a polynomial formula of degree ≤ 5
for the *n*th term of the sequence 14, 71, 182, 365, 638,
1019, 1526, 2177, ... Use the method of finite
differences to predict the next term. _____

Uses Objective H: Use polynomials to model real-world situations.

10. As part of an experiment, Chiang held a paper tube to her
eye and estimated the number of grid squares she could see
through the tube when the tube was held at various distances
above a sheet of grid paper. Her results are given in the table.

Distance Above Paper (cm)	1	2	3	4	5	6
Number of Squares Visible	30	39	50	63	78	95

a. What degree equation would you use to best model
the data? Explain your answer.

_____

_____

b. Predict how many squares Chiang could view
when the tube is held 7 cm above the paper. _____

Review Objective A, Lesson 5-4

In 11 and 12, solve the system.

11. $\begin{cases} \frac{1}{3}x - y = 6 \\ \frac{1}{2}x + 2y = -5 \end{cases}$

12. $\begin{cases} 2a + b - c = -9 \\ 3a + 3b + 2c = 4 \\ a + 2b - 2c = -12 \end{cases}$

LESSON MASTER

11-10 B

Skills Objective D: Determine an equation for a polynomial function from data points.

In 1 and 2, the data in the table can be modeled by a polynomial equation of the form $y = ax^2 + bx + c$.
a. List three equations which can be used to solve for a, b, and c.
b. Solve the system to find a formula which models the data.

1.

x	1	2	3	4	5	6	7	8
y	6	15	28	45	66	91	120	153

a. _____

b. _____

2.

x	1	2	3	4	5	6	7	8
y	-7	-16	-31	-52	-79	-112	-151	-196

a. _____

b. _____

In 3 and 4, write a polynomial formula which models the data.

3.

x	1	2	3	4	5	6	7	8
y	4	6	6	4	0	-6	-14	-24

_____

4.

x	1	2	3	4	5	6	7	8
y	8	15	34	71	132	223	350	519

_____

5. The data below can be modeled by an equation of the form $y = ax^4 + cx^2$. Find the equation.

x	0	1	2	3	4	5	6	7
y	0	3	24	99	288	675	1368	2499

_____

► **LESSON MASTER 11-10 B** *page 2*

Uses Objective H: Use polynomials to model real-world situations.

6. A statue is to be erected at the top of a number of square concrete steps as shown below. The top square is 10 ft by 10 ft by .5 ft. The second one is 20 ft by 20 ft by .5 ft. The third is 30 ft by 30 ft by .5 ft. Each additional square step is 10 ft longer on a side.

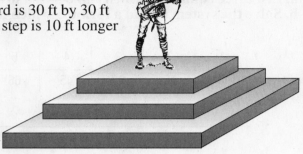

a. How many cubic feet of concrete are needed for

    i. the top step? _____   **ii.** the 2nd step? _____

    iii. the 3rd step? _____   **iv.** the 4th step? _____

    v. the 5th step? _____

b. Complete the table below. Be sure to give the *total* number of cubic feet of concrete needed.

Number of Steps	1	2	3	4	5
Cubic Feet of Concrete					

c. Write an equation to model the data.

_____

d. Use your equation to predict how many cubic feet of concrete would be needed for 8 stairs. _____

LESSON MASTER

12-1
B

Vocabulary

In 1 and 2, refer to the parabola below.

1. Identify the following.

   a. *focus* _____

   b. *directrix* _____

   c. *vertex* _____

   d. *axis of symmetry* _____

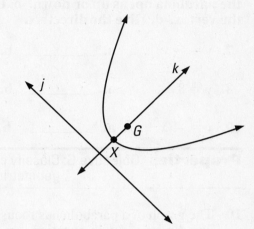

2. Explain what is true about all the
   points on the parabola. You may
   sketch additional points or segments
   and refer to them in your explanation.

   _____

   _____

   _____

Skills Objective B: Write equations for parabolas given sufficient conditions.

**In 3–5, write an equation for the parabola
satisfying the given conditions.**

3. focus $(0, -4)$ and directrix $y = 4$ _____

4. focus $(3, 0)$ and directrix $x = -3$ _____

5. Given $F = (6, 0)$ and line m with equation
   $x = -6$, write an equation for the set of points
   equidistant from F and m. _____

Properties Objective E: Find points on a parabola using its definition.

6. Find five points on the parabola with
   directrix w and focus U including
   the vertex of the parabola.

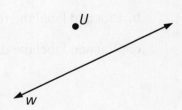

Properties Objective F: Identify characteristics of parabolas.

In 7–9, an equation for a parabola is given. **a.** Tell whether the parabola opens up or down. **b.** Give the focus. **c.** Give the vertex. **d.** Give the directrix.

7. $y = -\frac{1}{5}x^2$ **a.** _____ **b.** _____ **c.** _____ **d.** _____

8. $y = 8x^2$ **a.** _____ **b.** _____ **c.** _____ **d.** _____

9. $y = -4(x + 2)^2$ **a.** _____ **b.** _____ **c.** _____ **d.** _____

Properties Objective G: Classify curves as parabolas using algebraic or geometric properties.

10. The graph of a parabola has focus $F = (2, 1)$ and directrix d with equation $y = -1$.

    a. *Multiple choice.* Choose the points that lie on the parabola.

    (a) $A = (4, 1)$ (b) $B = (-2, 4)$

    (c) $C = (-1, 2)$

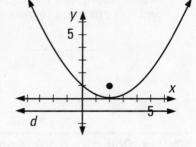

    _____

    b. Explain how you determined your answer in Part a.

    _____

    _____

    _____

Representations Objective J: Graph parabolas given sentences for them and vice versa.

11. **a.** Graph the parabola with equation $y = -\frac{1}{8}x^2$.

    b. Plot and label the focus.

    c. Plot and label the directrix.

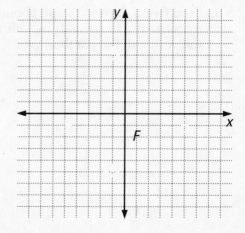

LESSON MASTER 12-2 B

Vocabulary

1. Write a definition for *circle*, including the meanings of *radius* and *center*.

_____

_____

_____

Skills Objective B: Write equations for circles given sufficient conditions.

In 2–7, write an equation for the circle satisfying the conditions.

2. center at $(0, 0)$, radius 9

_____

3. center at $(0, 0)$, radius .4

_____

4. center at $(3, -1)$, radius 3

_____

5. center at $(-2, -6)$, radius 11

_____

6. center at $(8, 0)$, radius $\frac{8}{5}$

_____

7. center at $(2, 5)$, radius $\sqrt{7}$

_____

Properties Objective F: Identify characteristics of circles.

In 8–11, identify the center and radius of each circle.

8. $(x - 4)^2 + (y + 6)^2 = 36$

center _____

radius _____

9. $x^2 + y^2 = 80$

center _____

radius _____

10. $(x + 2)^2 + (y + 4.5)^2 = 1$

center _____

radius _____

11. $(x - .6)^2 + (y + .9)^2 = 2.25$

center _____

radius _____

▶ **LESSON MASTER 12-2 B** *page 2*

Properties Objective G: Classify curves as circles using algebraic or geometric properties.

---

12. **a.** *True or false.* The points $(4, 4\sqrt{3})$, $(-4\sqrt{2}, 4\sqrt{2})$, $(0, 8)$, and $(-8, 0)$ all lie on the same circle with center $(0, 0)$. _____

   b. Explain how you determined your answer in Part a.

   _____

   _____

   _____

Uses Objective H: Use circles to solve real-world problems.

---

13. A sprinkler shoots a 10-foot stream of water in all directions. Consider a graph in which each unit represents one foot. Place the sprinkler at the origin.

   a. Write an equation to represent the boundary of the sprinkled area. _____

   b. A prize rose bush is located 8 ft east and 6 ft north of the sprinkler. Will the rose bush get sprinkled? Explain your thinking.

   _____

   _____

Representations Objective J: Graph circles given sentences for them and vice versa.

---

14. Graph the circle with equation $(x + 2)^2 + (y - 3)^2 = 9$.

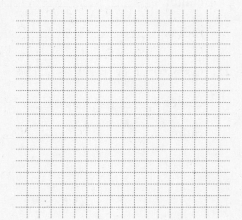

15. Write an equation for the circle graphed below.

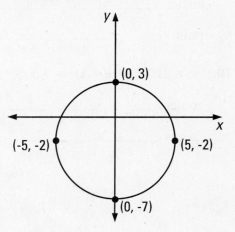

_____

LESSON MASTER 12-3 B

Vocabulary

1. Label the diagram at the right to identify the *boundary*, the *interior*, and the *exterior*.

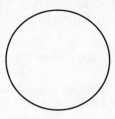

Skills Objective B: Write equations or inequalities for circles given sufficient conditions.

2. What equation describes the lower semicircle of the circle $x^2 + y^2 = 15$?

_____

3. a. Write a sentence describing all points in the interior of a circle whose center is (3, 4) and whose radius is 7.

_____

b. Use your answer to part a to show that (6, -1) is in the interior of the circle.

_____

_____

Uses Objective H: Use circles to solve real-world problems.

4. A parade float 8 feet high and 5 feet wide approached a semicircular arch with a diameter of 18 feet.

a. Will the float fit through the arch? Justify your answer.

_____

_____

_____

b. Find the radius of the smallest arch through which the float could pass.

_____

5. A semicircular mirror is made from four smaller mirrors as shown at the right. What are the least dimensions possible for the rectangular mirror out of which each end piece is cut?

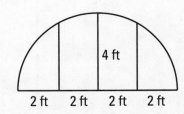

4 ft

2 ft   2 ft   2 ft   2 ft

_____

▶ **LESSON MASTER 12-3 B** *page 2*

6. A telephone company defines Zone 1 as a region within a 24-mile radius of the phone company's downtown office. For a flat rate of $56 per month, a city resident can make unlimited phone calls within Zone 1.

Consider a graph in which each unit represents one mile. Place the office at the origin.

a. Write an equation to represent the boundary of Zone 1.   _____

b. A resident made a call to a store located 20 miles east and 10 miles north of the office. Is the store located within Zone 1?   _____

Representations Objective J: Graph quadratic relations for circles or circular regions given sentences for them and vice versa.

In 7–10, graph the relation.

7. $(x + 3)^2 + y^2 \le 4$

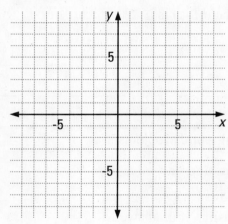

8. $x^2 + y^2 \ge 6$

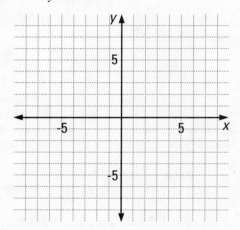

9. $(x + 2)^2 + (y - 4)^2 \le 3$

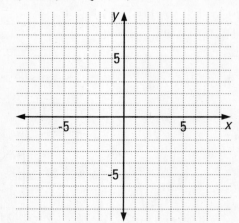

10. $5 \ge (x - 1)^2 + (y - 2)^2 \ge 1$

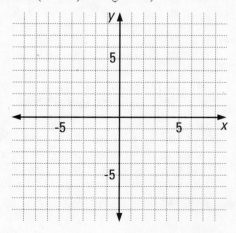

LESSON MASTER 12-4 B

Vocabulary

1. Refer to the ellipse at the right with foci P and Q.

   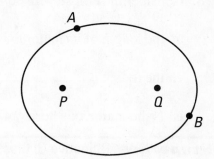

   a. Write an equation relating the distances among points P, Q, A, and B.

   _____

   _____

   b. Draw and label the vertices S and T of the ellipse.

   c. Draw the axes. Label the endpoints of each. Identify the major axis and the minor axis.   _____

   d. Draw and label the center C of the ellipse.

Skills Objective B: Write equations or inequalities for ellipses given sufficient conditions.

In 2–6, write an equation for an ellipse satisfying the conditions.

2. foci at (-7, 0) and (7, 0); focal constant 20   _____

3. foci at (0, 4) and (0, -4); focal constant 10   _____

4. foci at (0, 5) and (0, -5); major axis length 14   _____

5. foci at (-3, 0) and (3, 0); minor axis length $\sqrt{15}$ _____

6. center at origin; horizontal major axis 12, minor axis 8   _____

Properties Objective E: Find points on an ellipse using its definition.

7. Use the conic grid at the right with centers 8 units apart to draw the set of points P such that $PF_1 + PF_2 = 12$.

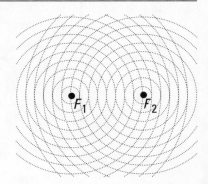

► **LESSON MASTER 12-4 B** *page 2*

Properties Objective F: Identify characteristics of ellipses.

8. Consider the ellipse with equation $\frac{x^2}{18} + \frac{y^2}{25} = 1$. Identify

   a. the length of its major axis. _____ **b.** the focal constant. _____

   c. the foci. _____ **d.** the vertices. _____

   e. Is the major axis horizontal or vertical? _____

Properties Objective G: Classify curves as ellipses using algebraic or geometric properties.

9. Does the point $(-5, 4\sqrt{3})$ lie on the ellipse with foci at $(-6, 0)$ and $(6, 0)$ and focal constant 20? _____

Uses Objective H: Use ellipses to solve real-world problems.

10. Grinsby's collar is on a 24-foot rope tied loosely around two trees which are 14 feet apart. A metal loop on the collar allows it to slide freely along the full length of the rope. Consider a graph in which each unit represents one foot. Place the origin halfway between the trees and place the trees on the *x*-axis. Write an equation to represent the boundary of Grinsby's play area.

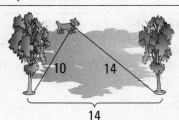

_____

Representations Objective J: Graph ellipses given sentences for them and vice versa.

11. Sketch the graph of $\frac{x^2}{9} + \frac{y^2}{25} = 1$.

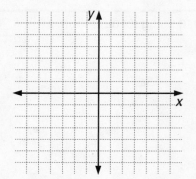

12. **a.** Write a sentence for the shaded region below.

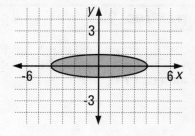

_____

   b. Is $(3, -\frac{\sqrt{3}}{2})$ in the shaded region? _____

LESSON MASTER

12-5 B

Skills Objective C: Find the area of an ellipse.

In 1–5, find the area of the ellipse satisfying the given conditions.

1. Its equation is $\dfrac{x^2}{25} + \dfrac{y^2}{121} = 1$. _____

2. Its equation is $\dfrac{x^2}{400} + \dfrac{y^2}{175} = 1$. _____

3. It has foci $(0, 5)$ and $(0, -5)$ and focal constant 14. _____

4. It has foci $(-2, 0)$ and $(2, 0)$ and minor axis length 6. _____

5. It has the image of the unit circle under $S_{5,6}$. _____

6. Which has a greater area: a circle of diameter 8 or an ellipse with axes of length 6 and 10? _____

7. Find the area of the shaded region at the right between a circle and ellipse with the same center.

   _____

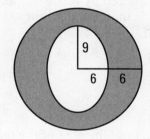

Properties Objective G: Classify curves as circles or ellipses using algebraic or geometric properties.

In 8–11, a scale change is given. a. Write an equation for the image of the circle $x^2 + y^2 = 1$ under the scale change. b. Tell if the image is a noncircular ellipse.

8. $S_{5,3}$

   a. _____

   b. _____

9. $S_{2,2}$

   a. _____

   b. _____

10. $S: (x, y) \rightarrow (5x, 5y)$

   a. _____

   b. _____

11. $S(x, y) = (.3x, 1.5y)$

   a. _____

   b. _____

12. Complete the following: An ellipse is a circle
if its major and minor axes are ___?___.   _____

13. Suppose you want to find the area of a circle. Can
you use the formula for the area of an ellipse, $A = \pi ab$?
Explain why or why not?

_____

_____

Uses Objective H: Use ellipses to solve real-world problems.

14. A mirror shaped like an ellipse has major axis 14 in.
and minor axis 9 in. Find the area of the mirror.   _____

15. A pond shaped like an ellipse is bordered by
a 4-ft wide walkway. The walkway is
bordered by fence shaped like an ellipse.
The major and minor axes of the fence are
48 ft and 32 ft.

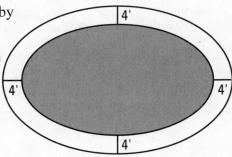

a. Find the area of the pond.   _____

b. Find the area of the walkway.   _____

Review Objective I, Lesson 2-6

16. Consider the equation $y = \dfrac{24}{x}$.

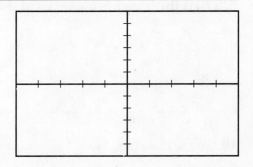

a. What type of variation is
described by the equation?

_____

b. Graph the equation in the
window $-5 \le x \le 5$, $-150 \le y \le 150$.
Sketch the graph at the right.

c. What type of curve describes the graph?

_____

d. Identify all asymptotes of the graph. _____

Name _____

Vocabulary

1. Refer to the hyperbola at the right with foci P and Q.

   a. Write an equation relating the distances among points P, Q, A, and B.

   _____

   b. Draw and label the vertices S and T of the hyperbola.

   c. Sketch and label the asymptotes j and k of the hyperbola.

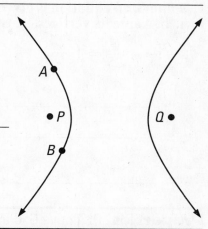

Skills Objective B: Write equations or inequalities for hyperbolas given sufficient conditions.

In 2–5, write an equation for the hyperbola satisfying the conditions.

2. foci at (-4, 0) and (4, 0); focal constant 6 _____

3. foci at (-10, 0) and (10, 0); focal constant 14 _____

4. vertices at (-5, 0) and (5, 0); containing the point (10, 3) _____

5. vertices at (-8, 0) and (8, 0); foci at (-12, 0) and (12, 0) _____

Properties Objective E: Find points on a hyperbola using its definition.

6. Use the conic grid at the right with centers 6 units apart to draw the set of points P such that $|PF_1 - PF_2| = 4$.

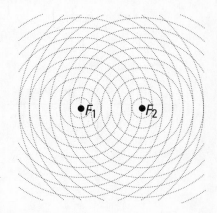

▶ **LESSON MASTER 12-6 B** *page 2*

Properties Objective F: Identify characteristics of hyperbolas.

**In 7 and 8, an equation is given for a hyperbola. a. Name its
foci. b. Name its vertices. c. Give equations of its asymptotes.**

7. $\dfrac{x^2}{144} - \dfrac{y^2}{25} = 1$ 8. $\dfrac{x^2}{10} - y^2 = 1$

   a. _____   a. _____

   b. _____   b. _____

   c. _____   c. _____

Properties Objective G: Classify curves as hyperbolas using algebraic or
geometric properties.

9. **a.** *Multiple choice.* Choose all of the points that lie
   on the hyperbola with foci $(-15, 0)$ and $(15, 0)$
   and focal constant 24.   _____

   (a) $A(0, 9)$ (b) $B(12\sqrt{3}, 9\sqrt{2})$ (c) $C(-12, 0)$ (d) $D(24, 15)$

   b. Explain how you determined your answer in Part a.

   _____

   _____

   _____

Representations Objective J: Graph hyperbolas given sentences for them
and vice versa.

10. Sketch the graph of $\dfrac{x^2}{25} - \dfrac{y^2}{4} = 1$ 11. Write an equation for the
hyperbola below.

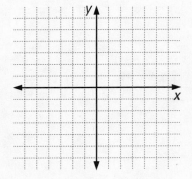

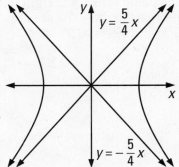
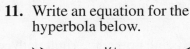

LESSON MASTER 12-7 B

Skills Objective A: Rewrite an equation for a conic section in the general form of a quadratic equation in two variables.

In 1–6, rewrite in the form $Ax^2 + Bxy + Cy^2 + Dx + Ey + F = 0$.

1. $\dfrac{x^2}{25} - \dfrac{y^2}{4} = 1$ _____

2. $y = 4(x - 2)^2 - 5$ _____

3. $(x + 8)(y - 7) = 30$ _____

4. $\dfrac{x^2}{100} + \dfrac{y^2}{25} = 1$ _____

5. $y = \pm 2\sqrt{x^2 - 3}$ _____

6. $xy = 72$ _____

Skills Objective B: Write equations for hyperbolas given sufficient conditions.

7. **a.** Find an equation for the hyperbola with foci at (8, 8) and (-8, -8) and focal constant 16. _____

   b. Find three points on the hyperbola.

   _____

   c. Verify that (-6, -4) is *not* on the hyperbola.

   _____

Properties Objective F: Identify characteristics of hyperbolas.

8. Identify the asymptotes of the hyperbola with equation $xy = 12$. _____

9. *True or false.* The graph of $y = \dfrac{k}{x}$ is a rectangular hyperbola. _____

10. Consider the hyperbola with equation $xy = 15$. Name its

    a. foci. _____

    b. asymptotes. _____

    c. focal constant. _____

▶ **LESSON MASTER 12-7 B** *page 2*

Properties Objective G: Classify curves as hyperbolas using algebraic or geometric properties.

11. Tell whether or not the graph of the equation is a hyperbola.

    a. $y = 6x$ _____   **b.** $xy = -10$ _____   **c.** $y = \dfrac{12}{x}$ _____

    d. $y = \dfrac{x}{24}$ _____   **e.** $\dfrac{x^2}{30} + \dfrac{y^2}{4} = 1$ _____   **f.** $\dfrac{x^2}{18} - \dfrac{y^2}{9} = 1$ _____

Uses Objective H: Use hyperbolas to solve real-world problems.

12. Mrs. Hastings is cutting h hair ribbons, each l inches long from a spool of 240 inches of ribbon. Give the equation for the conic section which describes the relationship between h and l. _____

Representations Objective J: Graph hyperbolas given sentences for them and vice versa.

13. Sketch the graph of $y = -\dfrac{20}{x}$.

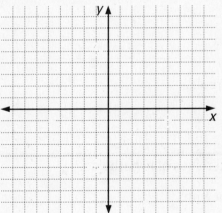

14. Sketch the graph of $xy \geq 32$.

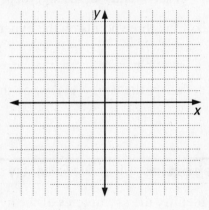

15. Refer to the hyperbola at the right.

    a. Write an equation for the hyperbola.

    _____

    b. Identify its foci.

    _____

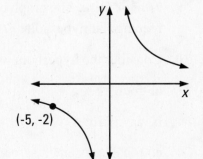

(-5, -2)

LESSON MASTER 12-8 B

Vocabulary

1. What is a *quadratic system?*

_____

2. What is a *quadratic-linear system?*

_____

Skills Objective D: Solve systems of one linear and one quadratic equation by substitution.

In 3–8, solve the system.

3. $\begin{cases} cd = 32 \\ 3c + d = 4 \end{cases}$

4. $\begin{cases} y = 4x \\ y = 2x^2 \end{cases}$

5. $\begin{cases} y = x^2 \\ 2x + 3y = 12 \end{cases}$

6. $\begin{cases} y = v^2 + 9 \\ y = \frac{1}{4}v \end{cases}$

7. $\begin{cases} xy = 169 \\ 3x + 4y - 91 = 0 \end{cases}$

8. $\begin{cases} m^2 + n^2 = 200 \\ n - m = 20 \end{cases}$

Uses Objective I: Use systems of quadratic equations to solve real-world
problems.

9. A rectangular playground has an area of
   2800 m² and a perimeter of 220 m.
   Find the dimensions of the playground.   _____

Representations Objective K: Solve systems of quadratic equations
graphically.

**In 10–12, give two equations whose graphs illustrate
the situation.**

10. a hyperbola and a line that intersect in exactly two points

   _____   _____

11. a circle and a line that intersect in exactly one point

   _____   _____

12. a parabola and a line that have no points in common

   _____   _____

In 13 and 14, graph the system and approximate the solutions.

13. $\begin{cases} 16x^2 + 9y^2 = 144 \\ \quad\;\; y = 2x \end{cases}$

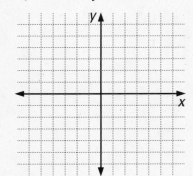

14. $\begin{cases} xy = 50 \\ y = -4x + 2 \end{cases}$

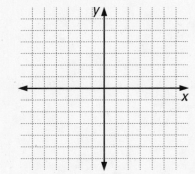

LESSON MASTER 12-9 B

Skills Objective D: Solve systems of two quadratic equations by substitution or linear combination.

In 1–6, solve the system by substitution or linear combination.

1. $\begin{cases} x^2 + y^2 = 6 \\ 4x^2 - y^2 = 9 \end{cases}$

2. $\begin{cases} ab = 48 \\ a^2 + b^2 = 160 \end{cases}$

3. $\begin{cases} y^2 + 4x^2 = 40 \\ y^2 - 4x^2 = 8 \end{cases}$

4. $\begin{cases} x^2 - y = 5 \\ x^2 + y^2 = 2 \end{cases}$

5. $\begin{cases} r^2 + s^2 = 16 \\ s = r^2 + 4 \end{cases}$

6. $\begin{cases} y = d^2 - 6 \\ 2d^2 + y^2 = 27 \end{cases}$

Uses Objective I: Use systems of quadratic equations to solve real-world problems.

7. An architect has designed a rectangular gallery with a floor area of 2352 sq. ft. The architect's clients want the floor area to be 2700 sq. ft, which can be accomplished by adding 3 ft to the width and 4 ft to the length in the original plans.

   a. Write a system of equations to describe this situation. _____

   b. What are the dimensions of the gallery in the original plan? _____

8. At football games last year, the snack shop took in $1200 in soft-drink sales. This year the price per drink was raised 15¢, 300 fewer drinks were sold, and $1365 was brought in. Find the price of the soft drinks and the number sold.

   a. last year. _____

   b. this year. _____

9. Monitoring Station A determines that the center of an
earthquake is 40 miles away. Station B, 20 miles west,
and 35 miles south of Station A, finds that it is 15 miles
from the center. Find all possible locations of the center relative to
Station A.

_____

_____

_____

Representations Objective K: Solve systems of quadratic equations
graphically.

In 10–12, give equations whose graphs fit the situation.

10. a hyperbola and an ellipse that intersect in exactly two points

_____   _____

11. a circle and a parabola that intersect in exactly three points

_____   _____

12. a parabola and a hyperbola that have no points in common

_____   _____

13. Graph $\begin{cases} x^2 + y^2 = 100 \\ xy = 32 \end{cases}$ and
approximate the solutions.

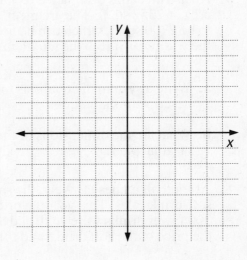

LESSON MASTER  **13-1 B**

Vocabulary

1. What is a *series*?

_____

_____

Skills Objective A: Calculate values of a finite arithmetic series.

In 2–9, evaluate the given arithmetic series.

2. $5 + 10 + 15 + \ldots + 75$ _____

3. $-10 + -14 + -18 + \ldots + -94$ _____

4. $-11 + -5 + 1 + \ldots + 37$ _____

5. the sum of the first 80 positive integers _____

6. the sum of the first 50 odd positive integers _____

7. the sum of the first 50 even positive integers _____

8. the sum of the first 35 terms of the sequence
   defined by $\begin{cases} a_1 = 12 \\ a_n = a_{n-1} + 3 \end{cases}$, for integers $n \geq 2$ _____

9. the sum of the first 100 terms of the sequence
   defined by $\begin{cases} a_1 = -5 \\ a_n = a_{n-1} - 2 \end{cases}$, for integers $n \geq 2$ _____

10. Consider the series $1 + 2 + 3 + \ldots + k$.

    a. How many terms are there? _____

    b. Suppose the sum is 15,753. Find k. _____

11. Consider the series $2 + 4 + 6 + \ldots + n$.

    a. How many terms are there? _____

    b. Suppose the sum is 1806. Find n. _____

12. Consider the series $1 + 3 + 5 + \ldots + m$.

    a. How many terms are there? _____

    b. Suppose the sum is 484. Find m. _____

▶ **LESSON MASTER 13-1 B** *page 2*

Uses Objective G: Solve real-world problems using arithmetic series.

13. A garden in the park is planted with 68 marigolds in the first row, 72 in the second row, and 4 more in each successive row. If the garden has 11 rows of marigolds, how many marigolds are there in all?   _____

14. A health club offers a special rate to encourage new members to continue their membership. The first month's fees are $70. Each successive month's fees drop $2 during the first year.

    a. What is the total amount of membership fees the first year?   _____

    b. During which month did the total reach $500?   _____

15. Setsuo jogged 6 blocks the first day, 7 blocks the second day, and continued to jog an additional block every day. In how many days will he have jogged a total of 35 miles? (Use 1 mile = 12 blocks.)   _____

Review Objective C, Lesson 7-5

In 16–20, give the first five terms of the geometric sequence described.

16. constant ratio -8, first term 3   _____

17. constant ratio $\frac{2}{3}$, first term 2187   _____

18. third term 500, fourth term 2500   _____

19. $g_n = 12(4)^{n-1}$, for integers $n \geq 1$ _____

20. $\begin{cases} g_1 = 16 \\ g_n = -2g_{n-1}, \text{ for integers } n \geq 2 \end{cases}$ _____

In 21 and 22, a sequence is given. a. Could the sequence be geometric? b. If yes, give its constant ratio.

21. 9, 18, 27, 36, . . .   22. $\frac{11}{6}$, 11, 66, 396, . . .

    a. _____   a. _____

    b. _____   b. _____

LESSON MASTER

13-2
B

Skills Objective B: Calculate values of a finite geometric series.

1. Find the sum of the first 12 terms of the geometric series with first term 8 and common ratio 2. _____

2. Find the sum of the first 5 terms of the geometric series with first term 16 and common ratio $\frac{1}{4}$. _____

3. Find the sum of the first 8 terms of the geometric series with first term -5 and common ratio -1.5. _____

4. Find the sum of the first 10 terms of the sequence defined by $\begin{cases} g_1 = 32 \\ g_n = .75g_{n-1} \end{cases}$, for integers $n \geq 2$ _____

5. Find the sum of the first 6 terms of the sequence defined by $\begin{cases} g_1 = 40 \\ g_n = -3g_{n-1} \end{cases}$, for integers $n \geq 2$ _____

6. Find the sum of the first 9 terms of the sequence defined by $\begin{cases} g_1 = -10 \\ g_n = -g_{n-1} \end{cases}$, for integers $n \geq 2$ _____

In 7–11, a geometric series is given. a. Tell how many terms are in the series. b. Give the value of the series.

7. $81 + 27 + 9 + 3 + 1 + \frac{1}{3} + \frac{1}{9}$

a. _____   b. _____

8. $1 + 2 + 4 + 8 + \ldots + 512$

a. _____   b. _____

9. $6 + 24 + 96 + \ldots + 6 \cdot 4^{11}$

a. _____   b. _____

10. $.005 + .01 + .02 + .04 + \ldots + .005 \cdot 2^8$

a. _____   b. _____

11. $10 + -40 + 1600 + \ldots + 10(-4)^{22}$

a. _____   b. _____

12. $1 - 1.5 + 2.25 - \ldots + 1.5^{10}$

   a. _____   **b.** _____

13. $1 + m + m^2 + m^3 + \ldots + m^{17}$

   a. _____   **b.** _____

Uses Objective G: Solve real-world problems using geometric series.

14. On each January 3rd for 19 years, Mrs. Redstar deposited $500 in a college account that earned an annual yield of 5.5%

   a. Write a geometric series that represents the value of the fund on January 3rd of the 20th year. You may use " . . . "as needed.

   _____

   _____

   b. Evaluate the series in Part **a**.   _____

   c. If the account had earned 5% rather than 5.5%, how much less would there have been in the account on January 3rd of the 20th year?   _____

15. The output of a certain industrial machine decreased 2.5% each year. In 1986, the machine produced 6,300,000 thingumajigs. Find the total number of thingumajigs produced from 1986 through 1995.   _____

16. At the right is a glass designer's plan for a stained-glass window. The designer will need to use leading for each segment shown in the diagram. The length of the side of the largest square is 100 cm.

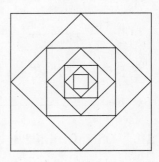

   a. What is the perimeter of

      i. the largest square?   _____

      ii. the next largest square?   _____

      iii. the third largest square?   _____

   b. Write a geometric series that represents the total length of leading needed for the window.

   _____

   c. Find the total length of leading needed.   _____

LESSON MASTER

13-3
B

Vocabulary

1. **a.** Explain the meaning of $\sum\limits_{i=1}^{9} 4^i$.

   _____

   b. What is the name of the Greek letter Σ? _____

   c. What is the variable i called? _____

2. Explain the meaning of 12!.

   _____

3. What is a *permutation*?

   _____

___

Skills Objective C: Use summation (Σ) or factorial (!) notation.

In 4–12, rewrite using Σ-notation or !-notation.

4. $5 + 10 + 15 + 20 + 25 + 30 + 35 + 40$ _____

5. $7 \cdot 6 \cdot 5 \cdot 4 \cdot 3 \cdot 2 \cdot 1$ _____

6. $-2 + 4 + -8 + \ldots + 256$ _____

7. $60 + 70 + 80 + \ldots + 940$ _____

8. $1 \cdot 2 \cdot 3 \cdot 4 \cdot 5 \cdot 6 \cdot 7 \cdot 8 \cdot 9 \cdot 10 \cdot 11 \cdot 12$ _____

9. $6 \cdot 5 \cdot 4 \cdot 3 \cdot 2 \cdot 1 \cdot 5 \cdot 4 \cdot 3 \cdot 2 \cdot 1$ _____

10. The sum of the cubes of the integers from 1 to 12 _____

11. $98 + 198 + 298 + \ldots + 1498$ _____

12. $\dfrac{5 \cdot 4 \cdot 3 \cdot 2 \cdot 1}{8 \cdot 7 \cdot 6 \cdot 5 \cdot 4 \cdot 3 \cdot 2 \cdot 1}$ _____

In 13–15, evaluate.

13. $8!$ _____ 14. $5! \cdot 3! \cdot 7!$ _____ 15. $\dfrac{18!}{14!}$ _____

▶ **LESSON MASTER 13-3 B** *page 2*

In 16–19, a series is given. a. Write the terms of the series.
b. Evaluate the series.

16. $\displaystyle\sum_{i=1}^{20} 11i$ **a.** _____

17. $\displaystyle\sum_{i=1}^{8} .3^i$ **a.** _____

_____

_____

b. _____

b. _____

18. $\displaystyle\sum_{i=1}^{500} (4i + 3)$ **a.** _____

19. $\displaystyle\sum_{i=-2}^{4} (6 \cdot 10^i)$ **a.** _____

_____

_____

b. _____

b. _____

Skills Objective D: Calculate permutations of *n* objects, *n* at a time.

20. **a.** List all the permutations of the letters S, M, A, R, T with the third term S.

b. How many permutations are possible? _____

21. How many permutations of the digits 1, 4, 6, 7,
9 are possible? _____

Uses Objective H: Solve problems involving permutations of *n* objects.

22. In how many ways can 12 children line up at
the water fountain? _____

23. In how many ways can 30 CDs be stacked
in a "tower" CD rack? _____

24. In how many different orders can a cast
of 10 be listed on a program? _____

25. A student takes 6 classes plus lunch in
a 7-period day. In how many different
orders can the student take the classes
if lunch must be 4th period? _____

LESSON MASTER 13-4 B

Vocabulary

1. Let *S* be a data set of *n* numbers.

   a. For what purposes are statistical measures of *S* used?

   _____

   b. What is the *mean* of *S*?

   _____

   c. What is the *median* of *S*?

   _____

   d. What is the *mode* of *S*?

   _____

   e. Complete the following: The *standard deviation*
      of *S* measures the ___?___ of the elements in *S*. _____

Uses Objective I: Use measure of central tendency or dispersion to describe data
            or distributions.

**In 2–5, a set of temperatures in degrees Fahrenheit is given.
For each set, find a. the mean, b. the median, and c. the mode.**

2. daily highs for one week in July:
   88, 91, 94, 94, 87, 89, 84

   a. _____ b. _____ c. _____

3. daily lows for one week in January:
   3, 0, -6, -11, -6, -3, -6

   a. _____ b. _____ c. _____

4. monthly highs for one year:
   33, 39, 48, 56, 69, 84, 96, 101, 89, 78, 52, 40

   a. _____ b. _____ c. _____

5. monthly lows for one year:
   -12, 8, 20, 31, 48, 61, 65, 74, 48, 20, 14, 8

   a. _____ b. _____ c. _____

▶ **LESSON MASTER 13-4 B** *page 2*

In 6–9, use the heights in inches
of the girls in two Brownie
troops listed at the right.

Troop 416: 39, 35, 36, 42, 44, 41, 37, 42

Troop 38: 42, 42, 37, 38, 42, 36, 37, 42

For each troop, find a. the mean, b. the median,
and c. the mode for the data.

6. Troop 416   a. _____ b. _____ c._____

7. Troop 38   a. _____ b. _____ c._____

8. What do you notice about your answers in Questions 6 and 7?

_____

9. Compute the standard deviation of the data for each troop.

a. Troop 416 _____   **b.** Troop 38 _____

c. What do your answers to Parts **a** and **b** tell you about the
heights of the girls in the two Brownie troops?

_____

10. The graph shows the
number of sit-ups done
by the members of a
karate team.

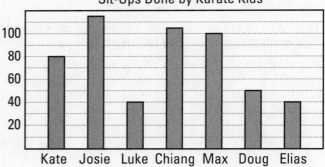

Sit-Ups Done by Karate Kids

a. Find the indicated
measure of central
tendency for the
data in the graph.

mean _____   median _____

mode _____   standard deviation _____

b. Which of these measures best describes the data? Explain your answer.

_____

_____

_____

_____

LESSON MASTER

13-5
B

Vocabulary

4. Complete the following: $\binom{n}{r}$ denotes the ___?___

element in row ___?___ of Pascal's triangle. _____

Skills Objective D: Calculate combinations.

2. Write $\dfrac{7 \cdot 6 \cdot 5 \cdot 4 \cdot 3 \cdot 2 \cdot 1}{4 \cdot 3 \cdot 2 \cdot 1 \cdot 3 \cdot 2 \cdot 1}$ in the form $\binom{n}{r}$. _____

3. Write $\binom{9}{7}$ using factorial symbols. _____

In 4–15, calculate.

4. $\binom{8}{3}$ _____   **5.** $\binom{6}{5}$ _____   **6.** $\binom{7}{6}$ _____

7. $\binom{8}{0}$ _____   **8.** $\binom{8}{8}$ _____   **9.** $\binom{18}{7}$ _____

10. $\binom{10}{1}$ _____   **11.** $\binom{24}{23}$ _____   **12.** $\binom{24}{1}$ _____

13. $\binom{16}{3}$ _____   **14.** $\binom{16}{13}$ _____   **15.** $\binom{29}{0}$ _____

Properties Objective F: Recognize properties of Pascal's triangle.

16. Row 0 and row 5 of Pascal's triangle are given below.
Fill in rows 1–4 and 6–10.

1

Row 1	_____
Row 2	_____
Row 3	_____
Row 4	_____
Row 5	1 5 10 10 5 1
Row 6	_____
Row 7	_____
Row 8	_____
Row 9	_____
Row 10	_____

▶ **LESSON MASTER 13-5 B** *page 2*

In 17–20, refer to Pascal's triangle in Question 16.

17. Draw a circle around the element denoted by $\binom{6}{4}$.

18. Draw a square around the element denoted by $\binom{10}{5}$.

19. Draw a triangle around the element denoted by $\binom{7}{1}$.

20. Draw an X through the element denoted by $\binom{5}{0}$.

21. Verify that for $n = 8$, $\binom{n}{4} + \binom{n}{5} = \binom{n+1}{5}$.

22. Refer to row 9 of Pascal's triangle in Question 16.
Write 84 two different ways using $\binom{n}{r}$ notation. _____

23. Show that $\binom{52}{12} = \binom{52}{40}$.

24. Show that $12! = 12 \cdot 11!$.

Review Objective A, Lesson 11-2

In 25–30, multiply and write the product in standard form.

25. $(a + b)^2$

26. $(x + 3)^2$

_____

_____

27. $(4m^2 + 3m - 2)(6m - 1)$

28. $(y - 2)(y + 3)(y - 5)$

_____

_____

29. $(a + b)^3$

30. $(x + 3)^3$

_____

_____

LESSON MASTER 13-6 B

Vocabulary

1. What is a *binomial expansion*?

   _____

   _____

Skills Objective E: Expand binomials.

2. **a.** Expand $(a + b)^6$.

   _____

   _____

   b. Let $a = 2m$ and $b = 3n^2$. Substitute these values
   for a and b in the polynomial you wrote in Part **a**
   to expand $(2m + 3n^2)^6$.

   _____

   _____

   _____

   c. Simplify Part **b**.

   _____

   _____

   d. Use your answer in Part **a** to expand $(5x^2 - y)^6$.

   _____

   _____

In 3–9, expand the binomial.

3. $(x^4 + 5)^3$ _____

4. $(3e - 7f)^4$ _____

5. $(m - n^4)^5$ _____

6. $(2r + 4s)^7$ _____

_____

_____

7. $(x^4 - 1)^8$ _____

_____

8. $(a^3 + b^7)^4$ _____

9. $(u - .5)^6$ _____

10. Consider $(1 + .06)^9$.

a. Find the sum of the first three terms of
the expansion. _____

b. Find $(1 + .06)^9$ using a calculator. _____

c. Do you think your answer to Part **a** is a reasonable
estimate of $(1 + .06)^9$? Why or why not?

_____

In 11–14, convert to an expression in the form $(a + b)^n$.

11. $\displaystyle\sum_{r=0}^{n} \binom{n}{r} x^{n-r} 5^r$

12. $\displaystyle\sum_{r=0}^{n} \binom{n}{r} (6p)^{n-r}(q)^r$

_____

13. $\displaystyle\sum_{r=0}^{n} \binom{n}{r} (2k)^{n-r}(3w)^r$

14. $\displaystyle\sum_{r=0}^{n} \binom{n}{i} \left(\frac{d}{2}\right)^{n-i}(-e)^i$

_____

Properties Objective F: Recognize properties of Pascal's triangle.

15. Explain the connection between Pascal's triangle and binomial expansion.

_____

_____

_____

_____

Name _____

Vocabulary

1. What is a *combination*?

_____

_____

Skills Objective D: Calculate combinations.

2. Consider the set {H, A, L, F}.

   a. Use exponential notation to tell how many
subsets of this set there are.   _____

   b. List the subsets.

   c. Check that your answers in Parts **a** and **b** agree.

   _____

   d. Use $\binom{n}{r}$ notation and tell how many subsets
have 2 elements.   _____

   e. Circle the subsets in Part **b** that have 2 elements.

   f. Check that your answers in Parts **d** and **e** agree.

   _____

3. Suppose a set has 7 elements. How many subsets have

   a. 2 elements? _____   **b.** 4 elements? _____   **c.** 7 elements? _____

4. Suppose a set has 12 elements. How many subsets have

   a. 0 elements? _____   **b.** 5 elements? _____   **c.** 7 elements? _____

5. a. Calculate $_8C_2$.   _____

   b. What does $_8C_2$ stand for?

   _____

Properties Objective F: Recognize properties of Pascal's triangle.

6. **a.** Calculate $_6C_0 + _6C_1 + _6C_2 + _6C_3 + _6C_4 + _6C_5 + _6C_6$. _____

   b. How is Part a related to Pascal's triangle?

   _____

   _____

Uses Objective H: Solve problems involving combinations.

7. Jennie has 12 close friends, but her mother will allow her to invite only 6 of them for a sleep over. In how many different ways can she make up her guest list? _____

8. Paul wants to take some tapes on a bus trip to Washington, D.C. His carrying case holds 16 tapes. In how many ways can he choose the 16 tapes from his collection of 74 tapes? _____

9. Consider 10 points in a plane such that no three are collinear.

   a. How many segments have these points as endpoints? _____

   b. How many triangles have these points as vertices? _____

   c. Look at your answers to Parts **a** and **b**. Since each triangle has three sides, why are there not three times as many segments as there are triangles?

   _____

10. Home Harvest Nursery carries 88 varieties of flowers. 12 varieties of ground cover, and 31 varieties of vegetables. The company is planning a newspaper advertisement.

    a. Page 1 of the advertisement will show 8 different types of flowers. In how many different ways can the flowers be chosen? _____

    b. Page 2 will show 4 different types of ground cover. In how many different ways can the ground cover be chosen? _____

    c. Page 3 will show vegetables. How many different displays of at least one type of vegetable are possible? _____

LESSON MASTER

13-8 B

Vocabulary

1. **a.** Give an example of two *independent events*.

   _____

   b. Give an example of two events that are *not* independent.

   _____

   _____

2. **a.** Give an example of two *mutually-exclusive events*.

   _____

   b. Give an example of two events that are *not* mutually exclusive.

   _____

3. List all of the features of a *binomial experiment*.

   _____

   _____

   _____

   _____

Uses Objective J: Solve problems using probability.

In 4–7, consider tossing a coin with $P(H) = 0.6$. You toss the coin 5 times.

4. **a.** Calculate the probability of 0 tails. _____

   b. Calculate the probability of exactly 1 tail. _____

   c. Calculate the probability of exactly 2 tails. _____

   d. Calculate the probability of exactly 3 tails. _____

   e. Calculate the probability of exactly 4 tails. _____

   f. Calculate the probability of exactly 5 tails. _____

5. In Question 4, which events are mutually exclusive?
   Explain your reasoning.

   _____

   _____

▶ **LESSON MASTER 13-8 B** *page 2*

6. a. Calculate the probability of at least 3 tails. _____

   b. Calculate the probability of at most 3 tails. _____

7. In Question 6, are the events in Parts **a** and **b** mutually exclusive? Explain your reasoning.

   _____

   _____

In 8 and 9, consider a 5-question multiple-choice quiz with three possible answers per question. If each question is answered by guessing, the probability of correctly answering any one question is $\frac{1}{3}$.

8. What is the probability of correctly answering exactly 3 questions correctly? _____

9. What is the probability of scoring at least 75% on the quiz? _____

In 10–13, suppose you are shooting ten baskets from the free-throw line. Recently you've had a 70% probability of making each basket. If this pattern continues, give the probability that you will get

10. exactly 5 baskets. _____   **11.** exactly 7 baskets. _____

12. exactly 10 baskets. _____   **13.** at least 7 baskets. _____

In 14–17, suppose a fair coin is tossed 12 times. Give the probability of each event.

14. exactly 2 heads _____   **15.** exactly 6 heads _____

16. exactly 10 tails _____   **17.** no more than 2 tails _____

18. Suppose a fair coin is tossed 5 times.

   a. What could the quantity $\binom{5}{4}$ represent?

   _____

   b. What could the quantity 2^5 represent?

   _____

   c. What could the quantity $\binom{5}{4}(.5)^4(.5)^1$ represent?

   _____

LESSON MASTER

13-9
B

Vocabulary

1. What is a *lottery*?

   _____

   _____

Uses Objective J: Solve problems using probability.

---

2. In the Guess-the-Number booth at the state fair, players select a 4-digit number using any combination of the numbers, 1 through 6, rolled on a die.

   a. What is the probability of picking the correct 4-digit number? _____

   b. What are the odds against winning? _____

   c. If the winner wins $1000, and it costs 50¢ to play, does the Guess-the Number booth gain money, lose money, or break even in the long run? Explain your reasoning.

   _____

   _____

   _____

3. In the state fair's Spin 6 game, a wheel with the numbers 1 through 36 is spun 6 times. Prizes are given for anyone who picks 3 out of the 6 numbers, 4 out of 6, 5 out of 6, or 6 out of 6.

   a. What is the probability of picking exactly 3 out of the 6 numbers? _____

   b. What is the probability of picking exactly 4 out of the 6 numbers? _____

   c. What is the probability of picking exactly 5 out of the 6 numbers? _____

   d. What is the probability of picking exactly 6 out of the 6 numbers? _____

▶ **LESSON MASTER 13-9 B** *page 2*

    e. The prizes in Spin 6 are $150 for picking exactly 3 out of 6 numbers, $2000 for 4 out of 6, and $75,000 for 5 out of 6.

       i. Based on the probabilities found in Parts **a** through **c**, do these prize amounts seem reasonable? Why or why not?

_____

_____

_____

_____

      ii. *Multiple choice.* Based on the other prize amounts and the probabilities found in Parts **a** through **d**, which prize would be appropriate for someone who chooses 6 out of 6 numbers correctly? Explain your choice. _____

        (a) $5 million   (b) 13\frac{1}{2}$ million   (c) $20 million

_____

_____

_____

  4. At the after-prom party, 5 balls are chosen from 20 balls numbered from 1 to 20. Each couple may choose one game ticket. Enough prizes were donated to be able to award one prize to roughly every 25 couples. If a prize is given to each couple who pick 3 out of 5 numbers, will there be enough prizes? Explain your reasoning.

_____

_____

Review   Objective I, Lesson 8-2

  5. *Multiple choice.* List all of the graphs that represent a function whose inverse is also a function. _____

    (a) 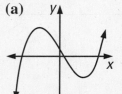   **(b)** 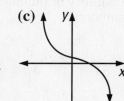   **(c)**   **(d)**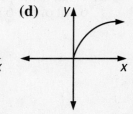

LESSON MASTER

13-10
B

Vocabulary

1. What is a *probability function*?

_____

_____

2. What is a *binomial probability distribution*?

_____

_____

3. Complete the following: Suppose a fair coin is tossed
14 times. When the probabilities are graphed as a
function of the number of heads, the graph approaches
a curve called ____?____.

_____

4. When test scores are *normalized*, what is true about the
distribution of the scores?

_____

_____

Uses Objective I: Use measures of central tendency or dispersion to describe
data or distributions.

**In 5–8, ACT scores range from 1 to 36, with a mean
near 21 and a standard deviation near 5. Assume the
scores are normally distributed.**

5. About what percent of students have a score
above 21? _____

6. About what percent of students have a score
below 16? _____

7. About what percent of students have a score
above 31? _____

8. About what percent of students have scores
between 16 and 26? _____

Representations Objective L: Graph and analyze binomial and normal
distributions.

In 9–10, consider the function P with $P(n) = \dfrac{\binom{7}{n}}{2^7}$.

9. Complete the table of values and graph P.

10. What name is given to P?

_____

_____

_____

_____

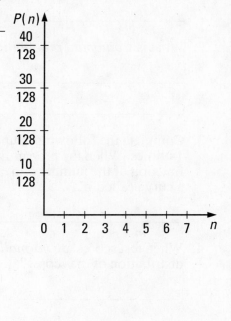

n	$P(n)$
0	
1	
2	
3	
4	
5	
6	
7	

In 11–13, consider the normal distribution with
mean 15 and standard deviation 4.

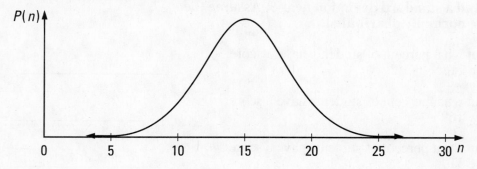

11. About what percent of the data are greater than 11? _____

12. About what percent of the data are between 7 and 23? _____

13. **a.** Shade the portions of the graph representing data
   more than two standard deviations away from 15.

   b. About what percent of the graph should you
   have shaded in Part **a**? _____

LESSON MASTER

13-11
B

Vocabulary

In 1–5, a situation involving sampling is described.
a. Describe the population. b. Identify the sample.

1. A company is testing brakes to see how many miles can be driven before they need replacing.

   a. _____

   b. _____

2. The school board is interviewing citizens to see how they will vote on an upcoming bond referendum.

   a. _____

   b. _____

3. The owner of a restaurant is asking its customers to list their favorite desserts.

   a. _____

   b. _____

4. A frozen-foods company is checking the weight of its pot pies.

   a. _____

   b. _____

5. A polling company is asking teenagers about their favorite electronics stores.

   a. _____

   b. _____

Uses Objective K: Give reasons for sampling.

6. List at least three reasons for sampling.

   _____

   _____

   _____

   _____

7. A juice company fills 6,000 cans of juice a day and randomly checks 1% of the cans to be sure they are properly filled.

   a. What is the population size in this situation? _____

   b. What is the sample size in this situation? _____

8. The Quincy Clock Company manufactures 2000 travel alarm clocks, 5000 stopwatches, and 3000 wall clocks each month. Suggest how the company might use stratified random sampling to test the accuracy of the timepieces.

_____

_____

_____

9. A spinner has 5 congruent regions numbered 1 through 5. It is hoped that the spinner is fair. The spinner is spun 500 times in an experiment, and the experiment is repeated many times.

   a. If the spinner is fair, what is the mean number of times a 2 should appear? _____

   b. What is the standard deviation? _____

   c. 68% of the time the number of 2s should be between what two numbers? _____

10. Suppose that 25% of the households are tuned to a particular TV show. Consider all the random samples of 1500 people.

   a. For these samples, what is the mean number of people tuned to the show? _____

   b. What is the standard deviation? _____

   c. 95% of the time the samples will have between what two numbers of people watching the show? _____

11. At MacKenzie Motors, 20% of the new-car orders are for black cars. Consider a random-number table.

   a. Which digits could represent black cars? _____

   b. Start in the row that matches the day of the month on which you were born and the column that represents the month. Read the next 200 digits and compute the percent of orders for black cars in this simulation. _____

LESSON MASTER 1-1 B — Questions on SPUR Objectives

Skills Objective A: Evaluate expressions and formulas, including correct units in answer.

In 1 and 2, consider the expression $\dfrac{5 \cdot 2^3 - 4}{9}$

1. Give the steps, in order, needed to evaluate the expression.

   Sample steps: 1) Raise 2 to the 3rd power.
   2) Multiply the power by 5. 3) Subtract 4
   from the product. 4) Divide the difference
   by 9.

2. Evaluate the expression. **4**

In 3–5, evaluate the expression $2n^2 + 4n - 5$ for the given value of n.

3. $n = 3$ **25**   4. $n = -2$ **-5**   5. $n = \frac{1}{2}$ **$-2\frac{1}{2}$**

In 6 and 7, evaluate the expression.

6. $8 \div 2 \cdot 6 - (3 - 9)$ **30**   7. $(4 - 6)^3 + 12 \div 3 - 7$ **-11**

In 8–10, evaluate the expression when $x = 4$, $y = -3$, and $z = 2$.

8. $\dfrac{x^2 - 2z}{y}$ **-4**   9. $y^4 - 3xz$ **57**   10. $\dfrac{x}{(y + z)^3}$ **-4**

11. The formula for the volume of a sphere is $V = \frac{4}{3}\pi r^3$. Find the volume of a sphere with a 9-cm radius. **$972\,\pi\ \text{cm}^3$**

12. For a polygon with n sides, the sum of the measures of the polygon's interior angles T is given by the formula $T = 180(n - 2)$. Find the value of T for an octagon. **1080°**

13. Near the surface of the moon, the distance d that a rock falls in t seconds is $d = \frac{1}{2}gt^2$. If $g = 5.3\ \frac{\text{ft}}{\text{sec}^2}$, how far will a rock fall in 8 seconds? **169.6 ft**

1 ▶

▶ **LESSON MASTER 1-1 B** *page 2*

Uses Objective I: Use addition, subtraction, multiplication, and division to write expressions which model real-world situations.

In 14–24, write an expression to describe the situation.

14. The enrollment at Shaw Elementary School was 1164. On Friday, n new students enrolled and w students withdrew. What is the new school enrollment? **$1164 + n - w$ students**

15. Sam drove at an average rate of m miles per hour for h hours. How far did he drive? **mh miles**

16. For D days, the total attendance at the Rocky Top Museum was P people. What was the average attendance per day? **$\dfrac{P}{D}$ people**

17. The model of a ship is one hundredth of the actual size. Find the length of a model ship if the actual ship is M meters long. **$\dfrac{M}{100}$ meters**

18. F feet of paper was taken from a roll of wrapping paper containing W feet. How much paper is left on the roll? **$W - F$ feet**

19. At North High School, the faculty f increased by t teachers. How many teachers are now on the faculty? **$f + t$ teachers**

20. The water level in Long Lake was L inches in 1992. It dropped I inches in 1993 and then rose K inches in 1994. What was the water level at the end of 1994? **$L - I + K$ in.**

21. Yesterday, s students were present at Wee Wons Nursery School. Today, 4 fewer students were present. What was the total attendance yesterday and today? **$2s - 4$ students**

22. Cutweld International ordered T tons of steel which came in s sheets of equal weight. What was the weight of each sheet of steel? **$\dfrac{T}{s}$ tons**

23. The original price of a compact disc was C dollars. What is the sale price after a 25% discount? **.75 C dollars**

24. If the markup on furniture is p percent, what is the selling price of a chair that cost the dealer d dollars? **$\left(1 + \dfrac{P}{100}\right)d$ dollars**

2

LESSON MASTER 1-2 B — Questions on SPUR Objectives

Vocabulary

1. A function is a correspondence between two variables such that each value of the **independent** variable corresponds to exactly one value of the **dependent** variable.

2. For the function with equation $y = \frac{1}{x^2}$, give
   a. the *domain*. **$\{x : x \neq 0\}$**
   b. the *range*. **$\{y : y > 0\}$**

Skills Objective A: Evaluate expressions and formulas and use correct units in answers.

3. In the formula $d = \dfrac{n(n-2)}{2}$, find d when $n = -10$. **$d = 60$**

4. If $T = kPV$, find T when $k = 0.68$, $P = 2.5$, and $V = 120$. **$T = 204$**

5. If $x = \dfrac{2b}{a}$, find x when $a = -1.2$ and $b = 0.45$. **$x = -0.75$**

6. A cone of radius r and height h has volume $V = \frac{1}{3}\pi r^2 h$. Find the volume of a cone with radius 6 inches and height 10 inches. **$V = 720\,\pi\ \text{in}^3$**

7. Total surface area of a right circular cylinder is $S = 2\pi rh + 2\pi r^2$. Find the total surface area of a tin can 15 cm high if its radius is 3 cm. **$S = 108\,\pi\ \text{cm}^2$**

In 8–10, evaluate the formula for the given value of the independent variable.

8. $r = 200(3)^n$, $n = -2$ **$r = \dfrac{200}{9}$**

9. $y = 4x^2 - 3x - 7$, $x = -3$ **$y = 38$**

10. $p = \dfrac{48}{n^3}$, if $n = -2$ **$p = -6$**

Properties Objective G: Determine whether a relation defined by a table, a list of ordered pairs, or a simple equation is a function.

11. Does the table describe b as a function of a? Justify your answer.

a	0	1	-1	2	-2
b	0	1	-1	8	-8

   Yes; each a-value is paired with exactly one b-value.

3 ▶

▶ **LESSON MASTER 1-2 B** *page 2*

12. Is the set $\{(2, 4), (4, 8), (8, 16), (16, 32)\}$ a function? Why or why not?

   Yes; each first coordinate is paired with exactly one second coordinate.

In 13–15, tell whether or not the equation describes a function.

13. $y = 12$ **yes**   14. $y = x^3$ **yes**   15. $xy = 0$ **no**

Properties Objective H: Determine the domain and the range of a function defined by a table, a list of ordered pairs, or a simple equation.

In 16–18, give the domain and the range of the function.

16. $\{(8, 4), (6, 3), (-12, -6), (21, 10.5), (0, 0)\}$
   Domain **$\{-12, 0, 6, 8, 21\}$** Range **$\{-6, 0, 3, 4, 10.5\}$**

17. m is a function of c.

c	0	1	-1	2	-2
m	1	2	2	5	5

   Domain **$\{-2, -1, 0, 1, 2\}$** Range **$\{1, 2, 5\}$**

18. $y = \dfrac{x + 5}{x}$
   Domain **$\{x : x \neq 0\}$** Range **all reals**

Uses Objective J: Evaluate functions to solve real-world problems.

19. The total surface area of a box is given by the formula $S = 2(\ell w + \ell h + hw)$. How much gold foil is needed to cover a brick 8 in. long, 3 in. wide, and 2 in. high? **92 in²**

20. John bought a boat with a down payment of $3,000 and monthly payments of $150.
   a. Write a formula for the amount paid p as a function of the number of months n he has been paying. **$p = 3000 + 150n$**
   b. Find the total paid for the boat if payments last for 3 years. **$8,400**

21. The formula $S = m + \dfrac{m^2}{20}$ gives the stopping distances in feet as a function of the car's speed m in miles per hour. How far does a car traveling 60 mph skid before it stops? **240 ft**

22. Use the formula $V = e^3$ to find the volume of air in a cube-shaped box with edges 15 centimeters long. **3375 cm³**

4

LESSON MASTER 1-3 B — Questions on SPUR Objectives

Vocabulary
In 1–3, tell how each is read.

1. $f(n)$ — **f of n**

2. $A: x \to \frac{x^2}{10}$ — **A maps x onto $\frac{x^2}{10}$.**

3. $S(y) = \frac{y^2}{8} + 5y + 17$ — **S of y equals $\frac{y^2}{8} + 5y + 17$.**

Skills Objective B: Use function notation.
In 4–6, suppose $B(x) = x^2 - x$. Evaluate the function for the given value of x.

4. $B(4)$ __**12**__   5. $B\left(\frac{1}{2}\right)$ __$-\frac{1}{4}$__   6. $B(-3)$ __**12**__

In 7–9, use the description $H: x \to \frac{x^2 - 2x}{4}$.

Evaluate the function for the given value.

7. $H: 2 \to$ __**0**__   8. $H: 4 \to$ __**2**__   9. $H: 0 \to$ __**0**__

10. If $g(y) = 3^y$ and $h(y) = y^3$, which is greater, $g(-1)$ or $h(-1)$? Justify your answer.
$g(-1)$; $g(-1) = 3^{-1} = \frac{1}{3}$; $h(-1) = (-1)^3 = -1$; $\frac{1}{3} > -1$

11. At a speed s, the minimum distance $D(s)$ a car travels between the time a driver decides to stop and the time the car comes to a complete stop is given by the function $D(s) = s + \frac{s^2}{20}$.

a. Complete the table.

Speed s of car (in mph)	10	20	30	40	50	60
Stopping distance $D(s)$ (in feet)	15	40	75	120	175	240

b. Determine the stopping distance for a car traveling 55 mph. Does this distance agree with the values you found in Part a? Why or why not?
206.25 ft; yes; the value should be between 175 ft and 240 ft.

c. Find the stopping distance for a car traveling 70 mph. __**315 ft**__

5 ▶

Uses Objective J: Use functions to solve real-world problems.
In 12–14, use the table below. $S(x)$ and $U(x)$ are the numbers of successful space launches by the Soviet Union and the United States, respectively, for the years 1980 through 1993.

	'80	'81	'82	'83	'84	'85	'86	'87	'88	'89	'90	'91	'92	'93
$S(x)$	89	98	101	98	97	97	91	95	90	74	75	59	54	47
$U(x)$	13	18	18	22	22	17	6	8	12	18	27	18	28	23

12. Describe what $U('87)$ represents.
The number of successful U.S. space launches in 1987 (8)

13. a. Calculate $S('88) - U('88)$. __**78**__
b. What does your answer to Part a represent?
The difference between Soviet and U.S. successful space launches in 1988

14. a. Calculate $\frac{U('89) - U('80)}{1989 - 1980}$. __$\frac{5}{9}$__
b. What does your answer to Part a represent?
The average rate of increase in U.S. successful space launches for the years 1980–1989

15. The cost of making a phone call from an airplane is \$9.50 for the first three minutes, and \$2.00 for each additional minute or fraction thereof. Describe this function
a. using Euler's notation. $f(x) = 9.50 + 2x$
b. using mapping notation. $F: x \to 9.50 + 2x$
c. Find the cost of a phone call lasting 7 minutes 20 seconds. __**\$19.50**__

16. The cost for gas in Northwoods is \$0.4685 per therm for the first 50 therms and \$0.3830 for each therm thereafter. In addition, there is a customer charge of \$4. Find the amount charged for 105.76 therms. __**\$48.78**__

17. In Northwoods, electricity costs \$0.10819 per kwh for the first 400 kwh and \$0.07093 for each kwh over 400. Find the amount charged for 725 kwh of electricity. Include a basic service charge of \$9.06. __**\$75.39**__

6

LESSON MASTER 1-4 B — Questions on SPUR Objectives

Vocabulary

1. State the *Vertical-Line Test for Functions.*
No vertical line intersects the graph of a function in more than one point.

Uses Objective J: Use functions to solve real-world problems.

2. The graph at the right gives the estimated percent $C(y)$ of high-school seniors, by year y of graduation, who have ever used cigarettes.

a. Estimate $C(1987)$.
≈ 67%
b. Estimate $C(1989) - C(1983)$. Tell what this number means.
≈ 5%; the difference in percents of h.s. seniors who used cigarettes in 1989 and 1983

3. The table below gives the sources for electric power in the United States for the years 1980-1989. Amounts are given in billions of kilowatt-hours produced. Let $y =$ the year, $C(y)$ the amount produced by coal that year, and $N(y)$ the amount by nuclear sources that year.

	1980	1981	1982	1983	1984	1985	1986	1987	1988	1989
Coal	1162	1203	1192	1259	1342	1402	1386	1464	1541	1551
Nuclear	251	273	283	294	328	384	414	455	527	529

a. On the grid at the right, graph the points $(y, C(y))$ and $(y, N(y))$ and connect each set of points with a smooth curve.
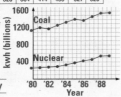
b. Which source for electricity shows a more rapid increase in usage? Use the table or your graph to justify your answer.
Coal: the slope of its graph is slightly steeper.

7 ▶

Representations Objective L: Determine the domain, the range, and values of a function from its graph.
In 4–6, a function is graphed.

4.
a. Give its range. __**all reals**__
b. Give its domain. __**all reals**__
c. For what values of x is $f(x) = 0$? __$x = 0$__

5.
a. Give its range. __$\{y : y > 0\}$__
b. Give its domain. __$\{x : x \neq 0\}$__
c. Find $g(-2)$. __**2**__

6.
a. Give its range. __$\{y : y \geq -3\}$__
b. Give its domain. __**all reals**__
c. For what values of x is $f(x) = 1$? __$x = 4, x = -4$__

Representations Objective M: Apply the Vertical-Line Test for a function.
In 7–10, determine whether or not the graph represents a function. How can you tell? **Sample explanations are given.**

7.
No; 2 points on same vertical line

8.
Yes; no 2 points on same vertical line

9.
Yes; no 2 points on same vertical line

10.
No; 2 points on same vertical line

8

LESSON MASTER 1-5 B

Questions on SPUR Objectives

Skills Objective C: Solve and check linear equations.

In 1–12, solve and check the equation. **Checks are not shown.**

1. $\frac{1}{4}x = 32$
   $x = 128$

2. $\frac{3}{5}n - 4 = 56$
   $n = 100$

3. $25 = \frac{5}{6}(m + 1)$
   $m = 29$

4. $24 = 1.2y$
   $y = 20$

5. $20 = \frac{5}{10c}$
   $c = \frac{1}{40}$

6. $4n - (n - 1) = 7$
   $n = 2$

7. $\frac{d}{4} + \frac{d}{6} = 5$
   $d = 12$

8. $\frac{1}{6}(60x + 24) = -x$
   $x = -\frac{4}{11}$

9. $5y + 42 = 3y + 60$
   $y = 9$

10. $\frac{6}{F} = 0.2$
    $F = 30$

11. $8k - 5 = 5 - 8k$
    $k = \frac{5}{8}$

12. $0.4(g - 20) - 0.2g = 36$
    $g = 220$

13. If $f(q) = 8q - (3 + 4q)$, for what value of q is $f(q) = 17$?
    $q = 5$

14. Use the function g defined as $g(e) = \frac{2}{e} - 6$.
    a. Find $g(8)$. $-5\frac{3}{4}$
    b. If $g(e) = -4$, find e. $e = 1$

Uses Objective K: Use linear equations to solve real-world problems.

15. A bag of mixed dried beans for soup contains $\frac{1}{8}$ pinto beans, $\frac{3}{8}$ white beans, $\frac{1}{4}$ kidney beans, and 8 ounces of navy beans. Find the weight of the

    a. entire bag of mix. 32 oz
    b. pinto beans. 4 oz
    c. white beans. 12 oz
    d. kidney beans. 8 oz

9 ▶

▶ LESSON MASTER 1-5 B *page 2*

16. How many bows each using two thirds of a yard of ribbon can be made from 20 yards of ribbon?
    30 bows

17. Nancy has 120 cm of wood molding to make a picture frame. If she wants the frame to be twice as long as it is wide, what should be the outside dimensions of the frame?
    40 cm by 20 cm

18. The total bill for a restaurant meal, including 8% tax and 15% tip (both on only the cost of the meal), was $9.84. What was the cost of the meal?
    $8

19. When Pedro called Gary, the call cost $1.58. If the rate for the call was 53¢ for the first three minutes and 15¢ for each additional minute or fraction thereof, how long did Pedro and Gary talk?
    10 minutes

20. Yuko needs materials for a felt banner. She needs a half yard each of green and blue felt and 1 yard of white felt. She also needs two wooden dowels at $1.25 each and cord costing $4. If she has only $12 to spend, how much can she afford to spend per yard for the felt?
    $2.75

21. Maria wishes to invest in bonds which pay 6% annual dividends. How much must she invest in order to realize $2,120 at the end of the first year?
    $2,000

22. After consecutive discounts of 10% and 20%, a winter coat was sale-priced at $144. What was the original price of the coat?
    $200

10

LESSON MASTER 1-6 B

Questions on SPUR Objectives

Skills Objective D: Rewrite formulas.

In 1 and 2, use this information: The formula for the distance d an object falls during time t when it is dropped near the earth's surface is $d = \frac{1}{2}gt^2$.

1. What is the ratio of d to t^2?
   $\frac{g}{2}$

2. Solve this formula for g.
   $g = \frac{2d}{t^2}$

3. The sum S of the measures of the angles of a polygon with n sides is $S = 180(n - 2)$. Solve for n.
   $n = \frac{S}{180} + 2$

4. Solve for n in the formula $t^2 = 8 - 2n$.
   $n = 4 - \frac{t^2}{2}$

5. In the formula for the volume of a sphere, $V = \frac{4}{3}\pi r^3$, find the value for π.
   $\pi = \frac{3V}{4r^3}$

In 6 and 7, use the formula $A = P + Prt$, which gives the total Amount A when a principal P is invested at a simple-interest rate r for a time of t years. The interest is represented by Prt.

6. Solve the formula for the principal P.
   $P = \frac{A}{1 + rt}$

7. Solve the formula for the interest rate r.
   $r = \frac{A - P}{Pt}$

8. The formula $A = P(1 + r)^t$ gives the amount A when a principal P is invested at a compound-interest rate r for a time of t years. Solve the formula for P.
   $P = \frac{A}{(1 + r)^t}$

9. The formula $C = \frac{5}{9}(F - 32)$ converts a temperature from degrees Fahrenheit to degrees Celsius. Solve for F.
   $F = \frac{9}{5}C + 32$

10. A formula for the perimeter of a rectangle is $P = 2(\ell + w)$. Solve for w.
    $w = \frac{P}{2} - \ell$

11. A formula for the area of a triangle is $A = \frac{1}{2}bh$. Solve the formula for the height h of the triangle.
    $h = \frac{2A}{b}$

12. A formula for the area of a trapezoid is $A = \frac{(a + b)h}{2}$. Solve the formula for the height h of the trapezoid.
    $h = \frac{2A}{a + b}$

11 ▶

▶ LESSON MASTER 1-6 B *page 2*

Uses Objective K: Use linear equations to solve real-word problems.

13. The volume of the Great Pyramid of Cheops in Giza, Egypt, was about 2,559,900 m³. Use the formula $V = \frac{1}{3}Bh$ to determine the original height of the pyramid if the area of its base B was about 52,600 m³.
    ≈ 146 m

In 14 and 15, use the formulas from Items 6 and 7.

14. Cindy and Tony invested $5,000 at an annual rate of 3.5%. Determine
    a. the amount of interest at the end of the first year. **$175**
    b. the total value at the end of the first year. **$5,175**

15. The annual rate of Cathy and Mike's investment was 4%. If the total value of their investment at the end of one year was $2,600, how much had they invested?
    $2,500

16. The temperature given on a bank thermometer was 25°C.
    a. Was this temperature above or below freezing? **above**
    b. Give the temperature in degrees Fahrenheit. Refer to the formula in Item 9. **77°F**
    c. Try to write a simple "rule of thumb" for estimating a Fahrenheit temperature when given a Celsius reading.
    Sample: Double the Celsius reading and add 32.

17. Young's formula, $C = \left(\frac{g}{g + 12}\right)A$, tells how much medicine C to give a child of age g under age 13 when the adult dosage A is known. If the dosage for a 12-year-old child is 600 mg, what is the dosage for someone 18 years old?
    1,200 mg

18. A pine-tree nursery plants each seedling in the center of a square 4 m on each side. How many seedlings can be planted in a rectangular field 200 m by 300 m?
    3,750 seedings

19. A 4-cubic-foot bag of peat moss is in the shape of a rectangular solid 32 in. long and 18 in. wide. How high is a stack of 4 bags if they are stacked on their largest sides? The formula for volume is $V = \ell wh$.
    48 in.

20. The building code for a ramp states that the ratio of the horizontal distance d to the height h of the ramp must be at least 12 to 1. How much horizontal distance must be allowed for a ramp that accompanies six 8-inch-high stairs?
    576 in.

12

LESSON MASTER 1-7 B

Questions on SPUR Objectives

Vocabulary

1. Give an informal definition of the term *sequence*.

Sample: an ordered list of numbers or items.

2. Consider the sequence 2, 3, 5, 6, 11, 13, 17, 19, ...

a. Tell how "$p_5 = 11$" is read. **p sub 5 equals 11.**

b. Name the third term. **5** **c.** Give p_8. **19**

Uses Objective E: Evaluate sequences.

3. a. Draw the next term in the following sequence of dots.

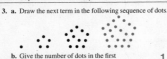

b. Give the number of dots in the first five terms of the sequence in Part a. **1, 5, 12, 22, 35**

c. Predict the number of dots in the tenth term of the sequence in Parts a and b. **145 dots**

In 4–7, give the first four terms of the sequence.

4. $a_n = 4n - 6$ **-2, 2, 6, 10** **5.** $a_n = n^2 + 8$ **9, 12, 17, 24**

6. $a_n = 12n$ **12, 24, 36, 48** **7.** $a_n = 2^n$ **2, 4, 8, 16**

8. Given $p_n = \frac{n^2 + n}{2}$, find p_6. $p_6 = 21$

9. Given $T_n = \frac{8n}{2n^2 - 1}$, find T_5. $T_5 = \frac{40}{49}$

In 10 and 11, *multiple choice.* Which is a formula for the *n*th term of the sequence?

10. 6, 10, 14, 18, 22, ... **b**
(a) $6 + 4n$ (b) $6 + 4(n - 1)$ (c) $6 + (n - 1)^2$

11. 3, 12, 27, 48, 75, ... **c**
(a) $3n$ (b) $4n^2 - 1$ (c) $3n^2$

13 ▶

▶ **LESSON MASTER 1-7 B** *page 2*

Uses Objective J: Use sequences to solve real-world problems.

12. Cary plans to read 3 books a month to help increase his reading speed. The sequence $b_n = 3n$ gives the number of books he will have read after n months. How many books will Cary have read in 8 months? **24 books**

13. Juan, who weighs 110 pounds, plans to lose $1\frac{1}{2}$ pounds a week so that he can wrestle in the 103-pound weight class. Juan's weight n weeks after he begins his diet is $w_n = 110 - 1.5n$.

a. If Juan diets for 8 weeks, what will he weigh? **98 lb**

b. When should Juan stop dieting in order to wrestle at 103 pounds? **after 5 wk**

14. On Sidewalk Day, *Abigail's Designs* has a "sliding-scale" sale on all merchandise. At the end of each hour, prices are reduced 10%. This means that the sale price of a $100 dress after hour h is given by $p_n = 100(0.9)^h$.

a. Find the sale price of the $100 dress after 4 hours. **$65.61**

b. Find the sale price of a $55 skirt after 7 hours. **$26.31**

15. Beth Garcia's beginning annual salary at Dontel was $22,000. She was promised an increase of 4% at the end of each year. So, $S_n = 22,000(1.04)^{n-1}$ gives Beth's salary in her nth year.

a. Find Beth's salary for her second year. **$22,880**

b. At this rate, what would Beth's salary be in her tenth year with Dontel? **$31,312.86**

16. The number of feet traveled during each second of free fall is given by the formula $d_n = 16 + 32(n - 1)$. Suppose a stone is dropped from the top of Chicago's Sears Tower, which is 1454 feet high.

a. How far will the stone travel during the eighth second? **240 feet**

b. What is the total distance the stone will have traveled after eight seconds? **1024 feet**

c. How long will it take for the stone to hit the ground? **≈ 10 seconds**

14

LESSON MASTER 1-8 B

Questions on SPUR Objectives

Skills Objective E: Evaluate sequences.

1. The first two terms of a sequence are 2 and 2. Each term after the second is the sum of the previous two terms. Write the next 6 terms. **4, 6, 10, 16, 26, 42**

In 2 and 3, give the first five terms of the sequence defined by the recursive formula.

2. The first term is 100. Each term after the first is one half of the previous term. **100, 50, 25, $\frac{25}{2}$, $\frac{25}{4}$**

3. The first term is -1. Each term after the first is 1 more than the cube of the previous term. **-1, 0, 1, 2, 9**

In 4–7, give the first six terms of the sequence defined by the recursive formula. The formula is given for integers $n \geq 2$.

4. $\begin{cases} s_1 = 5 \\ s_n = \boxed{ANS} + 6 \end{cases}$ **5, 11, 17, 23, 29, 35**

5. $\begin{cases} a_1 = -8 \\ a_n = \boxed{ANS} + 2 \end{cases}$ **-8, -6, -4, -2, 0, 2**

6. $\begin{cases} a_1 = 6 \\ a_n = 2 \cdot \boxed{ANS} \end{cases}$ **6, 12, 24, 48, 96, 192**

7. $\begin{cases} t_1 = 1 \\ t_n = (-1)^n \cdot \boxed{ANS} \end{cases}$ **1, 1, -1, -1, 1, 1**

In 8 and 9, *multiple choice.*

8. The explicit formula $x_n = 3(4)^{n-1}$ gives the same sequence as which recursive formula for integers $n \geq 2$? **b**

(a) $\begin{cases} x_1 = 6 \\ x_n = 3 + 3 \cdot \boxed{ANS} \end{cases}$ (b) $\begin{cases} x_1 = 3 \\ x_n = 4 \cdot \boxed{ANS} \end{cases}$ (c) $\begin{cases} x_1 = 3 \\ x_n = 3 + 4 \cdot \boxed{ANS} \end{cases}$

9. Which is a recursive definition for the sequence of squares of integers 1, 4, 9, 16, 25, 36, ... ? **c**

(a) $\begin{cases} s_1 = 1 \\ s_n = \boxed{ANS}^2, \\ \text{for integers } n \geq 2. \end{cases}$ (b) $\begin{cases} s_1 = 1 \\ s_n = \boxed{ANS} + 3, \\ \text{for integers } n \geq 2. \end{cases}$ (c) $\begin{cases} s_1 = 1 \\ s_n = \boxed{ANS} + 2n - 1, \\ \text{for integers } n \geq 2. \end{cases}$

15 ▶

▶ **LESSON MASTER 1-8 B** *page 2*

Skills Objective F: Write a recursive definition for a sequence.

In 10–12, a sequence is given. Write a recursive definition a. in words and b. in symbols.

Samples are given.

10. 891, 297, 99, 33, 11, ...

a. First term is 891; each succeeding term is $\frac{1}{3}$ the previous term.

b. $\begin{cases} t_1 = 891 \\ t_n = \frac{1}{3}(t_{n-1}), \\ \text{for } n \geq 2. \end{cases}$

11. 1, -5, -11, -17, -23, ...

a. First term is 1; each succeeding term is 6 less than the previous term.

b. $\begin{cases} s_1 = 1 \\ s_n = s_{n-1} - 6, \\ \text{for } n \geq 2. \end{cases}$

12. 5, 10, 20, 40, 80, ...

a. First term is 5; each succeeding term is twice the previous term.

b. $\begin{cases} a_1 = 5 \\ a_n = 2a_{n-1}, \\ \text{for } n \geq 2. \end{cases}$

Uses Objective J: Use sequences to solve real-world problems.

13. Becky invested $5000 in a savings account that pays 4% compounded annually. She plans to withdraw $100 at the end of each year. The recursive formula at the right gives her account balance at the end of the nth year.

$\begin{cases} B_0 = 5000 \\ B_n = 1.04 \cdot \boxed{ANS} - 100, \\ \text{for integers } n \geq 1 \end{cases}$

a. Give the account balance at the end of year 1. **$5100**

b. Give the account balance at the end of year 3. **$5312.16**

c. By how much will Becky's investment have increased after 5 years? **$541.63**

14. Tim received $20 from his parents on his first birthday, $25 on his second birthday, $30 on his third birthday, and so on.

$\begin{cases} b_1 = 20 \\ b_n = b_{n-1} + 5, \\ \text{for } n \geq 2. \end{cases}$

a. Write a recursive formula for this situation.

b. How much did Tim receive on his tenth birthday? **$65**

c. Find the total amount of money Tim's parents had given him for his ten birthdays. **$425**

16

ADVANCED ALGEBRA © Scott, Foresman and Company

LESSON MASTER 1-9 B

Questions on SPUR Objectives

Skills Objective E: Evaluate sequences.

In 1 and 2, give the first six terms of the sequence defined by the recursive formula.

1. The first term is -2. Each term after the first is -3 times the previous term.

$$-2, 6\ -18, 54, -162, 486$$

2. The first term is $\frac{1}{1000}$. Each term after the first is ten times the previous term.

$$\frac{1}{1000}, \frac{1}{100}, \frac{1}{10}, 1, 10, 100$$

In 3-8, give the first six terms of the sequence defined by the recursive formula. The formula is given for integers $n \geq 2$.

3. $\begin{cases} a_1 = 5 \\ a_n = 3a_{n-1} \end{cases}$

$$5, 15, 45, 135, 405, 1215$$

4. $\begin{cases} C_1 = 3 \\ C_n = 2C_{n-1} + 3 \end{cases}$

$$3, 9, 21, 45, 93, 189$$

5. $\begin{cases} d_1 = -4 \\ d_n = 8 - d_{n-1} \end{cases}$

$$-4, 12, -4, 12, -4, 12$$

6. $\begin{cases} e_1 = 2 \\ e_n = 1 \div e_{n-1} \end{cases}$

$$2, \frac{1}{2}, 2, \frac{1}{2}, 2, \frac{1}{2}$$

7. $\begin{cases} x_1 = 1 \\ x_n = 3x_{n-1} + 1 \end{cases}$

$$1, 4, 13, 40, 121, 364$$

8. $\begin{cases} m_1 = 3 \\ m_n = 3m_{n-1} \end{cases}$

$$3, 9, 27, 81, 243, 729$$

In 9 and 10, a sequence is defined. Find the designated term.

9. $\begin{cases} P_1 = -3 \\ P_n = (-1)^{n-1} \cdot (3P_{n-1}) \end{cases}$

$P_6 =$ ___ **729**

10. $\begin{cases} t_1 = -2 \\ t_n = (t_{n-1})^2 - 6 \end{cases}$

$t_5 =$ ___ **-2**

17

▶ **LESSON MASTER 1-9 B** *page 2*

Skills Objective F: Write a recursive definition for a sequence.

In 11 and 12, write a recursive definition in symbols for the given sequence. **Samples are given.**

11. 3, 7, 15, 31, 63, ...

$\begin{cases} s_1 = 3 \\ s_n = 2s_{n-1} + 1, \text{ for } n \geq 2. \\ \text{or } s_n = s_{n-1} + 2^n, \text{ for } n \geq 2. \end{cases}$

12. 2, 8, 18, 32, 50, ...

$\begin{cases} t_1 = 2 \\ t_n = t_{n-1} + 4n - 2, \\ \text{for } n \geq 2. \end{cases}$

Uses Objective A

13. Jon opened a savings account when he received his first pay check. He started with a deposit of $50 and then deposited $20 each week.

a. Write a recursive formula to describe this situation.

$\begin{cases} d_1 = 50 \\ d_n = d_{n-1} + 20, \\ \text{for } n \geq 2. \end{cases}$

b. How much had John deposited after 10 weeks? **$250**

14. Each year after he retired, Oscar Anderson sold two 20-acre parcels from his 400-acre farm for income.

a. Write a recursive formula to describe this situation.

$\begin{cases} f_1 = 400 \\ f_n = f_{n-1} - 40, \\ \text{for } n \geq 2. \end{cases}$

b. How many acres were left after 5 years? **200 acres**

c. In how many years will Oscar have fewer than 100 acres on his farm? **8 years**

In 15-17, use this information: Sara Kim was offered two jobs with a starting salary of $20,000. NA Publishing promised a raise of at least 4.5% every year, and Gary Press promised annual raises of at least $1,000.

15. Write a recursive formula to describe the salary plan

a. of NA Publishing.

$\begin{cases} N_1 = 20,000 \\ N_n = 1.045N_{n-1}, \\ \text{for } n \geq 2. \end{cases}$

b. of Gary Press

$\begin{cases} G_1 = 20,000 \\ G_n = G_{n-1}, + 1,000 \\ \text{for } n \geq 2. \end{cases}$

16. After how many years would Sara's salary reach at least $25,000

a. at NA Publishing? **6 yr**

b. at Gary Press? **5 yr**

17. Which company's annual salary would be higher after 10 years? **NA Publishing**

18

LESSON MASTER 2-1 B

Questions on SPUR Objectives

Vocabulary

In 1-3, use the direct variation equation $V = \frac{4}{3}\pi r^3$.

1. Identify the *constant of variation*. ___ $\frac{4}{3}\pi$

2. Identify the *independent variable*. ___ r

3. Identify the *dependent variable*. ___ V

Skills Objective A: Translate direct-variation language into formulas and formulas into direct-variation language.

In 4-8, translate into a variation equation. Let k be the constant of variation.

4. a varies directly as the cube of b. ___ $a = kb^3$

5. T is directly proportional to the fourth power of S. ___ $T = kS^4$

6. The actual distance D between two towns is directly proportional to d, the distance between them on a map. ___ $D = kd$

7. A person's weight w varies directly as the cube of his or her height h. ___ $w = kh^3$

8. Real-estate taxes T are directly proportional to property value V. ___ $T = kV$

9. Write the variation equation $y = kx^3$ in words.
y varies directly as the cube of x.

Skills Objective B: Solve direct-variation problems.

10. m is directly proportional to n. If $m = 48$ when $n = 12$, find m when $n = 3$. $m = 12$

11. y varies directly as the square of x. If $y = 63$ when $x = 3$, find y when $x = 9$. $y = 567$

12. s varies directly as g^4, and $s = 64$ when $g = 2$.

a. Find the constant of variation k. ___ $k = 4$

b. Find s when $g = 3$. ___ $s = 324$

13. c varies directly as the cube of d, and $c = 32$ when $d = 4$.

a. Find the constant of variation k. ___ $r = 0.5$

b. Find c when $d = 5$. ___ $c = 62.5$

19 ▶

▶ **LESSON MASTER 2-1B** *page 2*

Uses Objective F: Recognize direct-variation situations.

In 14-16, translate into a variation situation.

14. The price p of a pizza varies directly as the square of its diameter d. ___ $p = kd^2$

15. The rebate r is directly proportional to the number n of coupons submitted. ___ $r = kn$

16. The volume V of a spherical helium balloon is directly proportional to the cube of its radius r. ___ $V = kr^3$

Uses Objective G: Solve real-world problems involving direct variation.

17. When lightning strikes 8 miles away, the sound of the thunder is heard about 40 seconds later. The time it takes for the sound to travel is directly proportional to the distance. How long does it take the sound to travel if lightning strikes 6 miles away? **30 sec**

18. The distance a car travels before stopping after the driver brakes varies directly as the square of the speed of the car. If a car travels 30 feet after the driver brakes when the car's speed is 20 mph, how far will the car travel after the driver brakes if the car's speed is 60 mph? **270 ft**

19. The designers of the Parthenon, a Greek temple completed in 432 B.C., utilized the golden ratio. The outline of its face fits into a golden rectangle, in which the length varies directly as its height in the ratio 1.618 to 1. The length of the temple was about 31 m. What was the original height of the Parthenon? **≈ 19.2 m**

22. The rear wheel of a 5-speed bicycle turns 770 times in a mile. The table below lists the number of pedal turns for rear-wheel turns in each gear. The number of rear-wheel turns in each gear is directly proportional to the number of pedal turns.

Gear	First	Second	Third	Fourth	Fifth
Pedal turns	9	4	1	3	5
Rear-wheel turns	14	7	2	7	14

How many times must a person pedal in a mile in each gear?

a. First ___ **495**

b. Second ___ **440**

c. Third ___ **385**

d. Fourth ___ **330**

e. Fifth ___ **275**

20

251

LESSON MASTER 2-2 B

Questions on SPUR Objectives

Skills Objective A: Translate inverse-variation language into formulas and formulas into inverse-variation language.

In 1–6, translate into a variation equation.

1. P varies inversely with d.

$P = k/d$

2. e is inversely proportional to the cube of g.

$e = k/g^3$

3. m varies inversely with n^2.

$m = k/n^2$

4. The number n of baseballs that can fit into a carton is inversely proportional to the cube of a baseball's radius r.

$n = \dfrac{k}{r^3}$

5. The number of hours h it takes to travel a given distance varies inversely with the speed s of a car.

$h = \dfrac{k}{s}$

6. The weight W of a body varies inversely with the square of its distance d from the center of the earth.

$W = \dfrac{k}{d^2}$

Skills Objective B: Solve inverse-variation problems.

7. a is inversely proportional to b. If $a = \frac{1}{4}$ when $b = 2$, find a when $b = \frac{1}{2}$.

$a = 1$

8. y varies inversely as the square of v. If $y = 4$ when $v = -4$, find y when $v = 8$.

$y = 1$

9. m varies inversely as the cube of n. If $m = -2$ when $n = -5$, find m when $n = -2.5$.

$m = -16$

Uses Objective F: Recognize inverse-variation situations.

In 10–15, complete with "directly," "inversely," or "neither directly nor inversely."

10. The weight of a magazine varies __?__ as the number of pages it contains.

directly

11. The speed of a horse varies __?__ as the time it takes the horse to travel a given distance.

inversely

12. The temperature in Chicago varies __?__ with the number of the month of the year.

neither

13. The number of tiles it takes to tile a floor varies __?__ as the area of the tiles.

inversely

21 ▶

---

14. The distance needed to stop a moving vehicle varies __?__ as the speed of the vehicle.

directly

15. The amount of sunlight at a given time varies __?__ as the time of day.

neither

Uses Objective G: Solve real-world problems involving inverse variation.

16. The number n of square tiles needed to tile a floor varies inversely as the square of the length s of a side of each tile. If it takes 180 tiles with 6-in. sides to tile a floor, how many tiles with 9-in. sides will it take to tile the same floor?

80 tiles

17. The number n of citrus fruit that fit into a carton varies inversely as the cube of the diameter d of each fruit. A carton that holds 12 grapefruit with diameter 15 cm holds how many tangerines with diameter 5 cm?

324 tangerines

18. A lever is a simple machine which can be used to raise a weight at one end of a bar by pushing down at the other end of the bar. The diagram at the right shows how a 3-foot-long crowbar is used to pry an 80-pound boulder out of the ground. Recall that the weight needed to balance a lever is inversely proportional to the distance of the weight from the fulcrum.

a. If the fulcrum is 2 feet from the boulder, how much weight must be exerted at the other end of the bar to raise the boulder?

160 lb

b. Where could the fulcrum be placed in order for the lever to be more efficient? Justify your answer.

Sample: closer to the boulder; if the distance is 1 ft, only 40 lb would be needed.

19. It takes 4 workers 6 hours to pick the strawberries in a field.

a. How many hours would it take 6 workers to pick the strawberries in the same field?

4 hours

b. What is the constant of variation, and what does it represent?

$k = 24$; the product of the number of hours and the number of workers

22

LESSON MASTER 2-3 B

Questions on SPUR Objectives

Vocabulary

1. If y varies directly as x and x is multiplied by c, then y is multiplied by __?__ .

c

2. If y varies inversely as x^n and x is multiplied by a nonzero constant c, then y is __?__ by c^n.

divided

Properties Objective D: Use the Fundamental Theorem of Variation.

In 3–6, suppose that in a variation problem the value of x is doubled. How is the value of y changed?

3. if y varies directly as x^3?

y is multiplied by 8.

4. if y varies directly as x^4?

y is multiplied by 16.

5. if y varies inversely as x^2?

y is divided by 4.

6. if y varies inversely as $\sqrt{x}$?

y is divided by $\sqrt{2}$.

In 7–9, suppose that a varies directly as the fourth power of b. How does the value of a change if

7. b is doubled?

a is multiplied by 16.

8. b is multiplied by 5?

a is multiplied by 625.

9. b is multiplied by $\frac{1}{4}$?

a is multiplied by $\frac{1}{256}$.

In 10–12, suppose that m varies inversely as the square root of n. How does the value of m change if

10. n is doubled?

m is divided by $\sqrt{2}$.

11. n is multiplied by 4?

m is divided by 2.

12. n is multiplied by $\frac{1}{9}$?

m is divided by $\frac{1}{3}$.

In 13–15, tell what effect multiplying the x-values by $\frac{1}{3}$ has on the y values.

13. $y = 5x$

y is multiplied by $\frac{1}{3}$.

14. $y = 4x^2$

y is multiplied by $\frac{1}{9}$.

15. $y = \dfrac{8}{x}$

y is divided by $\frac{1}{3}$.

23 ▶

Review Previous course

In 16–21, graph the equation.

16. $4x + 3y = 24$

17. $y = \frac{1}{2}x + 6$

18. $xy = 12$

19. $y = x^2$

20. $y = 2^x$

21. $y = \dfrac{1}{x}$

24

252

LESSON MASTER 2-4 B

Questions on SPUR Objectives

Vocabulary

1. *Slope* measures the ___?___ of a line. **steepness**

2. *Multiple choice.* Tell which of the following is *not* a definition of slope. **c**
   (a) the rate of change of y with respect to x
   (b) $\dfrac{\text{change in vertical distance}}{\text{change in horizontal distance}}$
   (c) $\dfrac{\text{change in independent variable}}{\text{change in dependent variable}}$
   (d) $\dfrac{\text{rise}}{\text{run}}$

Skills Objective C: Find slopes.

In 3–5 find the slope of the line through the given points.

3. $(5, -2), (3, 8)$ **-5**

4. $(-9, 2), (-4, 0)$ **$-\dfrac{2}{5}$**

5. $(12, 8), (6, -3)$ **$\dfrac{11}{6}$**

6. Find the slope of each line graphed at the right.
   a. **0**
   b. **-2**
   c. **$\dfrac{1}{2}$**

Representations Objective E: Identify properties of variation functions.

In 7–9, give the slope of the line which is the graph of the equation.

7. $y = -7x$ **-7**

8. $y = \frac{1}{2}x$ **$\dfrac{1}{2}$**

9. $y = 0.2x$ **0.2**

Uses Objective I: Graph variation equations

In 10–13, graph the equation.

10. $y = -2x$

11. $y = \frac{1}{4}x$

12. $y = 1.5x$

13. $y = 3x$

Representations Objective J: Identify variation equations from their graphs.

14. Match each graph with its equation. The axes have the same scale.
   i. $y = 5x$ ii. $y = -5x$ iii. $y = \frac{3}{4}x$ iv. $y = -\frac{3}{4}x$

   a. **iv**
   b. **ii**

   c. **i**
   d. **iii**

LESSON MASTER 2-5 B

Questions on SPUR Objectives

Vocabulary

1. A graph *symmetric* to the y-axis coincides with its ___?___ image over the y-axis. **reflection**

2. *Multiple choice.* The graph of which equation is a *parabola*? **c**
   (a) $y = x^3$ (b) $y = 2^x$ (c) $y = 2x^2$

Skills Objective C: Find rates of change.

In 3 and 4, $y = 6x^2$.

3. Find the rate of change between $x = 2$ and $x = 5$. **42**

4. Find the rate of change between $x = -2$ and $x = 2$. **0**

In 5 and 6, $y = -2x^2$.

5. Find the rate of change between $x = 4$ and $x = 6$. **-20**

6. Find the rate of change between $x = 6$ and $x = 8$. **-28**

Properties Objective E: Identify properties of graphs of functions with equations of the form $y = kx^2$.

In 7–9, refer to the following equations.
   (a) $y = -4x$ (b) $y = \frac{1}{4}x$ (c) $y = -4x^2$ (d) $y = \frac{1}{4}x^2$

7. Which equations have a graph which is a parabola? **c, d**

8. Which equations have a graph which is symmetric with respect to the y-axis? **c, d**

9. Which equations have a straight-line graph? **a, b**

Uses Objective I: Graph equations of the form $y = kx^2$.

In 10 and 11, graph the equations on the same grid. Label the graphs.

10. a. $y = 5x^2$ b. $y = -5x^2$

11. a. $y = \frac{1}{2}x^2$ b. $y = -\frac{1}{2}x^2$

Representations Objective J: Identify variation equations from their graphs.

12. Match each graph with its equation. Axes have the same scale.
   i. $y = -3x$ ii. $y = \frac{1}{3}x^2$ iii. $y = 3x^2$ iv. $y = -\frac{1}{3}x^2$

   a. **iii**
   b. **iv**
   c. **i**

Representations Objective K: Recognize the effects of a change in scale or viewing window on a graph of a variation equation.

13. In the graph of $y = kx^2$ shown at the right, what type of number is k? **negative**

14. a. Sketch the graph of $y = 2x + 1$ on the window at the right.
    b. Sketch the graph of $y = 2x + 1$ on the second window at the right.
    c. Does the slope of the line $y = 2x + 1$ change when the viewing window is changed? Explain your answer.
    no; the slope appears different when the domain or range is changed.

   a.

   $-2 \le x \le 2$, x-scale = 1
   $-5 \le y \le 5$, y-scale = 1

   b.

   $-2 \le x \le 2$, x-scale = 1
   $-10 \le y \le 10$, y-scale = 1

LESSON MASTER 2-6 B

Questions on SPUR Objectives

Vocabulary

1. *Multiple choice.* Which is an equation for a *hyperbola*? **a**
   (a) $y = \frac{2}{x}$ (b) $y = \frac{x}{2}$ (c) $y = 2x$ (d) $y = \frac{2}{x^2}$

2. The parts of a hyperbola are called ___?___.   **branches**

3. Name the *asymptotes* of the graph of $\frac{2}{x^2}$.   **$x = 0, y = 0$**

Skills Objective C: Find rates of change.

In 4–7, find the rate of change between -2 and 2.

4. $y = \frac{8}{x}$ **2**

5. $y = \frac{8}{x^2}$ **0**

6. $y = \frac{8}{x}$ **-2**

7. $y = -\frac{8}{x^2}$ **0**

Properties Objective E: Identify properties of variation functions.

8. *True or false* Graphs of all variation functions pass through the point (0, 0).   **False**

In 9–12, refer to these equations.
   (a) $y = kx$ (b) $y = \frac{k}{x}$ (c) $y = kx^2$ (d) $y = \frac{k}{x^2}$

9. Which graphs have exactly one line of symmetry?   **b, c, d**

10. Which graphs have more than one part?   **b, d**

11. When $k < 0$, which graphs have points in the fourth quadrant?   **a, b, c, d**

12. When $k > 0$, which graphs have points in the third quadrant?   **a, b**

▶ LESSON MASTER 2-6B *page 2*

Uses Objective I: Graph inverse-linear variation and inverse-square variation equations.

In 13–16, graph the equation.

13. $y = \frac{8}{x}$
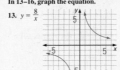

14. $y = -\frac{8}{x}$

15. $y = \frac{8}{x^2}$
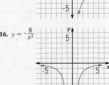

16. $y = -\frac{8}{x^2}$
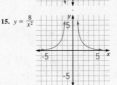

Representations Objective J: Identify inverse-linear and inverse-square functions from their graphs.

In 17–19, *multiple choice.* Choose the equation whose graph is most like that shown. Assume that the axes have the same scale.

17. **d**

   (a) $y = -\frac{3}{x}$
   (b) $y = 3x^2$
   (c) $y = -\frac{3}{x^2}$
   (d) $y = \frac{3}{x}$

18. **b**

   (a) $y = 2x^2$
   (b) $y = -2x^2$
   (c) $y = \frac{2}{x^2}$
   (d) $y = \frac{2}{x}$

19. **a**

   (a) $y = \frac{7}{x^2}$
   (b) $y = -7x^2$
   (c) $y = -\frac{7}{x}$
   (d) $y = 7x^2$

LESSON MASTER 2-7 B

Questions on SPUR Objectives

Uses Objective H: Fit an appropriate variation model to data.

In 1 and 2, *multiple choice.* Tell which equation is the best model for the graph shown at the left.

1.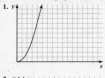
   (a) $y = kx$ **b**
   (b) $y = kx^2$
   (c) $y = \frac{k}{x}$
   (d) $y = \frac{k}{x^2}$

2.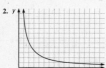
   (a) $y = kx$ **c**
   (b) $y = kx^2$
   (c) $y = \frac{k}{x}$
   (d) $y = \frac{k}{x^2}$

In 3–6, do steps a through d.
   a. Draw a graph to represent the situation.
   b. Write a general variation equation for the situation.
   c. Find the value of the constant of variation and rewrite the variation equation.
   d. Answer the question in the problem.

3. The amount of force needed to loosen a certain bolt is related to the length of a wrench as given in the table.

Force needed (lb)	3	7	10	15	30
Length of wrench (in.)	630	270	189	126	63

How many pounds of force would be needed to loosen the same bolt with a 21-inch wrench?

a.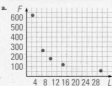

b. $F = \frac{k}{L}$

c. $F = \frac{1890}{L}$

d. **90 lb**

▶ LESSON MASTER 2-7B *page 2*

4. While studying gears, a physics class collected the data in the table relating the number of teeth in a gear and the speed of the gear in revolutions per minute. What would be the speed of a gear with 30 teeth?

Number of teeth	10	12	18	24	36
Speed (rpm)	108	90	60	45	30

a.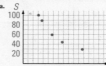

b. $S = \frac{k}{T}$

c. $S = \frac{1080}{T}$

d. **36 rpm**

5. The table to the right gives the number of square tiles of various sizes needed to floor a small restaurant kitchen. How many square tiles with 8-in. sides would be needed?

Length of tile side	4 in.	6 in.	9 in.	12 in.
Number of tiles	1944	864	384	216

a.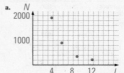

b. $N = \frac{k}{L^2}$

c. $N = \frac{31,104}{L^2}$

d. **486 tiles**

6. A packaging specialist studied the weights of 100 ball bearings of various diameters. The data are in the table.

Diameter of bearing (mm)	3	4	5	6	7	8
Weight of 100 bearings (grams)	12	28	54	93	147	220

What would be the weight of 100 ball bearings with 10-mm diameters?

a.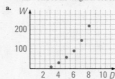

b. $W = kD^3$

c. $W = .43D^3$

d. **430 grams**

LESSON MASTER 2-8 B

Questions on SPUR Objectives

Vocabulary

1. If multiplying every x-value of a function by c results in multiplying the corresponding y-value by c^n, then y varies __?__ as the __?__ power of x.

directly **nth**

2. If multiplying every x-value of a function by c results in dividing the corresponding y-value by c^n, then y varies __?__ as the __?__ power of x.

inversely **nth**

Uses Objective H: Fit an appropriate variation model to data.

In 3 and 4, select the equation that could model the relationship shown in the graphs.

3.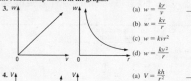

(a) $w = \frac{kr}{v}$

(b) $w = \frac{kv}{r}$

(c) $w = kvr^2$

(d) $w = \frac{kv^2}{r}$

b

4.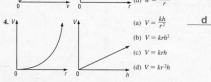

(a) $V = \frac{kh}{r^2}$

(b) $V = krh^2$

(c) $V = krh$

(d) $V = kr^2h$

d

5. A social scientist found a relationship between the average daily number of phone calls C between Unicity and other cities. The left graph displays data relating phone calls and the population P of the cities in millions. The right graph displays data relating phone calls and the distance D in miles between Unicity and the other cities.

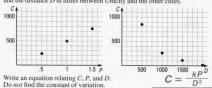

Write an equation relating C, P, and D. Do *not* find the constant of variation.

$$C = \frac{kP}{D^2}$$

33 ►

► LESSON MASTER 2-8B *page 2*

6. The Transportation Department studied the length of time traffic was halted as freight trains traveled across a road. The data in Table I relate speed s of a 100-car train to time T. The data in Table II relate length ℓ of a train traveling at 40 mph with time T.

I.

Speed s (mph)	20	30	40	50	60
Time T (min)	10	7	5	4	3

II.

Length ℓ (in cars)	20	40	60	80	100
Time T (min)	1	2	3	4	5

a. Graph the points from Table I.

c. Graph the points from Table II.

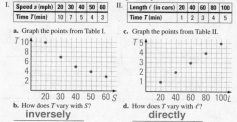

b. How does T vary with S?

inversely

d. How does T vary with ℓ?

directly

e. Write an equation relating T, S, and ℓ. Do *not* find the constant of variation.

$$T = \frac{k\ell}{S}$$

7. A packaging specialist for a toy company compiled the following data. Table I gives the data for the number of racquetballs r that fit in 30-cm-diameter cylindrical cans of height h. Table II gives data for the number of racquetballs r that fit in cans 48 cm high with diameter d.

I.

Height of can h (cm)	30	36	48	60	84
Number of racquetballs r	100	120	160	200	280

II.

Diameter of can d (cm)	30	35	40	45	50
Number of racquetballs r	160	210	270	340	425

a. Graph the points from Table I.

c. Graph the points from Table II.

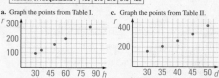

b. How does r vary with h?

directly

d. How does r vary with d?

directly

e. Write an equation relating r, h, and d. Do *not* find the constant of variation.

$$r = kd^2h$$

34

LESSON MASTER 2-9 B

Questions on SPUR Objectives

Skills Objective A: Translate joint- and combined-variation language into formulas and formulas into joint- and combined-variation language.

In 1–5, translate into a variation equation.

1. The area A of an ellipse varies jointly as its major semiaxis b and its minor semiaxis h.

$$A = kbh$$

2. The cost C of a square oak butcher block varies jointly as its thickness t and the square of a side s.

$$C = kts^2$$

3. The load L which will buckle a column is inversely proportional to the square of its length ℓ and directly proportional to the fourth power of its radius r.

$$L = \frac{kr^4}{\ell^2}$$

4. In the middle 1800s, the French scientist J. L. Poiseuille found that the rate r at which a fluid flows through a small tube varies directly with the product of the pressure p acting on the fluid and the fourth power of the diameter d of the tube.

$$r = kpd^4$$

5. The speed S of a 10-speed bike varies directly with the number of revolutions r per minute, directly with the number f of teeth on the front sprocket, and inversely with the number b of teeth on the back sprocket.

$$S = \frac{krf}{b}$$

6. In the formula $A = \pi ab$, A varies __?__ as __?__ and __?__.

jointly **a** **b**

7. If $g = \frac{2d}{t^2}$, g varies __?__ as __?__, and __?__ as __?__.

directly **d** **inversely** **t^2**

Skills Objective B: Solve problems involving joint or combined variation.

8. a varies directly as b and inversely as the square of c. When $b = -8$ and $c = 2$, $a = -6$.

a. Find a when $b = 4$ and $c = -2$.

$$a = 3$$

b. Give the constant of variation.

$$k = 3$$

9. m varies jointly as n and the cube of p. When $n = 3$ and $p = -2$, $m = -48$.

a. Find m when $n = -4$ and $p = 5$.

$$m = -1000$$

b. Give the constant of variation.

$$k = 2$$

35 ►

► LESSON MASTER 2-9B *page 2*

Uses Objective G: Solve real-world problems involving joint or combined variation.

10. The wind force F on a sail varies jointly as the area A of the sail and the square of the wind speed W. The force on a sail with area 500 ft² is 100 pounds when the wind speed is 20 mph.

a. What would the force be with a 30-mph wind?

225 lb

b. What would the force be if the sail is a triangle 20 ft high and 20 ft at the base and the wind speed is 40 mph?

160 lb

In 11 and 12, use this information: The speed s at which water flows through a pipe is directly proportional to the pressure p exerted by a pump and the fourth power of the radius r.

11. What effect will lime deposits on the inside of a pipe have on the speed of the water, if the pressure remains constant?

speed will increase.

12. If the speed of the water through a 2.5-cm-radius pipe is 600 cm per second when the pressure is 4 kg per cm²,

a. what would be the speed if the pressure is doubled?

1200 cm/sec

b. what would be the speed if the radius is 5 cm?

37.5 cm/sec

13. Bridge columns of a new material are 10 in. in diameter and 10 ft high. These columns are able to support up to 40 tons without collapsing. The weight w that collapses a column varies directly as the fourth power of its diameter d and inversely as the square of its height h. Give the maximum weight each column of this material with the given dimensions can support.

a. diameter, 20 in.; height, 10 ft

640 tons

b. diameter, 10 in.; height, 20 ft

10 tons

c. diameter, 20 in.; height, 20 ft

160 tons

Review Previous course.

In 14–16, solve the system of equations.

14. $\begin{cases} 10y - 20x = 20 \\ 4y + 2x = 28 \end{cases}$

15. $\begin{cases} 3a + 2c = -9 \\ 9a - c = 57 \end{cases}$

16. $\begin{cases} 10x + 2y = 60 \\ 3x - 4y = 41 \end{cases}$

$(x, y) = (2, 6)$ **$(a, c) = (5, -12)$** **$(x, y) = (7, -5)$**

36

255

LESSON MASTER 3-1 B
Questions on SPUR Objectives

Vocabulary

1. A function with an equation of the form $y = mx + b$ is a __?__ function. **linear**

2. Give an example of a *constant-decrease* situation.
Sample: Lanie bought a 32-oz jar of plant fertilizer. She uses $\frac{1}{2}$ oz every month.

Skills Objective A: Determine the slope and y-intercept of a line given its equation.

In 3–9, complete the table.

	Equation	Slope	y-intercept
3.	$y = -3x + 8$	-3	8
4.	$y = \frac{4}{5}x - 1$	$\frac{4}{5}$	-1
5.	$y = 6x$	6	0
6.	$y = x + 2$	1	2
7.	$y = \frac{8}{3}x + \frac{2}{3}$	$\frac{8}{3}$	$\frac{2}{3}$
8.	$y = ax + k$	a	k
9.	$y = dx$	d	0

Properties Objective E: Recognize properties of linear functions.

In 10–12, x is the independent variable, y is the dependent variable, and $y = mx + b$.

10. In a constant increase situation, is m positive, negative, or equal to zero? **positive**

11. In a constant decrease situation, is m positive, negative, or equal to zero? **negative**

12. The initial value of the independent variable occurs when $x =$ __?__ and $y =$ __?__. **0   b**

37 ▶

▶ **LESSON MASTER 3-1B** *page 2*

Uses Objective G: Model constant-increase or constant-decrease situations.

13. Mr. Reyes bought 100 coffee filters. On the average, he uses 5 per week. Write an equation relating the number of filters f left after w weeks.
$f = 100 - 5w$

14. Lynn has 42 computer magazines. She adds two more each month.

a. Write an equation relating the number of magazines c Lynn has after m months.
$c = 42 + 2m$

b. How many magazines are there after 6 months? **54 mag.**

c. After 2 years, will Lynn have 100 computer magazines? Why or why not?
No; $c = 42 + 2 \cdot 24 = 90$; she will have 90 magazines.

Uses Objective K: Model situations leading to piecewise-linear functions.

15. Graph this situation. Ai's temperature at 4:00 P.M. was 99.5°F. It rose at a steady rate of 0.3°F per hour for 6 hours. It then stayed constant for 4 hours, and then steadily fell 0.4°F per hour for 4 hours.

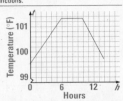

Representations Objective M: Graph or interpret graphs of piecewise-linear functions.

16. Refer to the graph below. Max walked to the library where he studied for awhile and then walked home.

a. How long did Max stay at the library? **1 hr**

b. Find Max's speed in blocks per hour on his way to the library. **20 hr bl.**

c. Find the total distance Max walked. **24 bl.**

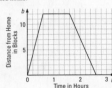

38

LESSON MASTER 3-2 B
Questions on SPUR Objectives

Skills Objective A: Determine the slope and y-intercept of a line given its equation.

In 1–8, complete the table.

	Equation	Slope	y-intercept
1.	$y = 9x + 5$	9	5
2.	$y = \frac{3}{8}x - 2$	$\frac{3}{8}$	-2
3.	$y = 7x$	7	0
4.	$y = 18$	0	18
5.	$2x + 5y = 12$	$-\frac{2}{5}$	$\frac{12}{5}$
6.	$3x - y = 16$	3	-16
7.	$6y = 3x - 4$	$\frac{1}{2}$	$-\frac{2}{3}$
8.	$y + 6 = 0$	0	-6

Skills Objective B: Find an equation for a line given a point on it and its slope.

9. Find an equation for the line with slope -6 and y-intercept 9.
$y = -6x + 9$

10. Find an equation for the line with slope $\frac{7}{4}$ and y-intercept -3.
$y = \frac{7}{4}x - 3$

11. Find an equation for the horizontal line through (5, -5).
$y = -5$

12. Find an equation for the line with slope -1 and y-intercept 0.
$y = -x$

13. Find an equation for the line with y-intercept -3 that is parallel to $y = -1.5x + 4$.
$y = -1.5x - 3$

14. Find an equation for the line with y-intercept 0 that is parallel to $y = 2x - 5$.
$y = 2x$

39 ▶

▶ **LESSON MASTER 3-2B** *page 2*

Properties Objective E: Recognize properties of linear functions.

15. As you move one unit to the right on the line, it rises 6 units. What is the slope of the line? **6**

16. As you move one unit to the right on the line, it drops 2 units. What is the slope of the line? **-2**

17. As you move three units to the right on the line, it rises 2 units. What is the slope of the line? **$\frac{2}{3}$**

18. As a line changes one unit horizontally, it changes $-\frac{2}{5}$ units vertically. What is the slope of the line? **$-\frac{2}{5}$**

19. What are the domain and the range of the function f when $f(x) = 6$?
domain **all real numbers**   range **6**

Representations Objective L: Graph or interpret graphs of linear equations.

In 20–23, graph the line described.

20. $y = -x + 4$

21. slope $= \frac{3}{2}$ and y-intercept $= -3$

22. $5x + 3y = 12$

23. y-intercept 2; parallel to $y = \frac{1}{2}x - 20$

40

256

LESSON MASTER 3-3 B

Questions on SPUR Objectives

Vocabulary

1. Write an expression that is a *linear combination* of *G* and *H*.
Sample: 2G + 7H

Uses Objective H: Model situations leading to linear combinations.

2. On a quiz show, 20 points are given for correct answers to regular questions, and 50 points are given for correct answers in the bonus round. Let *R* represent the number of regular questions answered correctly and *B* represent the number of bonus questions answered correctly.

   a. Write an expression that gives the total number of points earned.
   20R + 50B

   b. Suppose a contestant earned 650 points. Write an equation relating *R*, *B*, and the number of points earned.
   20R + 50B = 650

   c. Give three different possible solutions to the equation you wrote in Part b.
   Sample: R = 0, B = 13; R = 30, B = 1; R = 10, B = 9

   d. If the contestant answered 25 regular questions correctly and earned 650 points, how many bonus questions were answered correctly?
   3 bonus ques.

3. Helene bought *S* 60-minute audio tapes at $1.99 each and *L* 90-minute tapes at $2.99 each.

   a. Write an expression that gives the total amount Helene paid for the tapes.
   1.99S + 2.99L

   b. Suppose Helene spent $33.87 and bought 8 90-minute tapes. How many 60-minute tapes did she buy?
   5 60-min tapes

▶ **LESSON MASTER 3-3B** *page 2*

4. A chemist mixes *x* ounces of a solution that is 40% acid with *y* ounces of a solution that is 60% acid. The final solution contains 24 ounces of acid.

   a. Write an equation to model this situation. **.4x + .6y = 24**

   b. At the right, graph the solutions to the equation in Part a.

   c. Find three pairs of integer values for *x* and *y* that satisfy the equation in Part a.
   Sample: (0, 40), (60, 0), (30,20)

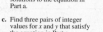

   d. If 10.5 ounces of the 40%-acid solution were used, how much of the 60%-acid is in the final solution? **33 oz**

5. Describe a situation that can lead to the expression 8.49*J* + 12.09*K*.
Sample: Pete bought J T-shirts at $8.49 each and K caps at $12.09 each.

Review Objective C, Lesson 2–4

In 6–13, write the slope of the line containing the given points.

6. (3, 4), (6, -2)   **-2**
7. (7, -4), (-1, 0)   **-½**
8. (0, 0), (2, 3)   **3/2**
9. (0, 16/3), (1, 4)   **-4/3**
10. (2, -4.5), (1.5, -4)   **-1**
11. (-5, 3), (-5, 2)   **undefined**
12. (-1, 8), (6, 8)   **0**
13. (50, 125), (100, 375)   **5**

LESSON MASTER 3-4 B

Questions on SPUR Objectives

Vocabulary

1. Write the *standard form* of a linear equation.
Ax + By = C

2. Describe the *x-intercept* of a graph.
Sample: the value of x at the point where a graph crosses the x- axis

Skills Objective A: Determine the slope and intercepts of a line given its equation.

In 3–9, complete the table.

	Equation	Slope	y-intercept	x-intercept
3.	$3x + 6y = 18$	$-\frac{1}{2}$	3	6
4.	$x - 4y = 10$	0.25	-2.5	10
5.	$-5y = 20$	0	-4	none
6.	$x = -7$	undefined	none	-7
7.	$2x - 9y - 45 = 0$	$\frac{2}{9}$	-5	$\frac{45}{2}$
8.	$2x = -25$	undefined	none	$-\frac{25}{2}$
9.	$Ax + By = C,$ $A \neq 0, B \neq 0$	$-\frac{A}{B}$	$\frac{C}{B}$	$\frac{C}{A}$

Properties Objective E: Recognize properties of linear functions.

10. Describe the values of the slope of
   a. a horizontal line. **slope is zero.**
   b. a vertical line. **slope is undefined.**
   c. an oblique line. **slope is any real number ≠ zero.**

▶ **LESSON MASTER 3-4B** *page 2*

In 11–14, determine whether the line with the given equation is *oblique, horizontal,* or *vertical.*

11. $y = -9x$ **oblique**
12. $3y = 15$ **horizontal**
13. $x - 7y = 10$ **oblique**
14. $-4x = 2$ **vertical**

Representations Objective L: Graph or interpret graphs of linear equations.

15. Graph $x = -3$

16. Graph $8y = 40$.

In 17 and 18, use the intercepts to graph the equation.

17. $3x + 5y = -15$

18. $28 = 14x - 7y$

In 19–21, graph a line with the given slope. **Samples are given.**

19. zero
20. undefined
21. negative

LESSON MASTER 3-5 B

Questions on SPUR Objectives

Vocabulary

1. Give the general form of a *point-slope equation* for a line.

$$y - y_1 = m(x - x_1)$$

Skills Objective B: Find an equation for a line given two points on it or given a point on it and its slope.

In 2–13, find an equation for the line with the given information. Write your equation in standard form with integers for A, B, and C.

Samples are given.

2. slope -1, through (4, -3) $x + y = 1$

3. slope $\frac{5}{4}$, through (6, 1) $5x - 4y = 26$

4. through (1, 4) and (-2, -2) $2x - y = -2$

5. through (1, 8) and (9, 8) $y = 8$

6. slope -4, y-intercept 6 $4x + y = 6$

7. slope 3, x-intercept -7 $3x - y = -21$

8. through (-3, 2) and (-3, 0) $x = -3$

9. slope -3, through (0, 0) $3x + y = 0$

10. x-intercept 2, y-intercept 5 $5x + 2y = 10$

11. through (-4, 1) parallel to $4x + 2y = 7$ $2x + y = -7$

12. through (6, 6) with undefined slope. $x = 6$

13. x-intercept 12, parallel to $x - 6y = 10$ $x - 6y = 12$

Properties Objective E: Recognize properties of linear functions.

14. Fill in the three blanks with the correct values. According to the Point-Slope Theorem, the line containing (4, -5) with slope 2 has equation $y - \underline{\ ?\ } = \underline{\ 2\ } (x - \underline{\ ?\ })$.

-5   2   4

15. *True or false.* The y-axis has a slope of zero. Justify your answer.
False; sample: y-axis is vertical, so its slope is undefined.

45 ▶

▶ **LESSON MASTER 3-5B** *page 2*

Uses Objective I: In a real-world context, find an equation for a line containing two points.

16. Card Carriers charges $36 to print 1,200 business cards and $56 for 2,700 cards. Assume the relationship between the price and the number of business cards is linear.

a. Write an equation giving price as a function of the number of cards printed. $y = \frac{1}{75}x + 20$

b. Find the set-up cost (the cost for printing 0 cards). $20

c. Find the cost of printing 6,000 cards. $100

17. Last week, Mr. Chinn sold $20,000 worth of newspaper advertisements and earned $800. The week before, he sold $26,000 worth of advertisements and earned $860. Assume the relationship between Mr. Chinn's weekly earnings and the value of the advertisements he sells is linear.

a. Write an equation giving Mr. Chinn's weekly earnings as a function of the value of the advertisements he sells. $y = .01x + 600$

b. In this situation, what do the slope and y-intercept mean?
Slope is rate of commission, 1%. y-intercept is base salary, without commission.

c. If in one week Mr. Chinn sells $30,000 worth of advertisements, how much will he earn? $900

Uses Objective K: Model situations leading to piecewise-linear functions.

18. Northstreet Disposal Company charges $30 to send out a truck to pick up debris. For the first 5 cubic yards of rubbish, the company charges an additional $10 per cubic yard. For each additional cubic yard, to a maximum of 45 cubic yards, the company charges $6.

a. What is the cost to have the following amount of rubbish removed?

3 cu yd $60   6 cu yd $86

30 cu yd $230   45 cu yd $320

b. Write an equation that gives the cost c for picking up y cubic yards of rubbish for the following values of y.

$0 \le y \le 5$ $c = 10y + 30$ $5 \le y \le 45$ $c = 6y + 50$

46

LESSON MASTER 3-6 B

Questions on SPUR Objectives

Vocabulary

1. a. What is the range of r, the *correlation coefficient* for a set of data? $-1 \le r \le 1$

   b. Suppose $r = -0.9$ for a line fit to a set of data. What does this tell you about the strength of the linear relationship between the variables?
   Sample: There is a strong linear relationship.

Uses Objective J: Fit lines to data.

2. The following data give the number of city-council members in six cities with various populations.

Population	45,000	16,000	320,000	108,000	61,000	176,000
City-Council Members	8	7	24	19	12	15

Sample equation is given for b.

a. Draw a scatterplot of the data.

b. Find an equation of the regression line.
$y = .000052x + 7.9$

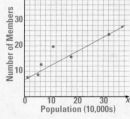

Number of Members — Population (10,000s)

c. Graph the regression line on your scatterplot.

d. Use your equation to predict the numbers of city-council members in a city with a population of 250,000. $\approx$ 21 members

e. Interpret the strength of the linear relationship based on the correlation coefficient.
Sample: It is reasonably strong, since $r \approx .89$.

47 ▶

▶ **LESSON MASTER 3-6B** *page 2*

3. The following data give the number of Frostee Treets sold and the high temperature on 10 different summer days.

Sample is given for b.

Temperature	88°	71°	84°	98°	95°	88°	80°	72°	77°	85°
Frostee Treets Sold	2,044	1,099	1,941	2,708	2,539	1,886	1,522	503	1,493	1,216

a. Draw a scatterplot of the data.

b. Find an equation of the regression line.
$y = 67.8x - 3984$

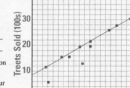

Treets Sold (100s) — Temperature (°F)

c. Graph the regression line on your scatterplot.

d. What does the slope in your equation mean in terms of this situation?
Sample: Each increase in temperature of 1° results in the sale of 68 Frostee Treets.

e. Use your equation to predict the number of Frostee Treets that would be sold on a 95° day. How close is this value to the actual data?
Sample: 2457 Frostee Treets; it is close, within about 3%.

f. Does this situation or the one described in Item 2 exhibit the stronger linear relationship? How do you know this?
Sample: this situation has the stronger linear relationship, since $|r|$ is closer to 1 ($r \approx .91$).

4. Use the regression line to determine whether (3.2, 4.08), (4.5, 4.925), and (6, 5.92) lie on a line. Explain your answer.
No; $r \approx .9998 \ne 1$

48

LESSON MASTER 3-7 B

Questions on SPUR Objectives

Vocabulary

1. Give an example of an *arithmetic sequence*. Then explain why it is an arithmetic sequence.

   Sample: 15, 20, 25, 30, . . . ; There is a constant difference, 5, between consecutive terms.

Skills Objective D: Evaluate or find recursive formulas for arithmetic sequences.

In 2–4, an arithmetic sequence is given.
a. Describe the sequence in words.
b. Write a recursive formula for the sequence.

2. 17, 28, 39, 50, . . .

   a. Arithmetic sequence with first term 17, constant difference 11

   b. $\begin{cases} a_1 = 17 \\ a_n = a_{n-1} + 11, \\ \quad \text{for } n \geq 2. \end{cases}$

3. 80, -160, -400, -640, . . .

   a. Arithmetic sequence with first term 80, constant difference -240

   b. $\begin{cases} a_1 = 80 \\ a_n = a_{n-1} - 240, \\ \quad \text{for } n \geq 2. \end{cases}$

4. $\frac{1}{3}, \frac{2}{3}, 1, \frac{4}{3}, \ldots$

   a. Arithmetic sequence with first term $\frac{1}{3}$, constant difference $\frac{1}{3}$

   b. $\begin{cases} a_1 = \frac{1}{3}, \\ a_n = a_{n-1} + \frac{1}{3}, \\ \quad \text{for } n \geq 2. \end{cases}$

In 5 and 6, an arithmetic sequence is described.
a. Write the first five terms of the sequence.
b. Write a recursive formula for the sequence.

5. An arithmetic sequence has first term 4 and constant difference 20.

   a. 4, 24, 44, 64, 84

   b. $\begin{cases} a_1 = 4 \\ a_n = a_{n-1} + 20, \\ \quad \text{for } n \geq 2. \end{cases}$

6. An arithmetic sequence has first term 0.3 and constant difference -0.1.

   a. 0.3, 0.2, 0.1, 0, -0.1

   b. $\begin{cases} a_1 = 0.3 \\ a_n = a_{n-1} - 0.1, \\ \quad \text{for } n \geq 2. \end{cases}$

▶ **LESSON MASTER 3-7B** *page 2*

Properties Objective F: Recognize properties of arithmetic sequences.

In 7 and 8, tell whether or not the sequence could be an arithmetic sequence. Justify your answer.

7. 400, 200, 100, 50, . . .

   No; the difference is not constant.

8. 49, 44, 39, 34, . . .

   Yes; there is a constant difference of -5.

Uses Objective G: Model situations involving arithmetic sequences.

9. Mrs. Machado contributed $50 to a local charity and pledged to donate another $5 every month thereafter.

   a. Write a sequence that shows Mrs. Machado's total contributions during the first six months.

   $50, $55, $60, $65, $70, $75

   b. Write a recursive formula for the sequence in Part a.

   $\begin{cases} a_1 = 50 \\ a_n = a_{n-1} + 5, \\ \quad \text{for } n \geq 2. \end{cases}$

10. Hector has an empty jar. Every workday he plans to add the 30¢ change from his bus fare.

    a. At the start, how much change is in the jar? 0¢

    b. Write a recursive formula that gives the amount of change in the jar after the nth workday.

    $\begin{cases} a_1 = 0 \\ a_n = a_{n-1} + 30, \\ \quad \text{for } n \geq 2. \end{cases}$

11. One afternoon, Matt bought an 85-ounce box of dishwasher detergent. Each morning he uses 3 ounces.

    a. Write a recursive formula for a sequence that gives the amount of detergent Matt will have left on the nth evening.

    $\begin{cases} a_1 = 85 \\ a_n = a_{n-1} - 3, \\ \quad \text{for } n \geq 2. \end{cases}$

    b. Find the amount of detergent left on the 10th evening.

    58 ounces

LESSON MASTER 3-8 B

Questions on SPUR Objectives

Skills Objective D: Evaluate or find explicit formulas for arithmetic sequences.

In 1–4, an arithmetic sequence is given.
a. Find a formula for the nth term.
b. Find a_{25}.

1. -22, -19, -16, -13, . . .

   a. $a_n = 3n - 25$

   b. 50

2. $\frac{7}{4}, \frac{9}{4}, \frac{11}{4}, \frac{13}{4}, \ldots$

   a. $a_n = \frac{1}{2}n + \frac{5}{4}$

   b. $\frac{55}{4}$

3. 3.2, 4.9, 6.6, 8.3, . . .

   a. $a_n = 1.7n + 1.5$

   b. 44

4. 75, 25, -25, -75, . . .

   a. $a_n = -50n + 125$

   b. -1125

In 5 and 6, a recursive formula for a sequence is given.
Write an explicit formula for the sequence.

5. $\begin{cases} a_1 = 20 \\ a_n = a_{n-1} + 12, \text{ for } n \geq 2. \end{cases}$

   $a_n = 12n + 8$

6. $\begin{cases} b_1 = 5.75 \\ b_n = b_{n-1} - 1.25, \text{ for } n \geq 2. \end{cases}$

   $b_n = -1.25n + 7$

7. Write a recursive formula for the sequence defined explicitly by $c_n = 45 + (n-1)5$.

   $\begin{cases} c_1 = 45 \\ c_n = c_{n-1} + 5, \\ \quad \text{for } n \geq 2. \end{cases}$

8. Write a recursive formula for the sequence defined explicitly by $d_n = 300n + 50$.

   $\begin{cases} d_1 = 350 \\ d_n = d_{n-1} + 300, \\ \quad \text{for } n \geq 2. \end{cases}$

In 9 and 10, two terms of an arithmetic sequence are given.
a. Write an explicit formula for the sequence.
b. Write a recursive formula for the sequence.

9. $s_2 = 12$ and $s_8 = 60$

   a. $s_n = 8n - 4$

   b. $\begin{cases} s_1 = 4 \\ s_n = s_{n-1} + 8, \\ \quad \text{for } n \geq 2. \end{cases}$

10. $a_5 = 1.6$ and $a_{10} = -0.9$

    a. $a_n = -.5n + 4.1$

    b. $\begin{cases} a_1 = 3.6 \\ a_n = a_{n-1} - .5, \\ \quad \text{for } n \geq 2. \end{cases}$

▶ **LESSON MASTER 3-8B** *page 2*

11. Find the 150th term of the arithmetic sequence $7g, 11g, 15g, 19g, \ldots$

    $603g$

Properties Objective F: Recognize properties of arithmetic sequences.

In 12–15, determine whether or not the given formula describes an arithmetic sequence. Justify your answer.

12. $a_n = 9n + 18$

    Yes; there is a constant difference of 9.

13. $t_n = 3n^2 + 4$

    No; there is not a constant difference.

14. $u_n = \frac{1}{2}n - 1$

    Yes; there is a constant difference of $\frac{1}{2}$.

15. $v_n = n - 30$

    Yes; there is a constant difference of -1.

Uses Objective G: Model situations involving arithmetic sequences.

16. A wading pool, filled to a depth of 36 inches, drains at the rate of about 3 inches per hour.

    a. Write an explicit formula that gives the depth of the water after n hours.

    $a_n = -3n + 36$

    b. How deep will the water be after 6 hours?

    18 inches

17. A vehicle emissions test center tests 320 vehicles every weekday.

    a. Write an explicit formula that gives the total number of cars tested after n days.

    $a_n = 320n$

    b. How many weeks will it take to test 240,000 cars?

    150 weeks

LESSON MASTER 3-9 B

Questions on SPUR Objectives

Vocabulary

1. Explain what is meant by the symbol $\lfloor x \rfloor$. Then give an example.

   Sample: $\lfloor x \rfloor$ **is the greatest integer less than or equal to** x; $\lfloor -4\frac{1}{2} \rfloor = -5.$

Skills Objective C: Evaluate expressions based on step functions.

In 2–9, evaluate each expression.

2. $\lfloor 15.7 \rfloor$ ___**15**___
3. $\lfloor -4.\overline{3} \rfloor$ ___**-5**___
4. $\lfloor 22 \rfloor$ ___**22**___
5. $\lfloor -2.008 \rfloor$ ___**-3**___
6. $\lfloor 12\frac{3}{4} \rfloor$ ___**12**___
7. $7 \cdot \lfloor 6 + 1.6 \rfloor$ ___**49**___
8. $\lfloor \sqrt{50} \rfloor$ ___**7**___
9. $\lfloor -8 \rfloor$ ___**-8**___

Uses Objective K: Model situations leading to step functions.

10. Hot dog buns come in packages of 8. Write an equation that shows the number p of complete packages that can be made from b buns.

    $p = \lfloor \frac{b}{8} \rfloor$

11. *Multiple choice.* A first-grade classroom receives a gross (144) of pencils. There are s students in the classroom. Which of the following represents the number of pencils each student may have?

    ___**a**___

    (a) $\lfloor \frac{144}{s} \rfloor$ (b) $\lfloor \frac{s}{144} \rfloor$ (c) $\frac{144}{s}$ (d) $\lfloor 144 \cdot s \rfloor$

12. Student Council is taking part in a clothing drive. They receive 30 passes to the local movie theater for participating in the drive, and for each 50 items of clothing, they receive another 10 passes.

    a. How many passes will the Student Council receive if they collect 736 items of clothing? ___**170 passes**___

    b. Let p represent the number of passes Student Council receives for collecting c items of clothing. Write an equation relating p and c.

    $p = 10 \lfloor \frac{c}{50} \rfloor + 30$

▶ **LESSON MASTER 3-9B** *page 2*

13. The table below gives the cost of a carton of milk at the Milbourne School cafeteria from the years 1965 through 1995. The year reflects the first year that cost was in effect.

    a. Find the cost of a carton of milk in each year.

    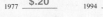

    1968 ___**\$.08**___   1977 ___**\$.20**___   1994 ___**\$.35**___

    b. Make a graph of the milk costs as a function of the year.

Year	Cost
1965	\$.08
1969	\$.12
1974	\$.18
1977	\$.20
1983	\$.25
1988	\$.30
1992	\$.35

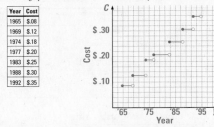

Representations Objective M: Graph or interpret graphs of step functions.

14. The graph at the right shows the cost of renting a chain saw. What would it cost to rent the saw for

    a. 3 hours? ___**\$18**___

    b. $5\frac{1}{2}$ hours? ___**\$30**___

15. a. Graph $f(x) = \lfloor x \rfloor + 1$.

    b. Give the domain and the range of the function f.

    domain: all real numbers;
    range: all integers

LESSON MASTER 4-1 B

Questions on SPUR Objectives

Vocabulary

1. A matrix has dimensions $m \times n$. What does this mean?

   Sample: **The matrix has** m **rows and** n **columns.**

Uses Objective G: Use matrices to store data.

2. In the 1970s, there were 800,368 immigrants to the United States from Europe, 1,588,178 from Asia, and 80,779 from Africa. In the 1980s, there were 705,630 immigrants from Europe, 2,066,455 from Asia, and 192,212 from Africa. Store this information in a 3×2 matrix.

$$\begin{array}{c}\text{Eu.}\\\text{As.}\\\text{Af.}\end{array} \begin{matrix} 1970\text{s} & 1980\text{s} \end{matrix} \\ \begin{bmatrix} 800{,}368 & 705{,}630 \\ 1{,}588{,}178 & 2{,}066{,}455 \\ 80{,}779 & 192{,}212 \end{bmatrix}$$

3. At Outfits East, 22% of last year's sales were children's clothing, 41% were women's, and 37% were men's. At Outfits West, 17% of the sales were children's clothing, 55% were women's, and 28% were men's. At Outfits North, 33% of the sales were children's clothing, 23% were women's, and 44% were men's. At Outfits South, 14% of last year's sales were children's clothing, 32% were women's, and 54% were men's. Store this information in a 4×3 matrix.

$$\begin{array}{c}\text{E}\\\text{W}\\\text{S}\\\text{N}\end{array} \begin{matrix} \text{C} & \text{W} & \text{M} \end{matrix} \\ \begin{bmatrix} 22\% & 41\% & 37\% \\ 17\% & 55\% & 28\% \\ 33\% & 23\% & 44\% \\ 14\% & 32\% & 54\% \end{bmatrix}$$

4. The matrix at the right gives the subscription figures for *The Metropolitan Sentinel* for a five-year period.

$$\begin{matrix} & \text{City} & \text{Suburbs} \end{matrix} \\ \begin{matrix} 1990 \\ 1991 \\ 1992 \\ 1993 \\ 1994 \end{matrix} \begin{bmatrix} 14{,}662 & 12{,}004 \\ 15{,}325 & 11{,}867 \\ 15{,}418 & 12{,}388 \\ 15{,}790 & 13{,}056 \\ 17{,}126 & 13{,}540 \end{bmatrix}$$

    a. What are the dimensions of this matrix? ___**5 × 2**___

    b. What does the element in row 1 column 2 represent?
    the number of suburban subscribers in 1990

    c. In what row and column is the entry 13,056? ___**row 4, column 2**___

    d. How many suburban subscribers were there in 1992? ___**12,388 subscribers**___

▶ **LESSON MASTER 4-1 B** *page 2*

Representations Objective I: Graph figures described by matrices.

In 5 and 6, draw the polygon described by the matrix.

5. $\begin{bmatrix} 4 & 0 & 5 \\ -2 & -3 & 1 \end{bmatrix}$

6. $\begin{bmatrix} -4 & -1 & 3 & 2 & -1 \\ 2 & 3 & 2 & -5 & -2 \end{bmatrix}$

In 7 and 8, write a matrix for the given polygon.

7. *DCBA*

$\begin{bmatrix} -2 & -4 & 4 & 4 \\ -3 & 4 & 0 & -5 \end{bmatrix}$

8. *GFEKJH*

$\begin{bmatrix} 3 & 0 & -3 & -3 & 4 & 5 \\ -5 & 0 & -3 & 5 & 3 & -5 \end{bmatrix}$

LESSON MASTER 4-2 B

Questions on SPUR Objectives

Skills Objective A: Add, subtract, and find scalar multiples of matrices.

In 1 and 2, express as a single matrix.

1. $\begin{bmatrix} 1 & 4 & -6 \\ 2 & -3 & -3 \end{bmatrix} + \begin{bmatrix} 3 & 0 & 6 \\ 4 & -3 & 8 \end{bmatrix}$
$\begin{bmatrix} 4 & 4 & 0 \\ 6 & -6 & 5 \end{bmatrix}$

2. $\begin{bmatrix} 5 & 2 \\ 2 & -1 \\ 5 & 4 \end{bmatrix} - \begin{bmatrix} -2 & 2 \\ 0 & -1 \\ -5 & 7 \end{bmatrix}$
$\begin{bmatrix} 7 & 0 \\ 2 & 0 \\ 10 & -3 \end{bmatrix}$

In 3–8, let $A = \begin{bmatrix} -7 & 2 & 6 \\ 9 & 0 & -2 \\ -5 & 3 & 3 \end{bmatrix}$ and $B = \begin{bmatrix} 4 & -7 & -2 \\ 5 & 5 & 0 \\ -2 & 9 & 6 \end{bmatrix}$. Calculate.

3. $3A$
$\begin{bmatrix} -21 & 6 & 18 \\ 27 & 0 & -6 \\ -15 & 9 & 9 \end{bmatrix}$

4. $-4B$
$\begin{bmatrix} -16 & 28 & 8 \\ -20 & -20 & 0 \\ 8 & -36 & -24 \end{bmatrix}$

5. $A + B$
$\begin{bmatrix} -3 & -5 & 4 \\ 14 & 5 & -2 \\ -7 & 12 & 9 \end{bmatrix}$

6. $2A + 3B$
$\begin{bmatrix} -2 & -17 & 6 \\ 33 & 15 & -4 \\ -16 & 33 & 24 \end{bmatrix}$

7. $B - A$
$\begin{bmatrix} 11 & -9 & -8 \\ -4 & 5 & 2 \\ 3 & 6 & 3 \end{bmatrix}$

8. $A - 5B$
$\begin{bmatrix} -27 & 37 & 16 \\ -16 & -25 & -2 \\ 5 & -42 & -27 \end{bmatrix}$

In 9–11, solve for a and b.

9. $\begin{bmatrix} 3 & a & -2 \\ -2 & 6 & 10 \end{bmatrix} + \begin{bmatrix} 3 & 8 & 0 \\ 1 & -1 & b \end{bmatrix} = \begin{bmatrix} 6 & 11 & -2 \\ -1 & 5 & 5 \end{bmatrix}$ $a = \underline{3}$ $b = \underline{-5}$

10. $\begin{bmatrix} 6 & 8 & 0 \\ a & 7 & 13 \end{bmatrix} - \begin{bmatrix} 1 & b & 4 \\ 3 & 7 & 6 \end{bmatrix} = \begin{bmatrix} -5 & 11 & -4 \\ 0 & 0 & 7 \end{bmatrix}$ $a = \underline{3}$ $b = \underline{-3}$

11. $4\begin{bmatrix} a & 7 \\ 5 & -4 \end{bmatrix} - 3\begin{bmatrix} 4 & b \\ 2 & 0 \end{bmatrix} = \begin{bmatrix} 14 & 31 \\ 14 & -16 \end{bmatrix}$ $a = \underline{6.5}$ $b = \underline{-1}$

▶ **LESSON MASTER 4-2 B** *page 2*

Properties Objective D: Recognize properties of matrix addition and scalar multiplication.

12. What addition of matrices is the same as $4\begin{bmatrix} 2 & 8 \\ 2 & -4 \end{bmatrix}$?

$\begin{bmatrix} 2 & 8 \\ 2 & -4 \end{bmatrix} + \begin{bmatrix} 2 & 8 \\ 2 & -4 \end{bmatrix} + \begin{bmatrix} 2 & 8 \\ 2 & -4 \end{bmatrix} + \begin{bmatrix} 2 & 8 \\ 2 & -4 \end{bmatrix}$

13. Suppose A is a 2×3 matrix and B is a matrix added to A.
a. What are the dimensions of $A + B$? $\underline{2 \times 3}$
b. Must $A + B = B + A$? $\underline{yes}$

Uses Objective H: Use matrix addition and scalar multiplication to solve real-world problems.

14. The matrices below show the number of books checked out from the school library during two consecutive weeks.

| | Nov. 3–7 | | Nov. 10–14 | |
	Fiction	Non Fiction	Fiction	Non Fiction
Freshmen	476	303	308	352
Sophomores	313	211	366	319
Juniors	416	336	347	288
Seniors	394	510	322	310

a. Subtract the left matrix from the right matrix. Call the difference D. Write D at the right.
$\begin{bmatrix} -168 & 49 \\ 53 & 108 \\ -69 & -48 \\ -72 & -200 \end{bmatrix}$

b. What is the meaning of the first column of D?
the differences in numbers of fiction books checked out during the two weeks

c. What is the meaning of the entry in row 4, column 2 of D?
Seniors checked out 200 less non-fiction books the second week.

15. The matrix below gives the prices in dollars of school rings in silver. The prices for gold are 6 times those for silver. Give the matrix that represents the prices of gold rings.

	Jade	Onyx
sizes 5-7	22	18
sizes 8-10	26	22
sizes 11+	32	28

	Jade	Onyx
5-7	132	108
8-10	156	132
11+	192	168

LESSON MASTER 4-3 B

Questions on SPUR Objectives

Skills Objective B: Multiply matrices.

In 1–8, calculate the product.

1. $\begin{bmatrix} -4 & 1 & 0 \end{bmatrix} \begin{bmatrix} 6 \\ 2 \\ -3 \end{bmatrix}$
$\begin{bmatrix} -22 \end{bmatrix}$

2. $\begin{bmatrix} -2 & -6 & 0 \\ 7 & 2 & 2 \end{bmatrix} \begin{bmatrix} 5 & 1 \\ 0 & 1 \\ 4 & 8 \end{bmatrix}$
$\begin{bmatrix} -10 & -10 \\ 43 & 32 \end{bmatrix}$

3. $\begin{bmatrix} 9 & -1 & 6 \\ 3 & 4 & 9 \\ 8 & -6 & 3 \end{bmatrix} \begin{bmatrix} 6 & 3 & -2 \\ 8 & 5 & 7 \\ 4 & 2 & 4 \end{bmatrix}$
$\begin{bmatrix} 70 & 34 & -1 \\ 70 & 38 & 27 \\ 12 & 0 & -46 \end{bmatrix}$

4. $\begin{bmatrix} -4 & 5 & 0 \\ 0 & 6 & 4 \\ 0 & -7 & 2 \\ 1 & 8 & 1 \end{bmatrix} \begin{bmatrix} 5 & 6 & 6 & 2 \\ 0 & 1 & 0 & 1 \\ 4 & -2 & -6 & 2 \end{bmatrix}$
$\begin{bmatrix} -20 & -19 & -24 & -3 \\ 16 & -2 & -24 & 14 \\ 8 & -11 & -12 & -3 \\ 9 & 12 & 0 & 12 \end{bmatrix}$

5. $\begin{bmatrix} 3.8 & 4.8 \\ 3.5 & 0 \\ .6 & 8.1 \end{bmatrix} \begin{bmatrix} 4.1 & -.3 & 2.6 \\ 5.5 & -1.7 & 5.2 \end{bmatrix}$
$\begin{bmatrix} 41.98 & -9.3 & 34.84 \\ 14.35 & -1.05 & 9.1 \\ 47.01 & -13.95 & 43.68 \end{bmatrix}$

6. $\begin{bmatrix} 5 & 5 \\ 7 & -3 \end{bmatrix} \begin{bmatrix} 6 & -2 \\ 4 & -8 \end{bmatrix}$
$\begin{bmatrix} 50 & -50 \\ 30 & 10 \end{bmatrix}$

7. $\begin{bmatrix} -5 & -9 \\ 7 & 2 \\ 0 & -4 \end{bmatrix} \begin{bmatrix} 5 & -1 & 2 \\ 0 & 0 & 2 \end{bmatrix}$
$\begin{bmatrix} -25 & 5 & -28 \\ 35 & -7 & 18 \\ 0 & 0 & -8 \end{bmatrix}$

8. $\begin{bmatrix} 0 & -4 & 8 \end{bmatrix} \begin{bmatrix} 2 & 6 & -2 \\ 1 & 1 & 1 \\ 3 & 7 & 4 \end{bmatrix} \begin{bmatrix} 9 & 0 & -1 \\ 3 & 2 & 1 \\ 3 & 4 & 8 \end{bmatrix}$
$\begin{bmatrix} 420 & 216 & 256 \end{bmatrix}$

Properties Objective D: Recognize properties of matrix multiplication.

9. If $\begin{bmatrix} 5 & 6 & 6 & 2 \\ 0 & 1 & 0 & 1 \end{bmatrix} \cdot H = \begin{bmatrix} 38 \\ 8 \end{bmatrix}$, what are the dimensions of H?
$\underline{4 \times 1}$

▶ **LESSON MASTER 4-3 B** *page 2*

10. The product of two matrices A and B exists only when the number of ____?____ of A is equal to the number of ____?____ of B.
columns **rows**

11. Suppose G, H, and M are matrices. If $G \cdot H = M$, the product of row i of G and column j of H is the element located in row ____?____ and column ____?____ of M.
$\underline{i}$ $\underline{j}$

12. a. Calculate $\begin{bmatrix} 0 & -4 & 8 \end{bmatrix} \begin{bmatrix} 2 & 6 & -2 \\ 1 & 1 & 1 \\ 3 & 7 & 4 \end{bmatrix} \begin{bmatrix} 9 & 0 & -1 \\ 3 & 2 & 1 \\ 3 & 4 & 8 \end{bmatrix}$
$\begin{bmatrix} 420 & 216 & 256 \end{bmatrix}$
b. How does your answer compare to your answer in Question 8? What does this illustrate?
It is the same; Associative Prop. for Matrix Multiplication.

Uses Objective H: Use matrix multiplication to solve real-world problems.

13. A band went to a football game in 2 vans, 6 cars, and one bus. There were 8 band members in each van, 5 in each car, and 38 in the bus. Write V, the vehicle matrix, and N, the matrix showing the number of band members in each vehicle. Calculate VN. Tell what VN represents.

$V = \begin{bmatrix} 2 & 6 & 1 \end{bmatrix}$ $N = \begin{bmatrix} 8 \\ 5 \\ 38 \end{bmatrix}$ $VN = \begin{bmatrix} 84 \end{bmatrix}$

the total number of band members who went to the game

14. Music Boosters ordered sweatshirts that cost $12 for small, $14 for medium, $17 for large, and $20 for extra large. In gray, they ordered 6 S, 8 M, 12 L, and 14 XL. In black, they ordered 2 S, 5 M, 10 L, and 15 XL. Write C, the cost matrix and N the matrix showing the number ordered. Calculate CN and tell what it represents.

$C = \begin{bmatrix} 12 & 14 & 17 & 20 \end{bmatrix}$ $N = \begin{bmatrix} 6 & 2 \\ 8 & 5 \\ 12 & 10 \\ 14 & 15 \end{bmatrix}$

$CN = \begin{bmatrix} 668 & 564 \end{bmatrix}$ **the total costs for the gray shirts and the black shirts**

LESSON MASTER 4-4 B

Questions on SPUR Objectives

Vocabulary

1. What are the *preimage* and *image* under a transformation?

   The preimage is the original figure; the image is the figure resulting from the transformation.

2. If a size change maps (x, y) onto (mx, my), the ___?___ is m.

   magnitude

Properties   Objective E: Recognize relationships between figures and their size-change images.

3. Suppose $C'D'E'F'$ is the image of quadrilateral $CDEF$ under a size change of magnitude k.

   a. How do the measures of $\angle D$ and $\angle D'$ compare?

   b. How do EF and $E'F'$ compare?

   $m\angle D = m\angle D'$
   $E'F' = k(EF)$

4. Under $S_{1/4}$, what is the image of each point?

   a. $(8, -4)$ **$(2, -1)$**   b. $(3, 12)$ **$\left(\frac{3}{4}, 3\right)$**

   c. $(0, -8)$ **$(0, -2)$**   d. $\left(5, \frac{1}{2}\right)$ **$\left(\frac{5}{4}, \frac{1}{8}\right)$**

Properties   Objective F: Relate size changes to matrices and vice versa.

5. Give the matrix for each size transformation.

   a. S_8 b. $S_{4/5}$ $\begin{bmatrix} \frac{4}{5} & 0 \\ 0 & \frac{4}{5} \end{bmatrix}$

   c. $S_{.75}$ $\begin{bmatrix} .75 & 0 \\ 0 & .75 \end{bmatrix}$ d. $S_{1.5}$ $\begin{bmatrix} 1.5 & 0 \\ 0 & 1.5 \end{bmatrix}$

6. What matrix is associated with the size transformation that maps $(-12, 6)$ onto $(-4, 2)$?

   $\begin{bmatrix} \frac{1}{3} & 0 \\ 0 & \frac{1}{3} \end{bmatrix}$

7. What is the magnitude of the size transformation associated with $\begin{bmatrix} 6 & 0 \\ 0 & 6 \end{bmatrix}$?

   6

Representations   Objective I: Graph figures and their size-change images.

8. Graph the polygon $\begin{bmatrix} -1 & 3 & 4 & 1 \\ 2 & 0 & 2 & 4 \end{bmatrix}$ and its image under S_2.

9. Graph the polygon $\begin{bmatrix} 6 & 3 & 3 \\ 0 & -3 & 6 \end{bmatrix}$ and its image under $S_{2/3}$.

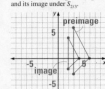

Review   Objective B, Lesson 4-3

In 10–13, calculate the product.

10. $\begin{bmatrix} 3 & 1 \\ 3 & -6 \end{bmatrix}\begin{bmatrix} 2 & 1 \\ 0 & -9 \end{bmatrix}$

    $\begin{bmatrix} 6 & -6 \\ 6 & 57 \end{bmatrix}$

11. $\begin{bmatrix} -8 & -6 \\ 0 & 3 \end{bmatrix}\begin{bmatrix} 5 & 2 & 5 & 0 \\ 1 & 0 & -4 & 8 \end{bmatrix}$

    $\begin{bmatrix} -46 & -16 & -16 & -48 \\ 3 & 0 & -12 & 24 \end{bmatrix}$

12. $\begin{bmatrix} 4 & -2 & 2 \\ 8 & 3 & -4 \\ 9 & 0 & -6 \end{bmatrix}\begin{bmatrix} -6 & 5 & 5 \\ 5 & 2 & 1 \\ 1 & -8 & 3 \end{bmatrix}$

    $\begin{bmatrix} -32 & 0 & 24 \\ -37 & 78 & 31 \\ -60 & 93 & 27 \end{bmatrix}$

13. $\begin{bmatrix} -3 & 4 & 3 \\ 8 & -2 & 4 \\ 0 & -7 & 2 \\ -1 & 6 & 1 \end{bmatrix}\begin{bmatrix} 2 & 1 & -9 & 2 \\ 4 & 7 & -1 & -1 \\ 0 & 2 & 3 & 1 \end{bmatrix}$

    $\begin{bmatrix} 10 & 25 & 29 & -1 \\ 8 & -6 & -62 & 30 \\ -28 & -49 & 11 & 13 \\ -26 & -43 & 17 & 7 \end{bmatrix}$

LESSON MASTER 4-5 B

Questions on SPUR Objectives

Vocabulary

1. Describe what happens to a figure under the scale change $S_{3,1/2}$.

   Sample: The figure stretches horizontally by magnitude 3 and shrinks vertically by magnitude $\frac{1}{2}$.

Properties   Objective E: Recognize relationships between figures and their scale-change images.

2. *True or false.* A figure and its scale-change image are similar.

   false

In 3–8, $\triangle A'B'C'$ is the image of $\triangle ABC$ under a scale change $S_{5,4}$.

3. If $A = (4, -2)$, what are the coordinates of A'?   **$(2, -8)$**

4. If $A' = (3, 12)$, what are the coordinates of A?   **$(6, 3)$**

5. Is $\triangle ABC$ similar to $\triangle A'B'C'$?   **no**

6. Is this scale change a size change?   **no**

7. In which direction is $\triangle ABC$ stretched?   **vertically**

8. In which direction is $\triangle ABC$ shrunk?   **horizontally**

Properties   Objective F: Relate scale-changes to matrices and vice versa.

In 9–11, give the scale change matrix corresponding to each given transformation.

9. $S_{5,2}$ $\begin{bmatrix} 5 & 0 \\ 0 & 2 \end{bmatrix}$

10. a vertical stretch of 2 and a horizontal shrink of $\frac{2}{3}$ $\begin{bmatrix} \frac{2}{3} & 0 \\ 0 & 2 \end{bmatrix}$

11. the transformation that maps $(3, -9)$ onto $(1.5, -3)$ $\begin{bmatrix} \frac{1}{2} & 0 \\ 0 & \frac{1}{3} \end{bmatrix}$

---

12. $\begin{bmatrix} 5 & 0 \\ 0 & .8 \end{bmatrix}$ is associated with what transformation?   **$S_{5,.8}$**

13. If $\begin{bmatrix} a & 0 \\ 0 & 4 \end{bmatrix}$ is associated with a size change, then $a =$ ___?___.   **4**

Representations   Objective I: Graph figures and their scale-change images.

14. Graph the polygon $\begin{bmatrix} -3 & 3 & 3 & 1 \\ -6 & 0 & 6 & 4 \end{bmatrix}$ and its image under $S_{2,2/3}$.

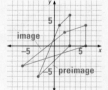

15. Graph the polygon $\begin{bmatrix} 4 & 3 & -3 \\ 1 & -3 & 4 \end{bmatrix}$ and its image under $\begin{bmatrix} 2 & 0 \\ 0 & 1 \end{bmatrix}$.

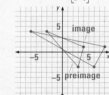

16. Graph the polygon $\begin{bmatrix} -3 & -3 & 0 \\ 0 & 5 & 5 \end{bmatrix}$ and its image under $\begin{bmatrix} \frac{2}{3} & 0 \\ 0 & 2 \end{bmatrix}$.

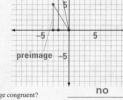

   a. What type of triangle is the preimage?   **right triangle**

   b. What type of triangle is the image?   **right triangle**

   c. Are the image and preimage congruent?   **no**

   d. Are the image and preimage similar?   **no**

LESSON MASTER 4-6 B

Questions on SPUR Objectives

Vocabulary

1. Suppose A' is the reflection image of A over line m.

   a. If A and A' are distinct points, how are A, A', and m related?

   m is the perpendicular bisector of $\overline{AA'}$.

   b. When are A and A' the same point?

   when A is on m

Properties Objective E: Recognize relationships between figures and their reflection images.

In 2–4, match the matrix with the reflection.

2. $\begin{bmatrix} 0 & 1 \\ 1 & 0 \end{bmatrix}$ __c__   3. $\begin{bmatrix} -1 & 0 \\ 0 & 1 \end{bmatrix}$ __a__   4. $\begin{bmatrix} 1 & 0 \\ 0 & -1 \end{bmatrix}$ __b__

(a) r_y (b) r_x (c) $r_{y=x}$

5. According to the Matrix Basis Theorem, if a transformation represented by a 2×2 matrix maps $(1, 0)$ onto (x_1, y_1) and $(0, 1)$ onto (x_2, y_2), then what is the matrix for the transformation?

$\begin{bmatrix} x_1 & x_2 \\ y_1 & y_2 \end{bmatrix}$

Properties Objective F: Relate reflections to matrices and vice versa.

In 6–8, translate the matrix equation into English.

6. $\begin{bmatrix} 0 & 1 \\ 1 & 0 \end{bmatrix}\begin{bmatrix} -3 \\ 8 \end{bmatrix} = \begin{bmatrix} 8 \\ -3 \end{bmatrix}$ The reflection image of the point __?__ over the line __?__ is the point __?__.

(-3, 8)   **$y = x$**   **(8, -3)**

7. $\begin{bmatrix} -1 & 0 \\ 0 & 1 \end{bmatrix}\begin{bmatrix} -3 \\ 8 \end{bmatrix} = \begin{bmatrix} 3 \\ 8 \end{bmatrix}$ The reflection image of the point __?__ over the __?__ is the point __?__.

(-3, 8)   **y-axis**   **(3, 8)**

8. $\begin{bmatrix} 1 & 0 \\ 0 & -1 \end{bmatrix}\begin{bmatrix} -3 \\ 8 \end{bmatrix} = \begin{bmatrix} -3 \\ -8 \end{bmatrix}$ The reflection image of the point __?__ over the __?__ is the point __?__.

(-3, 8)   **x-axis**   **(-3, -8)**

▶ **LESSON MASTER 4-6 B** *page 2*

9. a. Multiply the matrix for r_x by $\begin{bmatrix} 2 & 1 & 6 \\ -3 & 0 & 4 \end{bmatrix}$.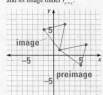

   b. Multiply the matrix for r_y by your answer to Part a.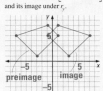

   c. Explain what happened.

   Sample: The reflection of the reflection image coincided with the preimage.

Representations Objective I: Graph figures and their reflection images.

10. Graph the polygon $\begin{bmatrix} 1 & -1 & -7 & -3 \\ 5 & 7 & 5 & 1 \end{bmatrix}$ and its image under r_y.

11. Graph the polygon $\begin{bmatrix} 1 & 6 & 5 \\ 1 & 2 & -2 \end{bmatrix}$ and its image under $r_{y=x}$.

In 12–14, give the coordinates of a point that is its own reflection image under the indicated reflection.

12. r_y **Sample: (0, 4)**

13. r_x **Sample: (3, 0)**

14. $r_{y=x}$ **Sample: (5, 5)**

LESSON MASTER 4-7 B

Questions on SPUR Objectives

Vocabulary

1. How do we write in symbols the composite of the transformation T_1 followed by the transformation T_2? What does it mean?

   $T_2 \circ T_1$; sample: If T_1 maps F onto F', and T_2 maps F' onto F'', then $T_2 \circ T_1$ maps F onto F''.

Properties Objective D: Recognize properties of matrix operations.

2. a. Write the identity matrix I.   b. Show that $I \cdot M = M \cdot I$ for all 2×2 matrices M.

   a. $I = \begin{bmatrix} 1 & 0 \\ 0 & 1 \end{bmatrix}$

   b. **(See below.)**

3. Name two other properties of 2×2 matrices that are shared by multiplication of real numbers.

   Associative Property; Closure

Properties Objective F: Relate transformations to matrices and vice versa.

4. Suppose T_1 has matrix $\begin{bmatrix} 4 & 0 \\ 0 & 4 \end{bmatrix}$ and T_2 has matrix $\begin{bmatrix} 1 & 0 \\ 0 & -1 \end{bmatrix}$. $\begin{bmatrix} 4 & 0 \\ 0 & -4 \end{bmatrix}$

   a. What is the matrix for $T_2 \circ T_1$?

   b. Explain what happens to a figure under $T_2 \circ T_1$.

   Sample: The figure undergoes a size change of magnitude 4 and is reflected over the x-axis.

(#2b) $\begin{bmatrix} 1 & 0 \\ 0 & 1 \end{bmatrix}\begin{bmatrix} a & b \\ c & d \end{bmatrix} = \begin{bmatrix} a+0 & b+0 \\ 0+c & 0+d \end{bmatrix} = \begin{bmatrix} a & b \\ c & d \end{bmatrix}$;

$\begin{bmatrix} a & b \\ c & d \end{bmatrix}\begin{bmatrix} 1 & 0 \\ 0 & 1 \end{bmatrix} = \begin{bmatrix} a+0 & 0+b \\ c+0 & 0+d \end{bmatrix} = \begin{bmatrix} a & b \\ c & d \end{bmatrix}$

▶ **LESSON MASTER 4-7 B** *page 2*

In 5–10, a point and its image under four composites of transformations are graphed. a. Match the composite to a graph. b. Calculate a matrix for the composite.

5. $r_x \circ r_x$
   a. __ii__   b. $\begin{bmatrix} 1 & 0 \\ 0 & 1 \end{bmatrix}$

6. $r_x \circ r_y$
   a. __i__   b. $\begin{bmatrix} -1 & 0 \\ 0 & -1 \end{bmatrix}$

7. $I \circ r_x$
   a. __vi__   b. $\begin{bmatrix} 1 & 0 \\ 0 & -1 \end{bmatrix}$

8. $S_2 \circ r_y$
   a. __iv__ $\begin{bmatrix} -2 & 0 \\ 0 & 2 \end{bmatrix}$

9. $r_x \circ r_{y=x}$
   a. __iii__   b. $\begin{bmatrix} 0 & -1 \\ 1 & 0 \end{bmatrix}$

10. $S_2 \circ S_{2.5}$
   a. __v__   b. $\begin{bmatrix} 5 & 0 \\ 0 & 5 \end{bmatrix}$

i.
ii.
iii.
iv.
v.
vi.

Representations Objective I: Graph figures and their transformation images.

11. Graph the polygon $\begin{bmatrix} 1 & 4 & 4 & 0 \\ -1 & -2 & -5 & -3 \end{bmatrix}$ and its image under $r_y \circ r_x$.

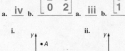

12. Graph the polygon $\begin{bmatrix} -4 & -2 & -4 \\ 2 & 2 & -2 \end{bmatrix}$ and its image under $r_{y=x} \circ S_{1/2}$.

LESSON MASTER 4-8 B

Questions on SPUR Objectives

Properties Objective E: Recognize relationships between figures and their rotation images.

In 1–3, match the matrix with the rotation.

1. $\begin{bmatrix} 0 & 1 \\ -1 & 0 \end{bmatrix}$ __b__   (a) R_{180}

2. $\begin{bmatrix} 0 & -1 \\ 1 & 0 \end{bmatrix}$ __c__   (b) R_{270}

3. $\begin{bmatrix} -1 & 0 \\ 0 & -1 \end{bmatrix}$ __a__   (c) R_{90}

Properties Objective F: Relate rotations to matrices and vice versa.

In 4 and 5, a composite of transformations is given. a. Find a matrix for the composite. b. Give a single transformation whose matrix is your answer to Part a.

4. $r_y \circ r_x$ $\begin{bmatrix} -1 & 0 \\ 0 & -1 \end{bmatrix}$
a. _____
b. R_{180}

5. $r_x \circ R_{180}$ $\begin{bmatrix} 1 & 0 \\ 0 & -1 \end{bmatrix}$
a. _____
b. r_x

6. Show how to find the matrix for R_{180} from the matrix for R_{90}.

$$R_{180} = R_{90} \circ R_{90} = \begin{bmatrix} 0 & -1 \\ 1 & 0 \end{bmatrix}\begin{bmatrix} 0 & -1 \\ 1 & 0 \end{bmatrix} = \begin{bmatrix} -1 & 0 \\ 0 & -1 \end{bmatrix}$$

Representations Objective I: Graph figures and their rotation images.

7. a. What rotation maps $\triangle FAN$ onto $\triangle F'A'N'$?
R_{90}

b. Give a matrix for the rotation in Part a.

$\begin{bmatrix} 0 & -1 \\ 1 & 0 \end{bmatrix}$

---

8. a. What rotation maps $\triangle WAVE$ onto $\triangle W'A'V'E'$?
R_{180}

b. Give a matrix for the rotation in Part a.

$\begin{bmatrix} -1 & 0 \\ 0 & -1 \end{bmatrix}$

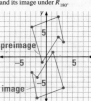

9. Graph the polygon $\begin{bmatrix} 0 & -5 & -6 \\ 0 & 1 & -6 \end{bmatrix}$ and its image under R_{90}.

10. Graph the polygon $\begin{bmatrix} -1 & -3 & 2 & 3 \\ -1 & 6 & 8 & 3 & 4 \end{bmatrix}$ and its image under R_{180}.

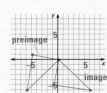

Review Objective B, Lessons 3-2 and 3-5

In 11–16, write an equation for the line satisfying the given conditions.

11. slope -3, through (3, 5)
$y = -3x + 14$

12. slope 5, through (2, -4)
$y = 5x - 14$

13. through (2, -3) and (4, 1)
$y = 2x - 7$

14. through (0, 3) and (2, -1)
$y = -2x + 3$

15. parallel to $y = 3x$, through (3, 4)
$y = 3x - 5$

16. parallel to $y = 4x - 9$, through (0, 0)
$y = 4x$

LESSON MASTER 4-9 B

Questions on SPUR Objectives

Skills Objective C: Determine equations of lines perpendicular to given lines.

In 1–8, find an equation for the line that goes through the given point and is perpendicular to the given line.

1. (4, 3); $y = -2x + 6$

$y = \frac{1}{2}x + 1$

2. (-1, 7); $y = -x - 4$

$y = x + 8$

3. (0, 0); $y = \frac{2}{3}x$

$y = -\frac{3}{2}x$

4. (5, 9); $y = 3$

$x = 5$

5. (5, 5); $x + 4y = 8$

$y = 4x - 15$

6. (-3, -1); $x = -1$

$y = -1$

7. (0, 6); $2x - 7y = 21$

$y = -\frac{7}{2}x + 6$

8. (.2, .8); $y = -.5x$

$y = 2x + .4$

In 9–12, find an equation of the perpendicular bisector of the line segment with the given endpoints.

9. (4, -2), (6, 6)

10. (10, 11), (-4, -3)

$y = -\frac{1}{4}x + \frac{13}{4}$ $y = -x + 7$

11. (0, 0), (3, 3)

12. (2, 5), (2, -9)

$y = -x + 3$ $y = -2$

Properties Objective E: Recognize relationships between figures and their rotation images.

13. The slope of a line is -4. What is the slope of the image of this line under R_{90}? $\frac{1}{4}$

14. The slope of a line is $\frac{8}{5}$. What is the slope of the image of this line under R_{90}? $-\frac{5}{8}$

15. The slope of a line is $-\frac{1}{3}$. What is the slope of the image of this line under R_{270}? 3

16. The equation of a line is $3x + 2y = -30$. What is the slope of the image of this line under R_{90}? $\frac{2}{3}$

17. A line contains (0, -2) and (-4, 5). What is the slope of the image of this line under R_{90}? $\frac{4}{7}$

18. Let $\triangle KID$ have matrix $\begin{bmatrix} 26 & 14 & 70 \\ 38 & -26 & -74 \end{bmatrix}$. Let $\triangle K'I'D' = R_{90}(\triangle KID)$. Find the slope of the given line.

a. $\overleftrightarrow{KD}$ $-\frac{28}{11}$ b. $\overleftrightarrow{K'D'}$ $\frac{11}{28}$

LESSON MASTER 4-10 B

Questions on SPUR Objectives

Properties Objective E: Recognize relationships between figures and their translation images.

1. Suppose $A'B'C'D'$ is the image of quadrilateral $ABCD$ under a translation.

   a. Are $ABCD$ and $A'B'C'D'$ congruent? **yes**

   b. Give two facts about $\overline{AB}$ and $\overline{A'B'}$.

   Samples: $\overline{AB}$ and $\overline{A'B'}$ are the same length; $\overline{AB}$ and $\overline{A'B'}$ are parallel

2. Under $T_{3,-2}$, what is the image of each point?

   a. (5, -1) **(8, -3)**   b. (-3, 13) **(0, 11)**

   c. (-9, 0) **(-6, -2)**   d. (1.75, 1.25) **(4.75, -.75)**

3. A translation $T_{h,k}$ maps (-4, 6) onto (-5, 3). Find the values of h and k. $h =$ **-1** $k =$ **-3**

Properties Objective F: Relate translations to matrices and vice versa.

4. Fill in the blanks to give a translation of the following matrix addition into English.

$$\begin{bmatrix} -4 & -4 & -4 \\ 5 & 5 & 5 \end{bmatrix} + \begin{bmatrix} 3 & 0 & 1 \\ 2 & -2 & -5 \end{bmatrix} = \begin{bmatrix} -1 & -4 & -3 \\ 7 & 3 & 0 \end{bmatrix}$$

A triangle with vertices at **(3, 2)** , **(0, -2)** , and **(1, -5)** is

translated **4** units **left** and **5** units **up** .

The vertices of the image are at **(-1, 7)** , **(-4, 3)** , and **(-3, 0)** .

5. What matrix is associated with the translation of a triangle under $T_{6,-2}$? $\begin{bmatrix} 6 & 6 & 6 \\ -2 & -2 & -2 \end{bmatrix}$

6. What matrix is the identity matrix for translating pentagons in the plane? $\begin{bmatrix} 0 & 0 & 0 & 0 & 0 \\ 0 & 0 & 0 & 0 & 0 \end{bmatrix}$

▶ **LESSON MASTER 4-10 B** *page 2*

Representations Objective I: Graph figures and their translation images.

7. represents polygon $ABCD$.

   a. Write the matrix that represents $T_{4,-1}$ for this polygon.

   $$\begin{bmatrix} 4 & 4 & 4 & 4 \\ -1 & -1 & -1 & -1 \end{bmatrix}$$

   b. Apply the matrix that represents $T_{4,-1}$ to the matrix for the polygon. Write the resulting matrix.

   $$\begin{bmatrix} 1 & 4 & 6 & 3 \\ 0 & -1 & 2 & 5 \end{bmatrix}$$

   c. Graph the preimage and image at the right.

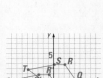

8. 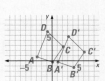 represents polygon $PQRST$.

   a. Write the matrix that represents $T_{-3,-2}$ for this polygon.

   $$\begin{bmatrix} -3 & -3 & -3 & -3 & -3 \\ -2 & -2 & -2 & -2 & -2 \end{bmatrix}$$

   b. Apply the matrix that represents $T_{-3,-2}$ to the matrix for the polygon. Write the resulting matrix.

   $$\begin{bmatrix} -4 & 1 & -1 & -3 & -8 \\ -3 & -2 & 1 & 1 & 0 \end{bmatrix}$$

   c. Graph the preimage and image at the right.

LESSON MASTER 5-1 B

Questions on SPUR Objectives

Vocabulary

1. a. What is the *intersection* of two sets? **the set consisting of those elements common to both sets**

   b. Is intersection the solution set of a compound sentence using *and* or *or*? **and**

2. What is the *union* of two sets? **the set consisting of those elements in either set or both sets**

   b. Is union the solution set of a compound sentence using *and* or *or*? **or**

Representations Objective H: Solve and graph linear inequalities in one variable.

In 3–10, graph all solutions on the number line.

3. $x \le 8$

4. $u > -6$

5. $n < 0$ and $n \ge -7$

6. $d > -4$ or $d < -8$

7. $-2 \le s \le 3$

8. $7 \ge y > -3$

9. g is from 1 to 6

10. c is between -4 and 4

In 11 and 12, write an inequality or a compound sentence that describes the graph.

11. **$h < 6$**

12. 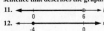 **$m \ge -4$**

▶ **LESSON MASTER 5-1 B** *page 2*

In 13 and 14, solve the inequality and graph its solution set on the number line.

13. $-20 + 6w \le 40$ **$w \le 10$**

14. $13 < y + 3(-4y + 8)$ **$y < 1$**

15. In some hospitals, newborns weighing less than 5 pounds are put on special watch. Graph these weights on the number line.

Representations Objective K: Solve systems of inequalities in one variable by graphing on a number line.

In 16 and 17, graph all solutions on the number line.

16. $\{p : p < 6\} \cap \{p : p > -5\}$

17. $\{y : y < 6\} \cup \{y : y \ge 10\}$

In 18 and 19, write an inequality or a compound sentence that describes the graph.

18. **$2 < x < 9$**

19. **$b \le -3$ or $b > 5$**

Review Objective L, Lesson 3-2

In 20 and 21, graph the line with the given equation.

20. $y = -4x + 2$

21. $2x - 6y = 12$

LESSON MASTER 5-2 B

Questions on SPUR Objectives

Vocabulary

1. Use the word *intersection* to describe the solution set for a system.
   Sample: The solution set for a system is the intersection of the solution sets for the individual sentences.

Properties Objective D: Recognize properties of systems of equations.

2. Does the ordered pair (3, -10) solve the system
   $\begin{cases} 3x + y = -1 \\ 2x + 3y = -17 \end{cases}$? Justify your answer.
   No; $3(3) + -10 \overset{?}{=} -1$, $-1 = -1$;
   $2(3) + 3(-10) \overset{?}{=} -17$, $-24 \neq -17$

3. Does the ordered pair (8, -3) solve the system
   $\begin{cases} 4x - 3y = 41 \\ -x - y = -5 \end{cases}$? Justify your answer.
   Yes; $4(8) - 3(-3) \overset{?}{=} 41$, $41 = 41$;
   $-(8) - (-3) \overset{?}{=} -5$, $-5 = -5$

4. Use the table at the right to solve the system $\begin{cases} y = 4x - 9 \\ y = 2x - 6 \end{cases}$.
   (1.5, -3)

x	y = 4x − 9	y = 2x − 6
-1	-13	-8
-0.5	-11	-7
0	-9	-6
0.5	-7	-5
1	-5	-4
1.5	-3	-3
2	-1	-2

5. a. Write a system that has (-5, 3) as a solution.
   Sample: $\begin{cases} x + y = -2 \\ x - y = -8 \end{cases}$
   b. Show that (-5, 3) is a solution to the system in Part a.
   $-5 + 3 = -2$; $-5 - 3 = -8$

Representations Objective I: Estimate solutions to systems by graphing.

In 6–9, a system is given. a. Graph the system.
b. Tell how many solutions the system has.
c. Estimate any solutions to the nearest tenth.

6. $\begin{cases} 2x + 4y = 6 \\ x + y = -1 \end{cases}$

a.

b. **1 solution**

c. **(-5, 4)**

7. $\begin{cases} 8x - 4y = 12 \\ y = 2x + 3 \end{cases}$

a.

b. **no solutions**

c. _____

8. $\begin{cases} y = \frac{4}{x} \\ y = x \end{cases}$

a.

b. **2 solutions**

c. **(2, 2), (-2, -2)**

9. $\begin{cases} y = \frac{2}{x} \\ y = x^2 \end{cases}$

a.

b. **1 solution**

c. **(1.3, 1.6)**

LESSON MASTER 5-3 B

Questions on SPUR Objectives

Skills Objective A: Solve 2 × 2 and 3 × 3 systems using substitution.

In 1–8, use substitution to solve the system. Then check.

Checks are not shown.

1. $\begin{cases} y = x - 7 \\ y = -2x + 5 \end{cases}$
   (4, -3)

2. $\begin{cases} y = 3x + 13 \\ y = x + 1 \end{cases}$
   (-6, -5)

3. $\begin{cases} 3m - 2n = 1 \\ 21m - 6n = 11 \end{cases}$
   $\left(\frac{2}{3}, \frac{1}{2}\right)$

4. $\begin{cases} xy = -4 \\ x = -4y \end{cases}$
   (-4, 1), (4, -1)

5. $\begin{cases} .25x + .1y = 78 \\ 7.5y - 1.5x = 990 \end{cases}$
   (240, 180)

6. $\begin{cases} 4a + 6b - 3c = -26 \\ b = a + 3 \\ c = -4a \end{cases}$
   (-2, 1, 8)

7. $\begin{cases} xy + z = 10 \\ z = -x + 1 \\ y = x + 1 \end{cases}$
   (3, 4, -2), (-3, -2, 4)

8. $\begin{cases} y = \frac{1}{2}x + 1 \\ x - 2y = -2 \end{cases}$
   infinitely many solutions

Properties Objective D: Recognize properties of systems of equations.

9. When you attempt to solve a system of two linear equations, you get the statement "5 = 19."
   a. What does this tell you about the solution?
   There is no solution.
   b. Describe the graph. **two distinct parallel lines**

10. When you attempt to solve a different system of two linear equations, you get the statement "8 = 8."
   a. What does this tell you about the solution?
   There are infinitely many solutions.
   b. Describe the graph. **one line**

Uses Objective F: Use systems of two or three linear equations to solve real-world problems.

11. At Wet Pets, a starter aquarium kit costs $15 plus 60¢ per fish. At Gills and Frills, the same kit is $13 plus 80¢ per fish.
   a. Give an equation for the cost c of f fish at each store.
   W. P. **$c = 15 + .6f$**   G. and F. **$c = 13 + .8f$**
   b. For what number of fish is the cost the same at the two stores?
   10 fish

12. A Valentine bouquet of 24 flowers contains pink carnations, red roses, and white mums. There are half as many mums as carnations and 4 more roses than carnations.
   a. Let c be the number of carnations, r the number of roses, and m the number of mums. Write a system of three equations satisfied by c, r, and m in this situation.
   $\begin{cases} c + r + m = 24 \\ m = \frac{1}{2}c \\ r = c + 4 \end{cases}$
   b. Solve the system to find how many of each type of flower are in the bouquet.
   C **8**, R **12**, M **4**

LESSON MASTER 5-4 B

Questions on SPUR Objectives

Skills Objective A: Solve 2 × 2 and 3 × 3 systems using the Linear Combinations Method.

In 1–8, use linear combinations to solve the system. Then check.

Checks are not shown.

1. $\begin{cases} 4x + y = -12 \\ 2x + 2y = -15 \end{cases}$

   $(-1.5, -6)$

2. $\begin{cases} 4x + 3y = 2.6 \\ 5x - 2y = 2.1 \end{cases}$

   $(.5, .2)$

3. $\begin{cases} 2a + b - 5c = -21 \\ a + 2b - 2c = -15 \\ a - 4b + c = 18 \end{cases}$

   $(-1, -4, 3)$

4. $\begin{cases} 8m - 2n = -16 \\ 2m - .5n = -4 \end{cases}$

   infinitely many solutions

5. $\begin{cases} 12x^2 - 5y^2 = 523 \\ 6x^2 + 2y^2 = 482 \end{cases}$

   $(8, 7), (-8, 7)$
   $(8, -7), (-8, -7)$

6. $\begin{cases} 4x + 5y = -14 \\ 8x + 10y = -20 \end{cases}$

   no solution

7. $\begin{cases} \frac{1}{4}x - y = -8 \\ \frac{1}{3}x + 4y = 14 \end{cases}$

   $(-12, 5)$

8. $\begin{cases} d + 9e - f = 13 \\ 3d + e + 2f = -7 \\ 2d + 2e + 2f = -6 \end{cases}$

   $(0, 1, -4)$

81 ▶

▶ **LESSON MASTER 5-4 B** page 2

Properties Objective D: Recognize properties of systems of equations.

For 9 and 10, consider the system $\begin{cases} 5x + 15y = -10 \\ x + 3y = k \end{cases}$.

9. For what value(s) of k will the system have infinitely many solutions?

   $k = -2$

10. For what value(s) of k will the system be inconsistent?

   $k \neq -2$

Uses Objective F: Use systems of two or three linear equations to solve real-world problems.

11. Five yards of fabric and three spools of thread cost $40.12. Two yards of the same fabric and ten spools of the same thread cost $23.88. Find the cost of a yard of fabric and the cost of a spool of thread.

   fabric $7.49/yd   thread $.89/spool

12. Two apples and six plums provide 300 calories. Three apples and five plums provide 350 calories. How many calories are provided by five apples and eight plums?

   575 calories

Review Objective B, Lesson 4-3

In 13 and 14, calculate the product.

13. $\begin{bmatrix} \frac{3}{4} & 1 \\ 3 & -1 \end{bmatrix}\begin{bmatrix} 8 & 12 \\ 0 & -2 \end{bmatrix}$

   $\begin{bmatrix} 6 & 7 \\ 24 & 38 \end{bmatrix}$

14. $\begin{bmatrix} -3 & -1 \\ 2 & 4 \end{bmatrix}\begin{bmatrix} 0 & 2 & -5 & 0 \\ 7 & 1 & -2 & 5 \end{bmatrix}$

   $\begin{bmatrix} -7 & -7 & 17 & -5 \\ 28 & 8 & -18 & 20 \end{bmatrix}$

82

LESSON MASTER 5-5 B

Questions on SPUR Objectives

Vocabulary

1. What do we call two matrices whose product is the identity matrix?

   inverse matrices

2. For the matrix $\begin{bmatrix} e & f \\ g & h \end{bmatrix}$, the number ___?___ is the determinant.

   $eh - fg$

Skills Objective B: Find the determinant and the inverse of a square matrix.

In 3–8, a matrix is given. a. Find its determinant. b. Find the inverse, if it exists. c. Check your answer to Part b by multiplying.

Checks are not shown.

3. $\begin{bmatrix} 3 & -1 \\ 0 & -2 \end{bmatrix}$

   a. -6

   b. $\begin{bmatrix} \frac{1}{3} & -\frac{1}{6} \\ 0 & -\frac{1}{2} \end{bmatrix}$

   c. _____

4. $\begin{bmatrix} -3 & -6 \\ -2 & 4 \end{bmatrix}$

   a. -24

   b. $\begin{bmatrix} -\frac{1}{6} & -\frac{1}{4} \\ -\frac{1}{12} & \frac{1}{8} \end{bmatrix}$

   c. _____

5. $\begin{bmatrix} \frac{1}{2} & 1 \\ -1 & \frac{1}{2} \end{bmatrix}$

   a. $\frac{5}{4}$

   b. $\begin{bmatrix} \frac{2}{5} & -\frac{4}{5} \\ \frac{4}{5} & \frac{2}{5} \end{bmatrix}$

   c. _____

6. $\begin{bmatrix} 0.5 & 1.5 \\ 0.5 & -0.5 \end{bmatrix}$

   a. -1

   b. $\begin{bmatrix} 0.5 & 1.5 \\ 0.5 & -0.5 \end{bmatrix}$

   c. _____

83 ▶

▶ **LESSON MASTER 5-5 B** page 2

7. $\begin{bmatrix} 1 & 0 \\ 0 & 1 \end{bmatrix}$

   a. 1

   b. $\begin{bmatrix} 1 & 0 \\ 0 & 1 \end{bmatrix}$

   c. _____

8. $\begin{bmatrix} -1 & 0 \\ 0 & -1 \end{bmatrix}$

   a. 1

   b. $\begin{bmatrix} -1 & 0 \\ 0 & -1 \end{bmatrix}$

   c. _____

9. Show that $\begin{bmatrix} -2 & 1 \\ 2 & -4 \end{bmatrix}$ and $\begin{bmatrix} -1 & -\frac{1}{2} \\ -\frac{1}{4} & 1 \end{bmatrix}$ are *not* inverses of each other.

$\begin{bmatrix} -2 & 1 \\ 2 & -4 \end{bmatrix}\begin{bmatrix} -1 & -\frac{1}{2} \\ -\frac{1}{4} & 1 \end{bmatrix} = \begin{bmatrix} \frac{7}{4} & 2 \\ -1 & -5 \end{bmatrix} \neq \begin{bmatrix} 1 & 0 \\ 0 & 1 \end{bmatrix}$

10. Consider the matrix $\begin{bmatrix} 5 & 4 \\ c & 8 \end{bmatrix}$. For what value(s) of c does the matrix lack an inverse?

   $c = 10$

In 11 and 12, a transformation is given. a. Write its matrix. b. Write the inverse of the matrix in Part a. c. Write the transformation represented by the matrix in Part b. d. Describe what the transformation does geometrically.

11. $S_{5,3}$

   a. $\begin{bmatrix} .5 & 0 \\ 0 & 3 \end{bmatrix}$

   b. $\begin{bmatrix} 2 & 0 \\ 0 & \frac{1}{3} \end{bmatrix}$

   c. $S_{2, 1/3}$

   d. $S_{5,3}$ horizontal shrink magnitude .5, vertical stretch magnitude 3; $S_{2, 1/3}$ horizontal shrink magnitude 2, vertical shrink magnitude $\frac{1}{3}$

12. R_{180}

   a. $\begin{bmatrix} -1 & 0 \\ 0 & -1 \end{bmatrix}$

   b. $\begin{bmatrix} -1 & 0 \\ 0 & -1 \end{bmatrix}$

   c. R_{180}

   d. R_{180} rotates each point of the plane 180° about the origin.

84

LESSON MASTER 5-6 B

Questions on SPUR Objectives

Vocabulary

1. Consider the system $\begin{cases} 3x + y = -1 \\ 4x + 6y = -34 \end{cases}$.

   a. Write the matrix form of the system.
   b. Identify its coefficient matrix.
   c. Identify its constant matrix.

$$\begin{bmatrix} 3 & 1 \\ 4 & 6 \end{bmatrix}\begin{bmatrix} x \\ y \end{bmatrix} = \begin{bmatrix} -1 \\ -34 \end{bmatrix} \qquad \begin{bmatrix} 3 & 1 \\ 4 & 6 \end{bmatrix} \qquad \begin{bmatrix} -1 \\ -34 \end{bmatrix}$$

Skills Objective C: Use matrices to solve systems of two or three linear equations.

In 2–7, use matrices to solve the system. Then check. **Checks are not shown.**

2. $\begin{cases} 3x - 4y = 9 \\ 8x - 10y = 20 \end{cases}$

   (-5, -6)

3. $\begin{cases} 4x + 3y = 0 \\ 2x + y = 6 \end{cases}$

   (9, -12)

4. $\begin{cases} 3a - 4b + 6c = 1 \\ 2a + 4b - 8c = 14 \\ 9a - 10b + 5c = 7 \end{cases}$

   (3, 2, 0)

5. $\begin{cases} 2g + 7h = 27 \\ 6g + 21h = 81 \end{cases}$

   infinitely many solutions

6. $\begin{cases} 4.2g + 5h = 64.1 \\ -5g - 2h = -52.2 \end{cases}$

   (8, 6.1)

7. $\begin{cases} 3x + 4y - 7z = -11 \\ 5x - y + z = -36 \\ x + y = -8 \end{cases}$

   (-7, -1, -2)

Properties Objective D: Recognize properties of systems of equations.

8. What is true of the coefficient matrix of every linear system that has exactly one solution?

   Its determinant is not zero.

Uses Objective F: Use systems of two or three linear equations to solve real-world problems.

9. Half a watermelon and a half pound of cherries cost $3.09. A whole watermelon and two pounds of cherries cost $8.16.

   a. Write a system of equations that can be used to find the cost of each type of fruit.

   $\begin{cases} .5w + .5c = 3.09 \\ w + 2c = 8.16 \end{cases}$

   b. Use matrices to solve the system and find the cost of each type of fruit.

   watermelon **$4.20**   cherries **$1.98/lb**

10. For the Summer Rock Festival, there is one price for students, one for adults, and another for senior citizens. The Rueda family bought 3 student tickets and 2 adult tickets for $104. The Cosentinos bought 5 student tickets, 1 adult ticket, and 2 senior tickets for $155. The Cragins bought 2 of each for $126.

    a. Write a system of equations that can be used to find the cost of each ticket.   **(See below.)**

    b. Use matrices to solve the system and find the cost of each ticket.

    students **$18**   adults **$25**   seniors **$20**

Review Objective H, Lesson 5-1

In 11–14, graph on the number line.

11. $e < 2$ and $e > -5$

12. $x \geq 3$ or $x < 0$

13. $\{r: r < 1\} \cap \{r: r > -8\}$

14. $\{k: k < 4\} \cap \{k: k \geq 2\}$

#10a $\begin{cases} 3s + 2a = 104 \\ 5s + 1a + 2n = 155 \\ 2s + 2a + 2n = 126 \end{cases}$

LESSON MASTER 5-7 B

Questions on SPUR Objectives

Vocabulary

1. **a.** A line drawn in a plane separates the plane into two distinct regions called __?__. The line itself is the __?__.

   half-planes   **boundary**

   b. Draw and label a diagram to illustrate the terms given in your answer to Part a.

   half-plane
   boundary
   half-plane

Representations Objective J: Graph linear inequalities in two variables.

2. The inequality $ax + by \leq c$ is graphed at the right. Match each point identified on the graph with the sentence it satisfies.

   P **b**   (a) $ax + by > c$
   Q **a**   (b) $ax + by = c$
   R **c**   (c) $ax + by < c$

In 3–6, write an inequality that describes the shaded region.

3.

   $y > -x - 2$

4.

   $y > -3.5$

5.

   $y \geq \frac{2}{3}x + 2$

6.

   $y \leq 3x - 1$

In 7–10, graph the given inequality on the coordinate plane.

7. $y < -1$

8. $y \geq -2x - 3$

9. $-2x - 3y > 9$

10. $x \geq 2.5$

Lesson 5-8 B (page 1)

LESSON MASTER 5-8 B — Questions on SPUR Objectives

Vocabulary

1. a. What is the *feasible set* for a system of inequalities?

   the set of solutions to the system

   b. What are the *vertices* of a feasible set?

   the intersections of the boundaries of the feasible set

Properties Objective E: Recognize properties of systems of inequalities.

2. A system of inequalities is graphed at the right. Does the given point satisfy the system?

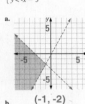

   a. (-2, 4) **no**   b. (0, 0) **no**

   c. (-2, 1) **no**   d. (2, 2) **yes**

   e. (0, 3) **yes**   f. (3, 0) **yes**

Representations Objective K: Solve systems of inequalities by graphing.

In 3 and 4, a system of linear inequalities is given.
a. Graph the feasible region. b. Find the coordinates of each vertex of the region.

3. $\begin{cases} y > 2x \\ y < -x - 3 \end{cases}$

   a.

   b. **(-1, -2)**

4. $\begin{cases} x \geq 0 \\ y \leq 3 \\ y < \frac{1}{2}x + 2 \end{cases}$

   a.

   b. **(0, 2), (2, 3)**

89 ▶

Lesson 5-8 B (page 2)

▶ **LESSON MASTER 5-8 B** *page 2*

In 5 and 6, graph the solution set.

5. $\begin{cases} y < x + 1 \\ x + 2y \geq -3 \end{cases}$

6. $\begin{cases} x \geq -2 \\ y \geq -3 \\ x + y \leq 1 \\ x - 3y \leq 12 \end{cases}$

In 7 and 8, write a system of inequalities that describes the shaded region.

7.

   $\begin{cases} y < 4 \\ y < \frac{5}{2}x - 1 \end{cases}$

8.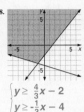

   $\begin{cases} y \geq \frac{4}{3}x - 2 \\ y \geq -\frac{1}{3}x - 4 \end{cases}$

9. A sack of Nutri-Plus parakeet seed contains 8 lb of white millet and 2 lb of red millet. A sack of Ultra-Grow parakeet seed contains 6 lb of white millet and 4 lb of red millet. Seed and Feed currently has 9,000 lb of white millet and 4,000 lb of red millet in stock.

   a. Let n be the number of sacks of Nutri-Plus and u be the number of sacks of Ultra-Grow that Feed and Seed can package. Give a system of inequalities satisfied by n and u.

   $\begin{cases} 8n + 6u \leq 9000; n \geq 0 \\ 2n + 4u \leq 4000; u \geq 0 \end{cases}$

   b. Graph the feasible set for the system in Part a and label the vertices.

90

Lesson 5-9 B (page 1)

LESSON MASTER 5-9 B — Questions on SPUR Objectives

Properties Objective E: Recognize properties of systems of inequalities.

1. *Multiple choice.* List all of the following shaded regions that could be the feasible region of a linear-programming problem. Explain your answer.

   (a)   (b)   (c)   (d)

   b, c; the feasible region must be convex.

In 2 and 3, use the graph at the right. It shows the feasible region of a linear-programming problem.

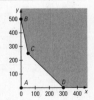

2. Name the points which could be solutions to the linear-programming problem.

   B, C, D

3. Find the point in the feasible region that minimizes $P = 2.8x + 1.5y$.

   C

Uses Objective G: Use linear programming to solve real-world problems.

In 4–8, refer to the following situation: Justine makes jewelry to sell at a flea market. She can currently make a pair of earrings with 20 beads in 30 minutes and a necklace with 30 beads in 30 minutes. She plans to use no more than 600 beads, work a maximum of 12 hours (720 minutes), and make at least 5 pairs of earrings and 5 necklaces. Let e be the number of pairs of earrings and n be the number of necklaces she can make. The system of inequalities for this problem is below.

$\begin{cases} 20e + 30n \leq 600 \\ 30e + 30n \leq 720 \\ e \geq 5 \\ n \geq 5 \end{cases}$

91 ▶

Lesson 5-9 B (page 2)

▶ **LESSON MASTER 5-9 B** *page 2*

4. Match each inequality in the system with the aspect of the situation.

   (i) $20e + 30n \leq 600$ (ii) $30e + 30n \leq 720$

   (iii) $e \geq 5$ (iv) $n \geq 5$

   a. the number of pairs of earrings   **iii**

   b. the number of necklaces   **iv**

   c. the total number of beads used   **i**

   d. the total number of minutes worked   **ii**

5. Graph the system of inequalities and determine the feasible region. Let e be the independent variable.

6. Give three possible combinations of earrings and necklaces Justine could make each week.

   Sample:
   10 ear., 10 neck.;
   12 ear., 8 neck.;
   5 ear., 5 neck.

7. List the vertices of the feasible region.

   (5, 5), (12, 12), (5, 16⅔), (19, 5)

8. Justine makes $3.25 profit on each pair of earrings and $5 profit on each necklace. She generally sells every piece of jewelry she makes.

   a. Write an expression for Justine's total profit in terms of e and n.

   $3.25e + 5n$

   b. Calculate the profits for your answers in Question 6.

   (See below.)

   c. How many pairs of earrings and how many necklaces should Justine make to maximize the profit?

   earrings **12 pairs**   necklaces **12**

   d. What is the maximum amount of profit she can make?

   $99

   #8b $82.50; $79; $41.25

92

269

LESSON MASTER **5-10** **B**   Questions on SPUR Objectives

Uses Objective G: Use linear programming to solve real-world problems.

In 1–5, refer to the following situation: Mr. Santos needs to borrow at least $50,000, some from a credit union and the rest from a bank. At both institutions, he will repay the amount he borrows after 5 years, but he will need to pay simple interest on the loans for each of the five years. He can borrow no more than $35,000 from the credit union, and he wants the amount borrowed from the bank to be no more than the amount borrowed from the credit union. The credit union charges 11.5% interest and the bank charges 13% interest. Mr. Santos wants to minimize his costs in a single year.

1. Let c be the amount borrowed from the credit union and b be the amount borrowed from the bank. Write a system of three inequalities for this situation.

$$\begin{cases} c + b \geq 50,000 \\ c \leq 35,000 \\ b \leq c \end{cases}$$

2. Graph the system of inequalities and determine the feasible region. Let c be the independent variable.

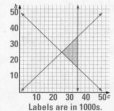
Labels are in 1000s.

3. List the vertices of the feasible region.
(25,000, 25,000)
(35,000, 15,000)
(35,000, 35,000)

4. Write the expression to be minimized.
$.115c + .13b$

5. a. According to the Linear-Programming Theorem, how can you find the least expensive plan for Mr. Santos?
Sample: Evaluate $.115c + .13b$ for each ordered pair in Question 3.

b. How much should Mr. Santos borrow from each institution?
credit union ___$35,000___   bank ___$15,000___

c. What is the minimum amount of interest Mr. Santos will need to pay in a year? $5,975

▶ **LESSON MASTER 5-10 B** *page 2*

In 6–10, refer to the following situation: A convention center designated a maximum of 34,000 square feet of floor space for trade-show exhibits. The space will be divided into two types of areas, wired and unwired zones. Wired zones are for exhibits that require electricity; each occupies 500 sq ft and accommodates 4 exhibits. Unwired zones are for exhibits that do not require electricity; each occupies 850 sq ft and accommodates 6 exhibits. There will be at least 10 of each type of zone, but no more than 40 wired zones. There is not enough space to accommodate all the companies that have applied to exhibit. Linear programming can be used to determine how many wired zones and unwired zones should be used to accommodate as many exhibits as possible.

6. Let w be the number of wired zones and u be the number of unwired zones. Write a system of inequalities to describe this situation.

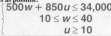
$$\begin{cases} 500w + 850u \leq 34,000 \\ 10 \leq w \leq 40 \\ u \geq 10 \end{cases}$$

7. Graph the system of inequalities and determine the feasible region. Let w be the independent variable.

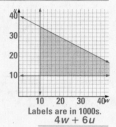

8. List the vertices of the feasible region.
(10, 10)
(40, 10)
(40, ≈16.5)
(10, ≈34.1)

Labels are in 1000s.

9. Write the expression to be maximized. $4w + 6u$

10. a. According to the Linear-Programming Theorem, how can you determine the numbers of wired zones and unwired zones that should be used to accommodate as many exhibits as possible?
Sample: Evaluate $4w + 6u$ for each ordered pair in Question 8.

b. How many of each type of zone should be planned?
wired ___40___   unwired ___60___

c. What is the maximum number of exhibits possible?   256 exhibits

---

LESSON MASTER **6-1** **B**   Questions on SPUR Objectives

Vocabulary

In 1–3, match the equation or expression with the English phrase.

1. $ax^2 + bx + c = 0$ ___b___   (a) the general quadratic expression in the variable x

2. $f:x \rightarrow ax^2 + bx + c$ ___c___   (b) the general quadratic equation in the variable x

3. $ax^2 + bx + c$ ___a___   (c) the general quadratic function in the variable x

Skills Objective A: Expand squares of binomials.

In 4–15, expand and simplify.

4. $(u + 8)^2$
$u^2 + 16u + 64$

5. $(v - 4)^2$
$v^2 - 8v + 16$

6. $(6x + 1)^2$
$36x^2 + 12x + 1$

7. $(a + 3b)^2$
$a^2 + 6ab + 9b^2$

8. $(5g - 4h)^2$
$25g^2 - 40gh + 16h^2$

9. $(\frac{1}{4} - b)^2$
$\frac{1}{16} - \frac{1}{2}b + b^2$

10. $(8q - \frac{1}{2})^2$
$64q^2 - 8q + \frac{1}{4}$

11. $(9d + 4e)^2$
$81d^2 + 72de + 16e^2$

12. $3(3 + c)^2$
$27 + 18c + 3c^2$

13. $(2x + 1)^2 + (2x - 1)^2$
$8x^2 + 2$

14. $\frac{3}{4}(6p + 4)^2$
$27p^2 + 36p + 12$

15. $-9(2k - 5)^2 - 2(k + 3)^2$
$-38k^2 + 168k - 243$

16. Solve for a: $x^2 + 14x + 49 = (x + a)^2$ $a = 7$

17. Solve for e: $x^2 - 40x + 400 = (x + e)^2$ $e = -20$

▶ **LESSON MASTER 6-1 B** *page 2*

Uses Objective G: Use quadratic equations to solve area problems.

18. Refer to the diagram at the right. Give the area of each region in standard form.

a. Shaded rectangle $2x^2 + x$
b. Larger rectangle $20x^2 + 22x + 6$
c. Unshaded region $18x^2 + 21x + 6$

19. Suppose a park district plans to build a rectangular playground 80 m by 60 m with a walkway w meters wide around it.

a. At the right, draw and label a diagram to represent this situation.

b. Write an expression in standard form for the total area of the playground and walkway.
$4w^2 + 280w + 4800$

c. Find the total area if $w = 3$. $5676m^2$

Review Objective C, Lesson 1–5; Objective H, Lesson 5–1

In 20–22, solve.

20. $4m + 12 = 9m + 67$
$m = -11$

21. $\frac{15}{a} = 4$
$a = \frac{15}{4}$

22. $0.45u + 0.6(4u) - 3.5(7u - 5.5) = -(20u + 22)$
$u = 25$

In 23 and 24, graph on the number line.

23. $y \leq 12$ and $y \geq 0$

24. $e > -2$ or $e < -11$

LESSON MASTER 6-2 B

Questions on SPUR Objectives

Vocabulary

1. Give an algebraic definition for the *absolute value* of x.
   Sample: $|x| = x$ for $x \geq 0$; $|x| = -x$ for $x < 0$.

2. Define the term and give an example. **Samples are given.**
   a. *square root* **x is a square root of k if and only if $x^2 = k$; $\sqrt{4} = 2$ or -2.**

   b. *rational number* **A rational number can be written as a/b, with a and b integers and $b \neq 0$; $\frac{5}{4}$.**

   c. *irrational number* **An irrational number is a real number that is not rational; $\sqrt{3}$**

Skills Objective C: Solve quadratic equations.

In 3–8, solve.

3. $w^2 = 144$ **$w = \pm 12$**   4. $m^2 = 66$ **$m = \pm\sqrt{66} \approx \pm 8.12$**

5. $a^2 = 3.61$ **$a = \pm 1.9$**   6. $\frac{25}{81} = x^2$ **$x = \pm\frac{5}{9}$**

7. $(x + 8)^2 = 0$ **$x = -8$**   8. $(2r - 6)^2 = 0$ **$r = 3$**

Properties Objective E: Apply the definition of absolute value and the Absolute Value-Square Root Theorem.

In 9–17, evaluate.

9. $|-55.3|$ **55.3**   10. $|711|$ **711**   11. $-|0.8|$ **-0.8**

12. $\sqrt{81}$ **9**   13. $\sqrt{(-13)^2}$ **13**   14. $\sqrt{67.2^2}$ **67.2**

15. $\sqrt{(3-8)^2}$ **5**   16. $-\sqrt{(-10)^2}$ **-10**   17. $-\sqrt{400}$ **-20**

18. When does $|x| = -x$?   **when $x \leq 0$**

In 19–22, solve.

19. $|x + 9| = 33$ **$x = 24$ or $x = -42$**   20. $|c - 5.2| = 3.1$ **$c = 8.3$ or $c = 2.1$**

21. $42 = |3x|$ **$x = \pm 14$**   22. $|\frac{2}{3}p - 8| = 2$ **$p = 15$ or $p = 9$**

Uses Objective G: use quadratic equations to solve area problems.

23. A square and a circle have the same area. The square has side 8. To the nearest hundredth, what is the radius of the circle?   **$r = 4.51$**

Representations Objective J: Graph the absolute-value functions and interpret the graphs.

In 24 and 25, a function is given. a. Graph the function.
b. Give the domain and the range of the function.

24. $f(x) = -2|x|$
    a.

    b. **all real numbers
    $\{y \mid y \leq 0\}$**

25. $g(x) = |-2x|$
    a.
    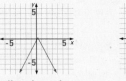
    b. **all real numbers
    $\{y : y \geq 0\}$**

LESSON MASTER 6-3 B

Questions on SPUR Objectives

Vocabulary

1. Write the general *vertex form* of an equation for a parabola.
   $y - k = a(x - h)^2$

2. If a parabola opens down, does it have a minimum or maximum y-value?
   maximum

Uses Objective I: Use the Graph-Translation Theorem to interpret equations and graphs.

In 3–6, a translation is described. a. Give an equation for the image of the graph of $y = x^2$ under this translation.
b. Name the vertex of the image.

3. 3 units right, 4 units down
   a. **$y + 4 = (x - 3)^2$**
   b. **$(3, -4)$**

4. 6 units left, 2 units up
   a. **$y - 2 = (x + 6)^2$**
   b. **$(-6, 2)$**

5. 7 units left
   a. **$y = (x + 7)^2$**
   b. **$(-7, 0)$**

6. 3 units up
   a. **$y - 3 = x^2$**
   b. **$(0, 3)$**

In 7–10, an equation and a translation are given.
a. Give an equation for the image of the graph of the equation under the translation. b. Give an equation for the axis of symmetry.

7. $y = 4x^2$ $T_{-3, 5}$
   a. **$y = 4(x + 3)^2 + 5$**
   b. **$x = -3$**

8. $y = -7x^2$ $T_{6, 2}$
   a. **$y = -7(x - 6)^2 + 2$**
   b. **$x = 6$**

9. $y = -\frac{7}{3}x^2$ $T_{-4, -4}$
   a. **$y = -\frac{7}{3}(x + 4)^2 - 4$**
   b. **$x = -4$**

10. $y = -\frac{1}{2}x^2$ $T_{0, -8}$
    a. **$y = -\frac{1}{2}x^2 - 8$**
    b. **$x = 0$**

In 11 and 12, assume parabola P is a translation image of parabola Q at the right.

11. What translation maps parabola P onto parabola Q?   **$T_{4, 5}$**

12. Parabola P has equation $y = -\frac{3}{2}x^2$.
    What is an equation of parabola Q?
    $y = -\frac{3}{2}(x - 4)^2 + 5$

Representations Objective J: Graph parabolas and interpret the graphs.

In 13–16, an equation for a parabola is given. a. Graph the parabola and show its axis of symmetry. b. Identify its vertex.
c. Write an equation for the axis of symmetry.

13. $y = 2(x - 3)^2$
    a.

    b. **$(3, 0)$**   c. **$x = 3$**

14. $y - 1 = (x + 4)^2$
    a.
    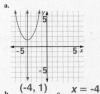
    b. **$(-4, 1)$**   c. **$x = -4$**

15. $y + 3 = x^2$
    a.
    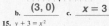
    b. **$(0, -3)$**   c. **$x = 0$**

16. $y - 5 = -2x^2$
    a.

    b. **$(0, 5)$**   c. **$x = 0$**

Name _____

LESSON MASTER **6-4** **B**   Questions on SPUR Objectives

Skills Objective B: Transform quadratic equations from vertex form to standard form.

In 1–6, write the equation in standard form.

1. $y + 6 = (x - 3)^2$

$$y = x^2 - 6x + 3$$

2. $y - 1 = 2(x - 4)^2$

$$y = 2x^2 - 16x + 33$$

3. $y = (x + 7)^2$

$$y = x^2 + 14x + 49$$

4. $y = -3(x + 5)^2 + 8$

$$y = -3x^2 - 30x - 67$$

5. $y + 14 = -x^2$

$$y = -x^2 - 14$$

6. $y - 2 = \frac{2}{3}(x - 9)^2$

$$y = \frac{2}{3}x^2 - 12x + 56$$

Uses Objective G: Use quadratic equations to solve problems dealing with velocity and acceleration.

7. Suppose a ball is thrown upward from a height of 5 feet with an initial velocity of 35 ft/sec.

   a. Write an equation relating the time t and the height h of the ball. $h = -16t^2 + 35t + 5$

   b. Find the height of the ball after 2 seconds. ___ **11 feet**

   c. Is the ball still in the air after 3 seconds? Explain.
   No; when $t = 3$, $h = -34$; when ball is in the air, $h \geq 0$.

8. Chizuko threw a stone upward at a speed of 10m/sec while standing on a cliff 40 m above the ground.

   a. What was the height of the stone after 3 seconds? ___ **25.9 m**

   b. Estimate how long it took for the stone to touch the ground. ___ **≈4 seconds**

101 ▶

Name _____

▶ **LESSON MASTER 6-4 B** *page 2*

9. Kenny is standing on a bridge 22 feet above the water. Suppose he drops a ball over the 3-foot railing.

   a. Write an equation relating the time t (in seconds) and the height h (in feet) of the ball above the water.

   $$h = -16t^2 + 25$$

   b. Graph the equation from Part a.

   c. Estimate how long it will take for the ball to hit the water. Explain your reasoning.
   1.25 seconds; when $h = 0$, $t = 1.25$.

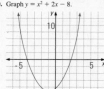

Representations Objective J: Graph quadratic functions and interpret the graphs.

10. Graph $y = x^2 + 2x - 8$.

11. Graph $y = -2x^2 + 7x + 5$.

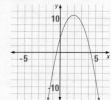

12. The height of a ball thrown upward is shown as a function of time on the graph.

   a. Estimate the initial height of the ball. ___ **2 m**

   b. Approximately when did the ball reach its maximum height? ___ **≈1.75 sec**

   c. What was the maximum height? ___ **16 m**

   d. When was the ball 8 m high? ___ **≈.5 sec and ≈3sec**

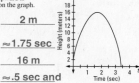

102

Name _____

LESSON MASTER **6-5** **B**   Questions on SPUR Objectives

Vocabulary

1. a. What is a *perfect-square trinomial?* **Sample is given for b.**
   the square of a binomial

   b. Give an example of a perfect-square trinomial. ___ $x^2 + 6x + 9$

Representations Objective B: Transform quadratic equations from standard form to vertex form.

In 2–7, fill in the blank to make the expression a perfect-square trinomial.

2. $y = x^2 + 8x +$ ___ **16**

3. $y = x^2 - 20x +$ ___ **100**

4. $y = x^2 + 5x +$ ___ $\frac{25}{4}$**, or 6.25**

5. $y = x^2 - \frac{2}{3}x +$ ___ $\frac{1}{9}$

6. $y = x^2 - bx +$ ___ $\frac{b^2}{4}$

7. $y = x^2 + \frac{b}{4}x +$ ___ $\frac{b^2}{64}$

In 8–17, transform the equation into vertex form.

8. $y = x^2 + 12x + 40$

$$y - 4 = (x + 6)^2$$

9. $y = x^2 - 10x + 10$

$$y + 15 = (x - 5)^2$$

10. $y = x^2 - 6x - 15$

$$y + 24 = (x - 3)^2$$

11. $y = x^2 + 3x + 7$

$$y - 4.75 = (x + 1.5)^2$$

12. $y = 6x^2 - 18x - 5$

$$y + 18.5 = 6(x - 1.5)^2$$

13. $y = -3x^2 + 15x$

$$y - 18.75 = -3(x - 2.5)^2$$

103 ▶

Name _____

▶ **LESSON MASTER 6-5 B** *page 2*

14. $y = x^2 - 9x + 4$

$$y + 16.25 = (x - 4.5)^2$$

15. $y = x^2 + 18x + 81$

$$y = (x + 9)^2$$

16. $y = \frac{1}{4}x^2 - 3x + 2$

$$y + 7 = \frac{1}{4}(x - 6)^2$$

17. $8y = 4x^2 + 24x - 6$

$$y + 5.25 = .5(x + 3)^2$$

In 18–21, find the vertex of the parabola determined by the equation.

18. $y = x^2 - 8x + 13$

(4, -3)

19. $y = -x^2 - 16x - 68$

(-8, -4)

20. $y = \frac{1}{2}x^2 - 3x + 8$

(3, 3.5)

21. $y = 4x^2 + 16x - 1$

(-2, -17)

22. *Multiple choice.* The graphs of which equation(s) have the same vertex as the graph of $y = x^2 + 14x + 52$? ___ **b, c**

   (a) $y = x^2 + 14x - 52$ (b) $y = -x^2 - 14x - 46$
   (c) $y = 2x^2 + 28x + 101$ (d) $y = x^2 + 6x + 2$

Review Objective D, Lesson 3-8

In 23–26, an arithmetic sequence is given.
a. Find a formula for the nth term. b. Find a_{20}.

23. 18, 11, 4, -3, -10, -17, . . .

   a. ___ $a_n = -7n + 25$

   b. ___ **-115**

24. 109, 129, 149, 169, 189, . . .

   a. ___ $a_n = 20n + 89$

   b. ___ **489**

25. 1.55, 2.56, 3.57, 4.58, 5.59, . . .

   a. ___ $a_n = 1.01n + .54$

   b. ___ **20.74**

26. $\frac{1}{3}, \frac{4}{3}, \frac{7}{3}, \frac{10}{3}, \ldots$

   a. ___ $a_n = n - \frac{2}{3}$

   b. ___ $\frac{58}{3}$

104

272

LESSON MASTER 6-6 B

Questions on SPUR Objectives

Uses Objective H: Fit a quadratic model to data.

1. Lola is studying geodesic domes, glass domes constructed of nearly equilateral connected triangles. She made some models of connected triangles with toothpicks, as pictured below. The side of the first figure is 1 toothpick long, the side of the second figure is 2 toothpicks long, and so on.

$\triangle$			
3 toothpicks	9 toothpicks	18 toothpicks	30 toothpicks

a. At the right, draw the next figure with side 5 toothpicks long.

b. How many toothpicks are required?

45 toothpicks

c. Use a quadratic model to find a formula for $t(s)$, the number of toothpicks in a figure whose side is s toothpicks long.

$t(s) = 1.5(s^2 + s)$

d. Use your formula to find the number of toothpicks in a figure with side 6 toothpicks long. Then, at the right, draw the figure with side 6 toothpicks long to verify that your formula is correct.

63 toothpicks

e. How many toothpicks would be required for a figure with a side 50 toothpicks long?

3,825 toothpicks

---

2. The table below gives the average amount donated to a university alumni fund last year.

Age of Alumnus A	24	30	40	50	60	70
Donation D	$28	$32	$47	$71	$88	$115

a. Draw a scatterplot of the data.

b. Fit a quadratic model to these data using data of your choice.

$D = .05A^2 - 2.1A + 49.4$

c. Plot your quadratic model on your scatterplot.

d. Use your model to predict the average amount donated by 80-year-old alumni.

$201

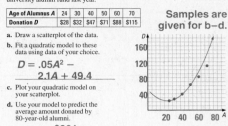

Samples are given for b–d.

3. The table below gives the prices of a company's color television sets.

Sizes (in.)	5	9	13	19	25	31	35
Price p ($)	$240	$158	$125	$275	$610	$1145	$1690

a. Draw a scatterplot of the data.

b. Fit a quadratic model to these data using the data for the 5-, 19-, and 31-in. televisions.

$p = 2.7s^2 - 62.1s + 483.3$

c. Plot your quadratic model on your scatterplot.

d. Use your model to predict the cost of a 39-inch television.

$2168

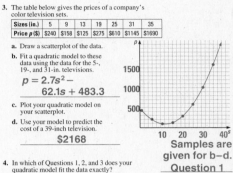

Samples are given for b–d.

4. In which of Questions 1, 2, and 3 does your quadratic model fit the data exactly?

Question 1

LESSON MASTER 6-7 B

Questions on SPUR Objectives

Vocabulary

1. Write the complete statement of the *Quadratic Formula Theorem.*

If $ax^2 + bx + c = 0$ and $a \neq 0$, then $x = \frac{-b \pm \sqrt{b^2 - 4ac}}{2a}$.

Skills Objective C: Solve quadratic equations.

In 2–15, use the Quadratic Formula to solve the equation.

2. $x^2 + 8x + 12 = 0$

$x = -6 \text{ or } x = -2$

3. $n^2 - 6n - 27 = 0$

$n = 9 \text{ or } n = -3$

4. $8c^2 + 2c - 3 = 0$

$c = \frac{1}{2} \text{ or } c = -\frac{3}{4}$

5. $-3x^2 - 7x + 40 = 0$

$x = \frac{8}{3} \text{ or } x = -5$

6. $x^2 - 16x + 64 = 0$

$x = 8$

7. $0 = w(w - 12)$

$w = 12 \text{ or } w = 0$

8. $2v^2 = 3v + 12$

$v = \frac{3 + \sqrt{105}}{4} \approx 3.3$

or $\frac{3 - \sqrt{105}}{4} \approx -1.8$

9. $0 = x^2 + 7x + 8$

$x = \frac{-7 + \sqrt{17}}{2} \approx -1.44$

or $\frac{-7 - \sqrt{17}}{2} \approx -5.56$

10. $5x^2 + 6x = 0$

$x = 0 \text{ or } x = -\frac{6}{5}$

11. $4m^2 - 12m + 9 = 0$

$m = \frac{3}{2}$

12. $e^2 + 2 = 3e + 11$

$e = \frac{3 + \sqrt{45}}{2} \approx 4.85$

or $\frac{3 - \sqrt{45}}{2} \approx -1.85$

13. $(4x + 1)(2x - 3) = 3(x + 4)$

$x = \frac{13 + \sqrt{649}}{16} \approx 2.41$

or $\frac{13 - \sqrt{649}}{16} \approx -.78$

14. $5(a^2 - 7a) = 10$

$a = \frac{7 + \sqrt{57}}{2} \approx 7.27$

or $\frac{7 - \sqrt{57}}{2} \approx -.27$

15. $(x - 11)^2 = (3x + 6)^2$

$x = 1.25 \text{ or } x = -8.5$

---

16. Consider the parabola with equation $y = 6x^2 - 5x - 4$.

a. Find its x-intercepts.

$\frac{4}{3}, -\frac{1}{2}$

b. Find the value(s) of x when $y = 8$.

$\frac{5 + \sqrt{313}}{12} \approx 1.89 \text{ or } \frac{5 - \sqrt{313}}{12} \approx -1.06$

Uses Objective G: Use quadratic equations to solve problems.

17. A square and a rectangle have the same area. The length of the rectangle is 8 less than twice the side of the square. The width of the rectangle is 3 less than the side of the square.

a. Let x represent the length of the side of the square. Write expressions for the dimensions of the rectangle.

length **$2x - 8$**   width **$x - 3$**

b. Write an equation that represents the situation. **$x^2 = (2x - 8)(x - 3)$**

c. Find the dimensions of the square and rectangle.

square **12 by 12**   rectangle **16 by 9**

18. The path of a ball hit by Giant Dennison is described by the equation $h(x) = -.005x^2 + 2x + 3$. Here, x is the distance (in feet) along the ground of the ball from home plate, and $h(x)$ is the height (in feet) of the ball at that distance.

a. How high was the ball when Giant hit it?

3 feet

b. Stretch Hanson caught the ball at the same height at which Giant hit it. How far from the plate was Stretch when he caught the ball?

400 feet

c. How high was the ball when it was 300 feet from the plate?

153 feet

d. How far from the plate was the ball when it was 75 feet high?

40 ft, 360 ft

19. A model rocket is launched straight up at an initial velocity of 150 ft/sec. The launch pad is 1 foot off the ground.

a. When will the rocket be 300 ft high?

2.875 sec
6.5 sec

b. Will the rocket ever reach a height of 500 ft? Why or why not?

No; when $h(t) = 500$, there is no real-number solution for t.

c. When will the rocket hit the ground?

≈ 9.4 sec

LESSON MASTER 6-8 B

Questions on SPUR Objectives

Vocabulary

1. What are *imaginary numbers*?

   square roots of negative numbers

2. a. What symbol is used to designate the *imaginary unit*? i

   b. What is the value of the imaginary unit? $\sqrt{-1}$

Skills Objective C: Solve quadratic equations.

In 3–12, solve.

3. $x^2 = -900$

   $x = \pm 30i$

4. $y^2 = -14$

   $y = \pm i\sqrt{14}$

5. $a^2 + 8 = -28$

   $a = \pm 6i$

6. $b^2 - 12 = -13$

   $b = \pm i$

7. $5d^2 = -20$

   $d = \pm 2i$

8. $-8g^2 = 24$

   $g = \pm i\sqrt{3}$

9. $3h^2 + 17 = -130$

   $h = \pm 7i$

10. $x^2 + 3x + 8 = 0$

    $x = \dfrac{-3 \pm i\sqrt{23}}{2}$

11. $(k-1)^2 + 20 = 5$

    $k = 1 \pm i\sqrt{15}$

12. $(m+5)(m-5) = -31$

    $m = \pm i\sqrt{6}$

▶ **LESSON MASTER 6-8 B** *page 2*

Skills Objective D: Perform operations with complex numbers.

13. Show that $4i$ is a square root of -16.

   $(4i)^2 = (4i)(4i) = 16i^2 = 16(-1) = -16$

14. Show that $i\sqrt{13}$ is a square root of -13.

   $(i\sqrt{13})^2 = (i\sqrt{13})(i\sqrt{13}) = i^2(13) = -1(13) = -13$

In 15–36, simplify.

15. $\sqrt{-11}$ $i\sqrt{11}$

16. $\sqrt{-100}$ $10i$

17. $\sqrt{-8}$ $2i\sqrt{2}$

18. $\sqrt{-75}$ $5i\sqrt{3}$

19. $\sqrt{-1296}$ $36i$

20. $\sqrt{-288}$ $12i\sqrt{2}$

21. $8i^2$ -8

22. $-5i^2$ 5

23. $6i + 9i$ $15i$

24. $10i - 16i$ $-6i$

25. $(7i)(3i)$ -21

26. $(6i)^2$ -36

27. $\sqrt{-16} + \sqrt{-4}$ $6i$

28. $\sqrt{-81} - \sqrt{-64}$ i

29. $\sqrt{-25}\sqrt{-100}$ -50

30. $\sqrt{-49}\sqrt{-49}$ -49

31. $\sqrt{-5}\sqrt{-10}$ $-5\sqrt{2}$

32. $\sqrt{-100}\sqrt{100}$ $100i$

33. $(i\sqrt{3})^2$ -3

34. $2i(3i + 9i)$ -24

35. $\dfrac{\sqrt{-36}}{\sqrt{-81}}$ $\dfrac{2}{3}$

36. $\dfrac{12i}{3i}$ 4

Review Multiplying binomials, previous course

In 37–40, multiply and simplify.

37. $(x+6)(x+2)$ $x^2 + 8x + 12$

38. $(m-5)(m+10)$ $m^2 + 5m - 50$

39. $(2n+1)(3n-6)$ $6n^2 - 9n - 6$

40. $(b-8c)(4b-3c)$ $4b^2 - 35bc + 24c^2$

LESSON MASTER 6-9 B

Questions on SPUR Objectives

Vocabulary

1. Give a complete definition for *complex number*. Be sure to identify the real part and the imaginary part.

   A complex number is of the form $a + bi$, where a and b are real numbers and $i = \sqrt{-1}$; a is the real part and b is the imaginary part.

In 2–6, name the real part and the imaginary part of the number.

	Real Part	Imaginary Part
2. $7 + 3i$	7	3
3. $-4 + i$	-4	1
4. $6i$	0	6
5. $\sqrt{15} - 2i$	$\sqrt{15}$	-2
6. 24	24	0

7. Give the complex conjugate of the number $a + bi$. $a - bi$

In 8 and 9, give the complex conjugate of the number.

8. $2 + 9i$ $2 - 9i$

9. $\sqrt{5} - i$ $\sqrt{5} + i$

Skills Objective D: Perform operations with complex numbers.

In 10–19, rewrite the expression in $a + bi$ form.

10. $\dfrac{8 + 4i}{4}$ $2 + i$

11. $\dfrac{9 - 24i}{3i}$ $-8 - 3i$

12. $-7i$ $0 - 7i$

13. 18π $18\pi + 0i$

14. $\sqrt{-16}$ $0 + 4i$

15. $-\sqrt{3}$ $-\sqrt{3} + 0i$

16. $\dfrac{2 - i}{3 + 5i}$ $\dfrac{1}{34} - \dfrac{13}{34}i$

17. $\dfrac{4 + i}{6 - i}$ $\dfrac{23}{37} + \dfrac{10}{37}i$

18. $\dfrac{7}{-2 + 2i}$ $\dfrac{-7}{4} - \dfrac{7}{4}i$

19. $\dfrac{12i}{10 + 3i}$ $\dfrac{36}{109} + \dfrac{120}{109}i$

▶ **LESSON MASTER 6-9 B** *page 2*

In 20–31, perform the operations and write the answer in $a + bi$ form.

20. $(12 + 3i) - (2 + 6i)$ $10 - 3i$

21. $(7 + i)(3 - 4i)$ $25 - 25i$

22. $(8 - i)(8 + i)$ $65 + 0i$

23. $(4 - 3i) + (10 + 2i)$ $14 - i$

24. $5(6 - 4i)$ $30 - 20i$

25. $7i(1 + 5i)$ $-35 + 7i$

26. $(3 + 9i)(3 - 9i)$ $90 + 0i$

27. $(5 - 2i)(1 - 3i)$ $-1 - 17i$

28. $(4 - i)^2$ $15 - 8i$

29. $(7i + 2)^2$ $-45 + 28i$

30. $(\sqrt{3} + i)^2$ $2 + 2i\sqrt{3}$

31. $(\sqrt{3} + i\sqrt{3})^2$ $0 + 6i$

In 32–37, suppose $p = 4 + i$ and $q = -3 - 2i$. Evaluate and write the answer in $a + bi$ form.

32. $2p - iq$ $6 + 5i$

33. pq $-10 - 11i$

34. q^2 $5 + 12i$

35. iq $2 - 3i$

36. $p^2 + 2p - 3$ $20 + 10i$

37. $(ip)^2 - (iq)^2$ $-10 + 4i$

LESSON MASTER 6-10 B — Questions on SPUR Objectives

Vocabulary

1. Consider the quadratic equation $ax^2 + bx + c = 0$.

   a. Give the *discriminant*.

   $$b^2 - 4ac$$

   b. What does the discriminant determine?

   the nature of the solutions — how many and whether the solutions are real or not real

2. What are the *roots* of an equation?

   the solutions

Skills Objective C: Solve quadratic equations.

In 3–6, solve.

3. $2x^2 - x + 15 = 0$

   $x = \dfrac{1}{4} \pm \dfrac{i\sqrt{119}}{4}$

4. $2h^2 - h - 15 = 0$

   $h = 3 \text{ or } h = -\dfrac{5}{2}$

5. $(3m + 1)^2 - 5 = 0$

   $m = -\dfrac{1}{3} + \dfrac{\sqrt{5}}{3} \approx .412$

   $\text{or} \quad -\dfrac{1}{3} - \dfrac{\sqrt{5}}{3} \approx -1.079$

6. $16x^2 - 72x + 81 = 0$

   $x = 2.25$

Properties Objective F: Use the discriminant of a quadratic equation to determine the nature of the solutions to the equation.

In 7–9, suppose D is the discriminant for a quadratic equation. Tell how many roots there are to the equation and tell whether they are *real* or *not real*.

7. $D = 0$ **one root** **real**

8. $D > 0$ **two roots** **real**

9. $D < 0$ **two roots** **not real**

10. Consider the equation $ax^2 + bx + c$. Complete the following statement: If a, b, and c are __?__ and $b^2 - 4ac$ is __?__, then the solutions to the equation are rational numbers.

    rational numbers   **a perfect square**

113 ▶

In 11–14, a quadratic equation is given. a. Calculate its discriminant. b. Give the numbers of real solutions. c. Tell whether the real solutions are *rational* or *irrational*.

11. $x^2 - 3x + 6 = 0$

   a. **-15**
   b. **no solutions**
   c. _____

12. $2x^2 - x - 40 = 0$

   a. **321**
   b. **2 solutions**
   c. **irrational**

13. $e^2 - 8e + 16 = 0$

   a. **0**
   b. **1 solution**
   c. **rational**

14. $5x^2 - 6x - 11 = 0$

   a. **256**
   b. **2 solutions**
   c. **rational**

In 15–20, give the number of real solutions.

15. $m^2 - 5m + 7 = 0$ **0**

16. $3x^2 - x - 10 = 0$ **2**

17. $8w^2 = 3w$ **2**

18. $5x^2 - 10x = 5$ **2**

19. $9 + 7x = 3 - 4x^2$ **0**

20. $5d^2 + 144 = 0$ **0**

Representations Objective K: Use the discriminant of a quadratic equation to determine the number of x-intercepts of the graph.

In 21–24, give the number of x-intercepts of the graph of the equation.

21. $y = 9x^2 - 30x + 25$ **1**

22. $y = -x^2 - 5x - 8$ **0**

23. $y + 13x = 14x^2 + 3$ **2**

24. $y = 2(x^2 - 2x) - 7$ **2**

In 25–27, suppose D is the discriminant for a quadratic equation. Sketch a possible graph of the equation.   **Samples are given.**

25. $D = 0$

26. $D > 0$

27. $D < 0$

114

LESSON MASTER 7-1 B — Questions on SPUR Objectives

Vocabulary

1. Consider the expression 6^4. Identify

   a. the base. **6**   b. the exponent. **4**   c. the power. **6^4**

2. Complete each equation to express the given power function.

   a. squaring function: $f(x) =$ **x^2**

   b. cubing function: $f(x) =$ **x^3**

   c. 8th power function: $f(x) =$ **x^8**

   d. identity function: $f(x) =$ **x**

   e. nth-power function: $f(x) =$ **x^n**, where n is **a positive integer**

Uses Objective F: Solve real-world problems which can be modeled by expressions with nth powers.

3. Consider a 10-question *true-false* test.

   a. Doreen has a 90% probability of answering each question correctly. What is the probability that Doreen will answer all 10 questions correctly? **$.9^{10} \approx .3487$**

   b. Mel has an 80% probability of answering each question correctly. What is the probability that Mel will answer all 10 questions correctly? **$.8^{10} \approx .1074$**

   c. Suppose someone decides to randomly guess at each answer. What is the probability that all 10 questions will be answered correctly? **$.5^{10} \approx .0010$**

4. Mrs. Montoyo has a computer golf game. She has a 60% chance of shooting par or better on each hole.

   a. What is the probability that Mrs. Montoyo will shoot par or better on each of the first 5 holes? **$.6^5 \approx .0778$**

   b. What is the probability that Mrs. Montoyo will shoot par or better on each of the holes in a 9-hole course? **$.6^9 \approx .0101$**

   c. What is the probability that Mrs. Montoyo will shoot par or better on each of the holes in an 18-hole course? **$.6^{18} \approx .0001$**

115 ▶

Representations Objective I: Graph nth power functions.

In 5–8, consider the following graphs. For what values of n, if any, could the graph represent a power function, $y = x^n$? If the graph cannot represent a power function, tell why.

5. **for even integers**

6. **for $n = 1$**

7. **The graph does not contain (0,0).**

8. **for odd integers**

9. The point $(-3, -243)$ is on the graph of a power function.

   a. Is the function an even or odd power function? **odd**

   b. Does the graph have a minimum or a maximum value? If so, what is its value? **no**

   c. Write an equation for the function. **$y = x^5$**

10. a. On the same coordinate grid, sketch graphs of $f(x) = x^2$ and $g(x) = x^4$.

    b. For what values(s) of x is $g(x) = f(x)$? **$x = 0, 1, -1$**

    c. For what values(s) of x is $g(x) > f(x)$? **$x > 1, x < -1$**

116

LESSON MASTER 7-2 B

Questions on SPUR Objectives

Skills Objective A: Evaluate b^n when $b > 0$ and n is a rational number.
Objective B: Simplify expressions using properties of exponents.

In 1–20, simplify.

1. $x^4 \cdot x^8$ x^{12}
2. $(r^5)^3$ r^{15}
3. $(3d^3)^4$ $81d^{12}$
4. $5m^2 \cdot 2m^6$ $10m^8$
5. $7y \cdot 2y^9$ $14y^{10}$
6. $(-4g)^2$ $16g^2$
7. $-(2r^3)^6$ $-64r^{18}$
8. $(x^2)^8(2x^4)^3$ $8x^{28}$
9. $\frac{c^6}{c^2}$ c^4
10. $\frac{u^{17}}{u^0}$ u^{17}
11. $\frac{12c^5}{4c^2}$ $3c^3$
12. $\frac{d^4 \cdot a^2}{a \cdot a^3}$ $\frac{d^4}{a^2}$
13. $\left(\frac{w}{3}\right)^5$ $\frac{w^5}{243}$
14. $\left(\frac{12}{n}\right)^2\left(\frac{n}{2}\right)^4$ $9n^2$
15. $\frac{(-5k^4)^4}{5^2k^{15}}$ $25k$
16. $\left(\frac{m}{n}\right)^8\left(\frac{n}{m}\right)^8$ 1
17. $4xy^4z^2 \cdot 3x^6y^9z^2$ $12x^7y^{13}z^4$
18. $a^2b^5c^8 \cdot b^4c^3d$ $a^2b^9c^{11}d$
19. $\frac{s^3 \cdot s^{10} \cdot u^8}{s \cdot s^{12} \cdot u}$ u^7
20. $(\pi r^3)(3r)^2$ $9\pi r^5$

In 21–31, evaluate and write in standard form.

21. $(-4)^4$ 256
22. $(-18)^0$ 1
23. $(-3)^7$ -2187
24. $(6^2)^3$ $46,656$
25. $4^3 \cdot 5^3$ 8000
26. $\frac{8^5}{8^3}$ 64
27. $8.9 \cdot 10^5$ $890,000$
28. $511 \cdot 10^0$ 511
29. $\frac{325 \cdot 10^9}{25 \cdot 10^6}$ $13,000$
30. $\frac{1.2 \cdot 10^{12}}{1.6 \cdot 10^{12}}$ $.75$
31. $(6.3 \cdot 10^3)(9.4 \cdot 10^7)$ $592,200,000,000$

Properties Objective E: Recognize properties of nth powers.

In 32–37, match the equation with the property it illustrates.

32. $(u^4)^5 = u^{20}$ c (a) Quotient of Powers Postulate
33. $\frac{e^{12}}{e^4} = e^8$ a (b) Power of a Product Postulate
34. $\left(\frac{c}{v}\right)^4 = \frac{c^4}{v^4}$ f (c) Power of a Power Postulate
35. $r^0 = 1$, for $r \neq 0$ e (d) Product of Powers Postulate
36. $(3b^6)^2 = 9b^{12}$ b (e) Zero Exponent Theorem
37. $g^3 \cdot g^8 = g^{11}$ d (f) Power of a Quotient Postulate

Uses Objective F: Solve real-world problems which can be modeled by expressions with nth powers.

38. A Merit Driver Citation is given to everyone who answers correctly all the questions in Parts I and II of the driving test. Each part has 7 questions. Suppose a person estimates that the probability of correctly answering a question in Part I is j and the probability of correctly answering a question in Part II is k. Assuming the questions are independent, what is the probability that this person will earn a Merit Driver Citation?

j^7k^7, or $(jk)^7$

39. The diameter of Saturn is about $1.2 \cdot 10^5$ km. Estimate Saturn's volume.

$2.88 \cdot 10^{14} \pi km^3 \approx 9 \cdot 10^{14} km^3$

In 40–44, find the average number of people per square mile.

State	Land Area (sq. mi)	Population (1992)	People per Sq.Mi
40. Michigan	$5.8 \cdot 10^4$	$9.4 \cdot 10^6$	≈ 162
41. Idaho	$8.3 \cdot 10^4$	$1 \cdot 10^6$	≈ 12
42. Texas	$2.6 \cdot 10^5$	$17.7 \cdot 10^6$	≈ 7
43. New Jersey	$7.4 \cdot 10^3$	$7.79 \cdot 10^6$	$\approx 1,053$
44. Alaska	$5.7 \cdot 10^5$	$.59 \cdot 10^6$	≈ 1

LESSON MASTER 7-3 B

Questions on SPUR Objectives

Skills Objective A: Evaluate b^n when $b > 0$ and n is a negative integer.
Objective B: Simplify expressions using the Negative-Exponent Theorem.

In 1–21, write as a decimal or a simple fraction. Samples are given.

1. 8^{-3} $\frac{1}{512}$
2. 6^{-1} $\frac{1}{6}$
3. $\left(\frac{5}{6}\right)^{-1}$ $\frac{6}{5}$
4. $\left(\frac{3}{2}\right)^{-3}$ $\frac{8}{27}$
5. $(-5)^{-2}$ $\frac{1}{25}$
6. $-(-3)^{-4}$ $-\frac{1}{81}$
7. $3^{-2} \cdot 3^{-1}$ $\frac{1}{27}$
8. $7^{-5} \cdot 7^3$ $\frac{1}{49}$
9. $4^{-6} \cdot 4^6$ 1
10. $9 \cdot 7^{-4}$ $\frac{9}{2401}$
11. $-\left(\frac{1}{7}\right)^{-3}$ -343
12. $\frac{8^4}{8^7}$ $\frac{1}{512}$
13. $\frac{5^{-2}}{5^3}$ $\frac{1}{3125}$
14. $\frac{7^2}{7^{-2}}$ 2401
15. $\frac{12}{12^3}$ $\frac{1}{144}$
16. $\frac{9^{-4} \cdot 13^{-2}}{9 \cdot 13^{-3}}$ $\frac{13}{59,049}$
17. 10^{-7} $.0000001$
18. $1.4 \cdot 10^{-3}$ $.0014$
19. $\frac{6 \cdot 10^4}{1.5 \cdot 10^8}$ $.0004$
20. $(8 \cdot 10^{-2})(22 \cdot 10^{-4})$ $\frac{176}{1,000,000}$
21. $\frac{2 \cdot 10^{-4}}{5 \cdot 10^2}$ $.0000004$

In 22–31, simplify and write the result using only positive exponents.

22. $x^8 \cdot x^{-6}$ x^2
23. $m^{-7} \cdot m^4$ $\frac{1}{m^3}$
24. $c^{-5} \cdot c^{-2}$ $\frac{1}{c^7}$
25. $(5b)^{-3}$ $\frac{1}{125b^3}$
26. $\frac{e^{-5}}{e}$ $\frac{1}{e^6}$
27. $\frac{s^{-8}}{s^{-2}}$ $\frac{1}{s^6}$
28. $(3c^{-2})^{-4}$ $\frac{c^8}{81}$
29. $(5^{-2} \cdot y^2)^2(2xy^4)^{-3}$ $\frac{1}{5000x^3y^8}$
30. $\left(\frac{4r^5}{3r^6}\right)^{-1}$ $\frac{3r}{4}$
31. $\left(\frac{5x}{10y}\right)^{-3}\left(\frac{2y}{15x^2}\right)$ $\frac{16y^4}{15x^5}$

---

32. Show why b^n and b^{-n} are reciprocals.

Sample: $b^n \cdot b^{-n} = b^n \cdot 1/b^n = 1$

33. In the expression b^n, for what value(s) of n must b be a nonzero number?

$n \leq 0$

Uses Objective F: Solve real-world problems which can be modeled by expressions with negative-integer exponents.

In 34–36, meanings are given for several prefixes used in the metric system. a. Write the number using negative exponents. b. Write the number as a decimal. c. Write the number as a simple fraction.

34. micro: one millionth
   a. 10^{-6} b. $.000001$ c. $\frac{1}{1,000,000}$
35. nano: one billionth
   a. 10^{-9} b. $.000000001$ c. $\frac{1}{1,000,000,000}$
36. pico: one trillionth
   a. 10^{-12} b. $.000000000001$ c. $\frac{1}{1,000,000,000,000}$

37. The cost C of operating an electrical appliance is one-thousandth of the product of W, the number of watts; t, the time in hours; and k, the cost per kilowatt-hour.
   a. Write a formula for C using positive exponents. $C = \frac{Wtk}{10^3}$
   b. Write a formula for C using negative exponents. $C = Wtk \cdot 10^{-3}$

38. $1 \text{ foot}^2 \approx 2.2957 \cdot 10^{-5}$ acres, and 1 acre $= 1.5625 \cdot 10^{-3}$ miles^2. So 1 square foot $\approx$ ___?___ square miles. Fill in the blank with a number in scientific notation. $3.5870 \cdot 10^{-8}$

LESSON MASTER 7-4 B

Questions on SPUR Objectives

Vocabulary

1. The original amount of money placed in an investment is called the __?__ .

principal

2. If a savings account earns *compound interest*, what does this mean?

Sample: The interest, as well as the principal, earns interest.

3. The annual rate of interest earned after all the compounding has taken effect is called the __?__ .

yield

Uses Objective G: Apply the compound-interest formula.

4. Write the General Compound-Interest Formula and explain what each variable represents.

$A = P(1 + r/n)^{nt}$; A = amount after t years; P = amount invested; r = rate; n = number of times interest is compounded; t = number of years

5. Norio had invested $800 in a savings account that paid 4.2% interest compounded annually. How much money was in the account after 4 years, if he left the money untouched?

$943.11

6. Mrs. Rubino has put $2,500 in a 5-year CD (certificate of deposit) that pays 7.4% compounded quarterly. How much will the CD be worth when it matures?

$3607.12

7. When their daughter was 2 years old, the Nashans paid $7,000 for a 15-year college bond for her. The bond pays 7.1% compounded monthly. Their banker told them that if the money is left alone, it will triple in value. Is the banker right?

no

---

8. Nancy has $4,000 in a savings account that pays 3.9% interest compound semi-annually. Suppose the money is left untouched for 10 years.

   a. How much money is in the account after the first five years?

   $4852.13

   b. How much money is in the account after 10 years?

   $5885.79

   c. Does the account earn more interest during the first five years or the second five years? Explain why this is so.

   second five years; sample: The account earns interest on the interest.

9. Blanca invested $1,800 in an account that pays 4.4% compounded daily (365 days a year). If she leaves the money alone, how much will be in the account after 2.5 years?

$2009.29

10. Find the effective annual yield on an account that pays 6% compounded quarterly.

≈ 6.14%

Review Objective F, Lesson 3–8

In 11–14, determine whether or not the given formula describes an arithmetic sequence. Justify your answer.

11. $a_n = 4n + 15$ **Yes; constant difference is 4.**

12. $a_n = 2n^2 + 5$ **No; there is no constant difference.**

13. $a_n = \frac{1}{3}n$ **Yes; constant difference is $\frac{1}{3}$.**

14. $a_n = \frac{1}{n}$ **No; there is no constant difference.**

LESSON MASTER 7-5 B

Questions on SPUR Objectives

Vocabulary

1. What is another name for *geometric sequence*?

exponential sequence

Skills Objective C: Describe geometric sequences explicitly and recursively.

In 2–11, give the first five terms of the geometric sequence described.

2. constant ratio 4, first term 1

1, 4, 16, 64, 256

3. constant ratio .3, first term 8

8, 2.4, .72, .216, .0648

4. constant ratio $\frac{5}{4}$, first term 20

20, 25, $\frac{125}{4}$, $\frac{625}{16}$, $\frac{3125}{64}$

5. constant ratio -5, first term -5

-5, 25, -125, 625, -3125

6. first term 6, second term 18

6, 18, 54, 162, 486

7. fourth term 20, fifth term 5

1280, 320, 80, 20, 5

8. $g_n = 10(3)^{n-1}$, for integers $n \geq 1$

10, 30, 90, 270, 810

9. $g_n = 2(-.1)^{n-1}$, for integers $n \geq 1$

2, -.2, .02, -.002, .0002

10. $\begin{cases} g_1 = \frac{1}{2} \\ g_n = 6g_{n-1} \end{cases}$, for integers $n \geq 2$

$\frac{1}{2}$, 3, 18, 108, 648

11. $\begin{cases} g_1 = 10 \\ g_n = -g_{n-1} \end{cases}$, for integers $n \geq 2$

10, -10, 10, -10, 10

In 12–15, a sequence is given. a. Is the sequence geometric? b. If yes, give its constant ratio.

12. 7, 21, 63, 189, . . .

   a. **yes**

   b. **3**

13. 8, 16, 24, 32, . . .

   a. **no**

   b. _____

14. $\frac{3}{2}, -\frac{3}{4}, \frac{3}{8}, \frac{3}{16}, \ldots$

   a. **yes**

   b. **$-\frac{1}{2}$**

15. $\frac{9}{5}, \frac{13}{5}, \frac{17}{5}, \frac{21}{5}, \ldots$

   a. **no**

   b. _____

In 16–19, the first four terms of a geometric sequence are given. a. Give a recursive formula for the sequence. b. Give an explicit formula for the sequence.

16. 8, 88, 968, 10,648, . . .

   a. $\begin{cases} g_1 = 8 \\ g_n = 11g_{n-1}, \\ \quad n \geq 2 \end{cases}$

   b. $g_n = 8(11)^{n-1}, n \geq 1$

17. 12, -36, 108, -324, . . .

   a. $\begin{cases} g_1 = 12 \\ g_n = -3g_{n-1}, \\ \quad n \geq 2 \end{cases}$

   b. $g_n = 12(-3)^{n-1}, n \geq 1$

18. $\frac{3}{4}, \frac{3}{16}, \frac{3}{64}, \frac{3}{256}, \ldots$

   a. $\begin{cases} g_1 = \frac{3}{4} \\ g_n = \frac{1}{4}g_{n-1}, n \geq 2 \end{cases}$

   b. $g_n = \frac{3}{4}\left(\frac{1}{4}\right)^{n-1}, n \geq 1$

19. -2.5, 3.5, -4.9, 6.86, . . .

   a. $\begin{cases} g_1 = -2.5 \\ g_n = -1.4g_{n-1}, \\ \quad n \geq 2 \end{cases}$

   b. $g_n = -2.5(-1.4)^{n-1}, n \geq 1$

In 20–22, find the tenth term of the geometric sequence described.

20. first term 20, constant ratio .9

≈ 7.75

21. $g_n = 7(-2)^{n-1}$, for integers $n \geq 1$

-3584

22. $\begin{cases} g_1 = 4^2 \\ g_n = \frac{3}{2}g_{n-1} \end{cases}$, for integers $n \geq 2$

$\frac{19,683}{32}$, or ≈ 615.09

Uses Objective H: Solve real-world problems involving geometric sequences.

23. A ball is dropped from a height of 2 m and rises to 60% of its previous height each time it bounces. Find the height the ball reaches after its eighth bounce.

≈ .056 m

24. The population in Manrose County approximately doubled every decade from 1920 through 1970. If there were 1,650 residents in 1920, about how many were there in 1970?

52,800 res.

25. A sheet of a certain type of glass allows 90% of the light to pass through. How much light will pass through a triple thickness of this glass?

72.9%

LESSON MASTER 7-6 B

Questions on SPUR Objectives

Vocabulary

1. If u is an nth root of h, what equation relates the three variables? $u^n = h$

Skills Objective A: Evaluate b^n when $b > 0$ and n is a rational number.
Objective B: Simplify expressions or solve equations with exponents of the form $\frac{1}{n}$.
Objective D: Solve equations of the form $x^n = b$, where n is a rational number.

In 2–9, write as a decimal or a simple fraction. **Samples are given.**

2. $81^{\frac{1}{2}}$ 9

3. $(-125)^{\frac{1}{3}}$ -5

4. $-16^{\frac{1}{4}}$ -2

5. $1.44^{\frac{1}{2}}$ 1.2

6. $1^{\frac{1}{8}}$ 1

7. $\left(\frac{8}{27}\right)^{\frac{1}{3}}$ $\frac{2}{3}$

8. $(-32)^{\frac{1}{5}}$ -2

9. $343^{\frac{1}{3}}$ 7

In 10–15, use a calculator to approximate to the nearest thousandth.

10. $5^{\frac{1}{2}}$ 2.236

11. $22^{\frac{1}{3}}$ 2.802

12. $10^{\frac{1}{4}}$ 1.778

13. $2^{\frac{1}{10}}$ 1.072

14. $262{,}144^{\frac{1}{6}}$ 8

15. $(-.5)^{\frac{1}{9}}$ .926

In 16–23, solve.

16. $c^{\frac{1}{2}} = 5$ $c = 25$

17. $p^{\frac{1}{4}} = 20$ $p = 160{,}000$

18. $g^{\frac{1}{3}} = -6$ $g = -216$

19. $n^{\frac{1}{4}} = .2$ $n = .0000128$

20. $5m^{\frac{1}{2}} = 10$ $m = 4$

21. $-10r^{\frac{1}{3}} = 40$ $r = -64$

22. $b^{\frac{1}{4}} - 4 = 4$ $b = 4096$

23. $\frac{2}{3}\left(x^{\frac{1}{2}}\right) + 9 = 15$ $x = 81$

▶ **LESSON MASTER 7-6 B** *page 2*

In 24–27, an equation is given. **a.** Give the exact real solution(s). **b.** Approximate the solution(s) to the nearest thousandth.

24. $d^3 = 14$
   a. $d = 14^{\frac{1}{3}}$
   b. $d \approx 2.410$

25. $w^2 = 218$
   a. $w = \pm 218^{\frac{1}{2}}$
   b. $w \approx 14.765$

26. $m^5 + 9 = 6$
   a. $m = -3^{\frac{1}{5}}$
   b. $m \approx -1.246$

27. $2v^{10} = 24$
   a. $v = \pm 12^{\frac{1}{10}}$
   b. $v \approx 1.282$

Properties Objective E: Recognize properties of nth roots.

In 28–30, show that the given number is an 8th root of 390,625.

28. 5 $5^8 = 390{,}625$

29. -5 $(-5)^8 = 390{,}625$

30. 5i $(5i)^8 = 390{,}625 i^8 = 390{,}625$

In 31–34, use the Number of Real Roots Theorem to determine the number of real roots possible.

31. 4th root(s) of 20   2

32. 5th root(s) of 18   1

33. 6th root(s) of -12   0

34. 9th root(s) of -7   1

Uses Objective F: Solve real-world problems which can be modeled by expressions with nth roots.

35. The volume of a cube is 20 cubic feet.
   a. What is the exact length of an edge of the cube? $20^{\frac{1}{3}}$ ft
   b. What is the length of an edge of the cube to the nearest hundredth?   2.71 ft

36. Some bacteria double every 20 minutes. What is the ratio of the number of bacteria one minute to the number of bacteria the previous minute? $\approx 1.035{:}1$

LESSON MASTER 7-7 B

Questions on SPUR Objectives

Vocabulary

1. Write as a power of m.
   a. the 8th power of the cube root of m $m^{\frac{8}{3}}$
   b. the 7th power of the 5th power m $(m^5)^7$

Skills Objective A: Evaluate b^n when $b > 0$ and n is a rational number.
Objective B: Simplify expressions or solve equations using the Rational-Exponent Theorem.
Objective D: Solve equations of the form $x^n = b$, where n is a rational number.

In 2–11, write as a decimal or simple fraction. **Samples are given.**

2. $27^{\frac{4}{3}}$ 81

3. $64^{\frac{7}{6}}$ 128

4. $64^{\frac{5}{3}}$ 1024

5. $1^{\frac{7}{8}}$ 1

6. $100^{1.5}$ 1000

7. $.36^{2.5}$ .07776

8. $32^{\frac{2}{5}} \cdot 32^{\frac{2}{5}}$ 64

9. $.008^{\frac{7}{3}}$ .0000128

10. $\left(\frac{64}{9}\right)^{\frac{3}{2}}$ $\frac{512}{27}$

11. $\frac{2}{5} \cdot \left(\frac{8}{125}\right)^{\frac{2}{3}}$ $\frac{8}{125}$

In 12–17, use a calculator to approximate to the nearest hundredth.

12. $100^{\frac{3}{4}}$ 31.62

13. $8^{\frac{7}{6}}$ 11.31

14. $7.51^{\frac{5}{3}}$ 216.29

15. $45^{.3}$ 3.13

16. $64{,}078^{1.2}$ 586,206.65

17. $.006^{\frac{5}{12}}$ .12

In 18–25, simplify.

18. $a^{\frac{3}{4}} \cdot a^{\frac{1}{2}}$ $a^{\frac{5}{4}}$

19. $m^{3.6} \cdot m^{1.8}$ $m^{5.4}$

20. $u^{\frac{2}{3}} \cdot u^{\frac{6}{5}}$ $u^{\frac{28}{15}}$

21. $k^{\frac{4}{5}} \cdot k$ $k^{\frac{9}{5}}$

22. $\left(r^{\frac{5}{8}}\right)^3$ $r^{\frac{15}{8}}$

23. $\left(f^{\frac{3}{4}} g^{\frac{1}{4}}\right)^{\frac{2}{3}}$ $fg^{\frac{1}{6}}$

24. $(64y^3)^{\frac{7}{6}}$ $128y^{\frac{7}{2}}$

25. $(16e^{\frac{4}{3}})^{\frac{3}{4}}$ $8e$

▶ **LESSON MASTER 7-7 B** *page 2*

In 26–31, solve. If the solution is not an integer, round to the nearest hundredth.

26. $n^{\frac{3}{2}} = 27$ $n = 9$

27. $v^{\frac{5}{4}} = 32$ $v = 16$

28. $2g^{\frac{2}{3}} = 98$ $g = 343$

29. $a^{\frac{9}{4}} = 24$ $a \approx 40.76$

30. $m^{1.5} = .064$ $m = 0.16$

31. $\frac{d^{\frac{2}{5}}}{6} + 2 = 8$ $d = 7776$

Properties Objective E: Recognize properties of rational powers.

32. Consider the expression $x^{\frac{m}{n}}$. The Rational Exponent Theorem applies to which values of
   a. x?   reals ≥ 0
   b. m and n?   integers > 0

Uses Objective F: Solve real-world problems which can be modeled by expressions with rational powers.

In 33–35, recall from Lesson 7-6 that the ratio of the frequencies of consecutive keys on a piano is the 12th root of 2, or $2^{\frac{1}{12}}$. The frequency of the A below middle C is tuned to 220 hertz. The frequency F of a note n notes above A can be found by using the following formula: $F = 220 \cdot 2^{\frac{n}{12}}$. Find the frequency of the note.

33. E above middle C (7 notes above A) ≈ 330 hertz

34. F♯ above middle C (9 notes above A) ≈ 370 hertz

35. A above middle C (12 notes above A)   440 hertz

In 36 and 37, use Kepler's formula $d = 1.82r^{\frac{2}{3}}$ which gives the average distance d (in million of miles) of the sun from a planet with period of revolution r (in days).

36. Venus orbits the sun every 224.7 days. Find the distance from the sun to Venus to the nearest million miles. ≈ 67 mil. mi

37. Jupiter is about 484 million miles from the sun. Estimate Jupiter's period of revolution in *years*. ≈ 12 years

LESSON MASTER 7-8 B

Questions on SPUR Objectives

Skills Objective A: Evaluate b^n when $b > 0$ and n is a rational number.
Objective B: Simplify expressions or solve equations using properties of exponents.
Objective D: Solve equations of the form $x^n = b$, where n is a negative rational number.

In 1–8, write as a decimal or a simple fraction. Samples are given.

1. $64^{-\frac{4}{3}}$ $\dfrac{1}{256}$ 2. $100^{-\frac{3}{2}}$ $\dfrac{1}{1,000}$

3. $625^{-\frac{1}{4}}$ $\dfrac{1}{5}$ 4. $81^{-.75}$ $\dfrac{1}{27}$

5. $\left(\dfrac{25}{49}\right)^{-\frac{5}{2}}$ $\dfrac{16,807}{3,125}$ 6. $\left(\dfrac{1}{27}\right)^{-\frac{1}{3}}$ 3

7. $6 \cdot 32^{-\frac{4}{5}}$ $\dfrac{3}{8}$ 8. $9.3 \cdot 10,000^{-\frac{1}{2}}$ $.093$

In 9–14, use a calculator to approximate to the nearest thousandth.

9. $40^{-\frac{3}{2}}$ $.109$ 10. $5^{-\frac{1}{3}}$ $.117$

11. $1.21^{-\frac{1}{2}}$ $.909$ 12. $24^{-.8}$ $.079$

13. $12 \cdot 3.8^{-\frac{7}{3}}$ 4.928 14. $7.5 \cdot 16^{-2.2}$ $.017$

In 15–22, simplify. Use only positive exponents in your answer.

15. $\left(\dfrac{a}{b}\right)^{-\frac{1}{2}}$ $\left(\dfrac{b}{a}\right)^{1/2}$ 16. $\left(\dfrac{1}{h}\right)^{-\frac{3}{4}}$ $h^{3/4}$

17. $e^{-\frac{2}{3}}$ $\left(\dfrac{1}{e}\right)^{2/3}$ 18. $(r^3)^{-\frac{3}{8}}$ $\left(\dfrac{1}{r}\right)^{9/8}$

19. $v^{-\frac{1}{2}} \cdot w^3$ $\dfrac{w^3}{v^{1.2}}$ 20. $(x^{-\frac{3}{2}} y^{\frac{1}{4}})^{-2}$ $\dfrac{x^3}{y^{1/2}}$

21. $\dfrac{a^{-\frac{4}{3}}}{a^{\frac{2}{3}}}$ $\dfrac{1}{a^2}$ 22. $\dfrac{-20xy^2}{4x^3y^{-\frac{3}{4}}}$ $\dfrac{-5y^{1/4}}{x^2}$

In 23–28, solve. If the solution is not an integer, round to the nearest hundredth.

23. $m^{-\frac{3}{2}} = 64$ $m \approx .06$ 24. $a^{-\frac{1}{4}} = .7$ $a \approx 4.16$

25. $y^{-8} = 16$ $y \approx .03$ 26. $c^{-\frac{5}{3}} = 10$ $c \approx .25$

27. $u^{-4} = 318$ $u \approx .24$ 28. $9p^{-\frac{1}{3}} = 45$ $p \approx .01$

Properties Objective E: Recognize properties of negative rational exponents.

29. *Multiple choice.* List the expression(s) below that are equivalent to $a^{-\frac{a}{q}}$.   **a, c, e, f**

(a) $\dfrac{1}{a^{\frac{p}{q}}}$ (b) $(a^{-p})^q$ (c) $(a^{-1})^{\frac{p}{q}}$

(d) $\left(\dfrac{1}{a}\right)^{\frac{q}{p}}$ (e) $((a^{-1})^p)^{\frac{1}{q}}$ (f) $\left(\dfrac{1}{a}\right)^{\frac{p}{q}}$

Uses Objective F: Solve real-world problems which can be modeled by expressions with nth powers or nth roots.

30. Carbon 14 dating is used to estimate the age of a fossil less than 50,000 years old. When an organism dies, the Carbon 14, or ^{14}C, in the organism decomposes at a constant rate. The amount of ^{14}C is reduced to half in about 5750 years. The amount of ^{14}C is reduced to the fraction $2^{-\frac{x}{5750}}$ after x years.

Approximately what fraction of a living organism's ^{14}C is left after the given time period? Express the answer as a percent.

a. 2,875 years $\approx 70.7\%$ b. 11,500 years 25%

c. 25,000 years $\approx 4.9\%$ d. 50,000 years $\approx .2\%$

Review Objective I, Lesson 4-7

31. Graph the polygon $\begin{bmatrix} 2 & 5 & 3 & 0 \\ 1 & -1 & -4 & -3 \end{bmatrix}$ and its image under $r_x \circ r_x$.

32. Graph the polygon $\begin{bmatrix} -3 & -1 & -3 \\ 2 & 2 & -1 \end{bmatrix}$ and its image under $r_{x=y} \circ S_2$.

LESSON MASTER 8-1 B

Questions on SPUR Objectives

Vocabulary

1. Define the *composite* $g \circ f$ of two functions f and g.
Sample: the function that maps x onto $g(f(x))$ and whose domain is the set of all values in the domain of f for which $f(x)$ is in the domain of g

Skills Objective A: Find values and rules for composites of functions.

In 2–11, let $f(x) = -2x^2$ and $g(x) = 6x + 1$.

2. Evaluate $f(g(2))$. -338 3. Evaluate $g(f(2))$. -47

4. Evaluate $f(g(-3))$. -578 5. Evaluate $f \circ g(-3)$. -578

6. Evaluate $f(f(0))$. 0 7. Evaluate $g(g(0))$. 7

8. Evaluate $f(g(0))$. -2 9. Evaluate $g(f(0))$. 1

10. Find an expression for $f(g(x))$. $-72x^2 - 24x - 2$

11. Find an expression for $g(f(x))$. $-12x^2 + 1$

In 12–21, $r(n) = \dfrac{1}{2n}$ and $s(n) = -4n - 8$.

12. Evaluate $r(s(1))$. $-\dfrac{1}{24}$ 13. Evaluate $s(r(1))$. -10

14. Evaluate $r(r(3))$. 3 15. Evaluate $s(s(-2))$. -8

16. Find an expression for $r(s(n))$. $-\dfrac{1}{8n + 16}$

17. Find an expression for $s(r(n))$. $-\dfrac{2}{n} - 8$

18. State the restrictions, if any, on the domain of $r \circ s$. $n \neq -2$

19. State the restrictions, if any, on the domain of $s \circ r$. $n \neq 0$

20. State the restrictions, if any, on the domain of $r \circ r$. $n \neq 0$

21. State the restrictions, if any, on the domain of $s \circ s$.   none

---

In 22 and 23, rules for functions g and h are given. Does $g \circ h = h \circ g$? Justify your answer.

22. $g: m \to m - 9$ $h: m \to m + 9$
Yes; $g \circ h(m) = (m + 9) - 9 = m$, and $h \circ g(m) = (m - 9) + 9 = m$.

23. $g(n) = 3n + 5$ $h(n) = 3n - 5$
No; $g \circ h(n) = 3(3n - 5) + 5 = 9n - 10$, but $h \circ g = 3(3n + 5) - 5 = 9n + 10$.

In 24–26, suppose $p(x) = x^2$ and $q(x) = x^4$. Write an expression for

24. $p \circ q(x)$. x^8 25. $q \circ p(x)$. x^8 26. $p(x) \cdot q(x)$. x^6

Review Objective L, Lessons 3-2 and 3-4

In 27–30, graph the equation.

27. $y = 2x - 5$

28. $6y = 24$

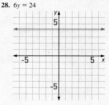

29. $3x + 4y = -12$

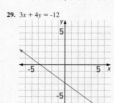

30. $y = -x$

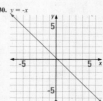

LESSON MASTER 8-2 B

Questions on SPUR Objectives

Vocabulary

1. How is the *inverse* of a relation obtained?
   Sample: Switch the order of the coordinates for each ordered pair in the relation.

Skills Objective B: Find the inverse of a relation.

In 2–7, a function is defined. a. Describe the inverse of the function. b. Tell if the inverse is a function.

2. $f(x) = \{(2, 8), (6, -1), (-4, 4), (0, -1)\}$
   a. **$\{(8, 2), (-1, 6), (4, -4), (-1, 0)\}$**
   b. **no**

3. $y = 5x$
   a. **$y = \frac{1}{5}x$**
   b. **yes**

4. $y = 9x - 2$
   a. **$y = \frac{x}{9} + \frac{2}{9}$**
   b. **yes**

5. $y = x^2 + 5x + 4$
   a. **$y = \frac{-5 \pm \sqrt{9 + 4x}}{2}$**
   b. **no**

6. $y = |x| + 1$
   a. **$y = x - 1$ or $y = -x + 1$**
   b. **no**

7. $y = -x^3$
   a. **$y = -x^{\frac{1}{3}}$**
   b. **yes**

Properties Objective F: Apply properties of inverse relations and functions.

8. Complete the following: According to the Horizontal-Line Test for Inverses, if no horizontal line intersects the graph of a function f in more than one point, then ___?___.
   the inverse of f is itself a function

9. How are the domain and range of a function g related to the domain and range of the inverse of g?
   Sample: The domain of g is the range of the inverse of g, and the range of g is the domain of the inverse of g.

▶ **LESSON MASTER 8-2 B** *page 2*

10. How is the graph of a function related to the graph of its inverse?
    Sample: The graphs are reflection images of each other over the line $y = x$.

Representations Objective I: Make and interpret graphs of inverses of relations.

11. Identify all of the graphs which represent a function whose inverse is also a function. **a, b**

(a)   (b) (c) (d)

12. The graph of a function is shown on the grid at the right.
    a. On the same grid, sketch the graph of the inverse of the function.
    b. Is the inverse also a function? Why or why not?
    Yes; the graph passes the Horizontal-Line Test for Inverses.

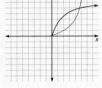

13. a. At the right, graph the inverse of the function with equation $y = -2x^2$.
    b. Is the inverse also a function? Why or why not?
    No; the graph does not pass the Vertical-Line Test for Functions.

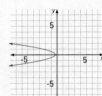

LESSON MASTER 8-3 B

Questions on SPUR Objectives

Skills Objective B: Find the inverse of a relation.

In 1–10, write an equation for the inverse in $f(x)$ notation.

1. $h(x) = 8x$
   $h^{-1}(x) = \frac{1}{8}x$

2. $f(x) = x + 9$
   $f^{-1}(x) = x - 9$

3. $g(t) = 2t - 7$
   $g^{-1}(t) = \frac{1}{2}(t + 7)$

4. $f(a) = -4a + 3$
   $f^{-1}(a) = -\frac{1}{4}(a - 3)$

5. $h(x) = \frac{7}{x}$
   $h^{-1}(x) = \frac{7}{x}$

6. $g(x) = \frac{x - 5}{2}$
   $g^{-1}(x) = 2x + 5$

7. $f(z) = -5(z + 10)$
   $f^{-1}(z) = -\frac{1}{5}(z + 50)$

8. $m(x) = \frac{1}{2}x^2$, when $x \geq 0$
   $m^{-1}(x) = \sqrt{2x}$

9. $f(x) = x^7$, when $x \geq 0$
   $f^{-1}(x) = x^{\frac{1}{7}}$

10. $g(x) = x^{\frac{1}{8}}$, when $x \geq 0$
    $g^{-1}(x) = x^8$

Properties Objective F: Apply properties of inverse relations and functions.

11. Consider the function f defined by $f(x) = -5x + 12$. **$f^{-1}(x) = -\frac{1}{5}(x - 12)$**
    a. Write a rule for $f^{-1}(x)$.
    b. Find $f \circ f^{-1}(x)$. **x**
    c. Find $f^{-1} \circ f(x)$. **x**

In 12–15, two functions f and g are defined over the domain $x \geq 0$. a. Find $f(g(x))$. b. Find $g(f(x))$. c. Tell if f and g are inverses and explain why or why not.

12. $f(x) = x + 4$ and $g(x) = \frac{1}{4}x$
    a. **$\frac{1}{4}x + 4$**
    b. **$\frac{1}{4}(x + 4)$**
    c. **no; $f(g(x)) \neq g(f(x)) \neq x$**

13. $f(x) = x^{\frac{4}{7}}$ and $g(x) = x^{\frac{7}{4}}$
    a. **x**
    b. **x**
    c. **yes; $f(g(x)) = g(f(x)) = x$**

▶ **LESSON MASTER 8-3 B** *page 2*

14. $f(x) = -x$ and $g(x) = -x$
    a. **x**
    b. **x**
    c. **yes; $f(g(x)) = g(f(x)) = x$**

15. $f(x) = x^1$ and $g(x) = x^{-1}$
    a. **x^{-1}**
    b. **x^{-1}**
    c. **no; $f(g(x)) = g(f(x)) \neq x$**

Representations Objective I: Make and interpret graphs of inverses of relations.

16. Consider the function $g: x \rightarrow x^2 - 1$, when $x \geq 0$.
    a. Graph g at the right.
    b. Write a formula for g^{-1}.
    $g^{-1}(x) = \sqrt{x + 1}$
    c. Graph g^{-1} at the right.

    d. Describe how the graphs of g and g^{-1} are related.
    Sample: They are reflection images of each other over the line $y = x$.
    e. Explain why, if the domain of g is taken as the set of real numbers, the inverse of g is not a function.
    Sample: The graph of g does not pass the Horizontal-Line Test for Inverses.

17. *Multiple choice.* A function h is graphed at the right. Which of the following domains for h gives a function whose inverse is also a function?
    a
    (a) $\{x: 1 \leq x \leq 6\}$
    (b) $\{x: x \leq 7\}$
    (c) $\{x: -5 \leq x \leq 5\}$

LESSON MASTER 8-4 B

Questions on SPUR Objectives

Vocabulary

1. Complete the following definition.

When m is __?__ and n is __?__ , $\sqrt[n]{m}$ = __?__ .

nonnegative   an integer ≥ 2 $m^{\frac{1}{n}}$

Skills Objective C: Evaluate radicals.
Objective D: Rewrite or simplify expressions with radicals.

In 2–7, evaluate.

2. $\sqrt[3]{512}$ _____ **8**   3. $\sqrt{169}$ _____ **13**

4. $\sqrt{10,000}$ _____ **10**   5. $\sqrt[3]{.008}$ _____ **.2**

6. $\sqrt[6]{\frac{64}{729}}$ _____ **$\frac{2}{3}$**   7. $\sqrt{50,625}$ _____ **15**

In 8–11, approximate to the nearest hundredth.

8. $\sqrt[5]{10}$ _____ **1.58**   9. $\sqrt[7]{8}$ _____ **1.30**

10. $\sqrt[4]{716,448}$ _____ **29.09**   11. $\sqrt{0.00029}$ _____ **.07**

In 12–15, rewrite using a single radical. Assume that the variables represent nonnegative real numbers.

12. $\sqrt[4]{\sqrt{\sqrt{u}}}$ $\sqrt[8]{u}$ 13. $\sqrt{\sqrt{45y}}$ $\sqrt[4]{45y}$

14. $\sqrt[4]{\sqrt{\sqrt{e^3m}}}$ $\sqrt[16]{e^3m}$ 15. $\sqrt[5]{\sqrt[4]{\sqrt{y}}}$ $\sqrt[20]{y}$

In 16–19, write without a radical sign and simplify. Assume that the variables represent nonnegative real numbers.

16. $\sqrt{r^5}$ _____ $r^{\frac{5}{2}}$ 17. $\sqrt[6]{y^4}$ _____ $y^{\frac{2}{3}}$

18. $\sqrt[4]{a^4}$ _____ a 19. $\sqrt[3]{u^{15}}$ _____ u^5

Properties Objective G: Apply properties of radicals and nth-root functions.

20. Consider the statement $\sqrt[6]{m^6} = m$.

a. For which values of m is the statement true? _____ $m \geq 0$

b. If the statement is not true for all real numbers, give a counterexample to justify that.
Sample: If $m = -2$, $\sqrt[6]{(-2)^6} = 2 \neq -2$.

21. Suppose $r \geq 0$ and a and b are integers such that $a \geq 1$ and $b \geq 2$. Write two other expressions equivalent to $\sqrt[b]{r^a}$.

Samples: $r^{\frac{a}{b}}$; $(r^a)^{\frac{1}{b}}$; $(\sqrt[b]{r})^a$

Uses Objective H: Solve real-world problems which can be modeled by equations with radicals.

22. The frequency F of a note that is n notes above a note with frequency f can be found by using the following formula:
$F = f \cdot 2^{\frac{n}{12}}$.

a. Write this formula using radical notation. $F = f \sqrt[12]{2^n}$

b. Suppose you want to know the frequency F of a note 5 notes above the note with frequency f. Write a formula for F using radical notation. $F = f \sqrt[12]{32}$

23. Suppose the probability of spinning a B six times in a row is p. Use radical notation to give the probability of spinning a B on a single spin. $\sqrt[6]{p}$

Review Objective B, Lesson 7-2

In 24–27, simplify.

24. $d^4 \cdot d^8$ d^{12} 25. $(-4e^5)^2$ $16e^{10}$

26. $\frac{18a^4}{9a}$ $2a^3$ 27. $\left(\frac{m}{4}\right)^3$ $\frac{m^3}{64}$

LESSON MASTER 8-5 B

Questions on SPUR Objectives

Vocabulary

1. Explain how to find the *geometric mean* of a set of n positive numbers.

Sample: Multiply the numbers and take the nth root of the product.

Skills Objective D: Rewrite or simplify expressions with radicals.

In 2–4, *multiple choice*. Identify the expression that is *not* equivalent to the given expression.

2. $\sqrt{96}$ _____ **c**

(a) $\sqrt{48} \cdot \sqrt{2}$ (b) $\sqrt[3]{12} \cdot \sqrt[3]{8}$ (c) $8\sqrt[3]{12}$

(d) $2\sqrt{12}$ (e) $\sqrt{16} \cdot \sqrt{6}$ (f) $\sqrt{4} \cdot \sqrt{24}$

3. $\sqrt[3]{5} \cdot \sqrt[3]{250}$ _____ **b**

(a) $\sqrt[3]{5} \cdot \sqrt[3]{125} \cdot \sqrt[3]{2}$ (b) $2\sqrt[3]{5}$ (c) $\sqrt[3]{5^4} \cdot \sqrt[3]{2}$

(d) $\sqrt[3]{1250}$ (e) $\sqrt[3]{25} \cdot \sqrt[3]{50}$ (f) $5\sqrt[3]{2}$

4. $\sqrt[6]{128y^{14}}$ _____ **d**

(a) $\sqrt[6]{128} \cdot \sqrt[6]{y^{12}} \cdot \sqrt[6]{y^2}$ (b) $\sqrt[6]{2^6 \cdot 2 \cdot y^6 \cdot y^6 \cdot y^2}$ (c) $\sqrt[6]{2^7} \cdot \sqrt[6]{y^{14}}$

(d) $64y^{12} \cdot \sqrt[6]{2y^2}$ (e) $\sqrt[6]{128} \cdot \sqrt[6]{y^{14}}$ (f) $2y^2\sqrt[6]{2y^2}$

In 5–14, simplify. Assume that the variables are nonnegative.

5. $\sqrt[3]{250}$ $5\sqrt[3]{2}$ 6. $\sqrt[4]{48}$ $2\sqrt[4]{3}$

7. $\sqrt[4]{50,000x^7}$ $10x\sqrt[4]{5x^3}$ 8. $\sqrt[3]{27x^6y^4}$ $3x^2y\sqrt[3]{y}$

9. $\sqrt[6]{x^{12}y^6}$ x^2y 10. $\sqrt[4]{81m^5}$ $3m\sqrt[4]{m}$

11. $\sqrt[3]{5} \cdot \sqrt[3]{125}$ **5**   12. $\sqrt[3]{9} \cdot \sqrt[3]{48}$ $6\sqrt[3]{2}$

13. $\sqrt[3]{2u^7} \cdot \sqrt[3]{4u^2}$ $2u^3$ 14. $\sqrt[5]{3^2x} \cdot \sqrt[5]{3^4x^8}$ $3x\sqrt[5]{9x^4}$

---

15. Find the geometric mean of the following set of numbers. Round to the nearest hundredth.
18, 27, 84, 33.6, 4   _____ **22.28**

16. The chart at the right gives the period of revolution for the nine planets in our solar system. Find the geometric mean of these periods.
8.86 years

Planet	Period of Revolution (years)
Mercury	0.24
Venus	0.62
Earth	1
Mars	1.88
Jupiter	11.86
Saturn	29.46
Uranus	84
Neptune	165
Pluto	248

Properties Objective G: Apply properties of radicals and nth-root functions.

17. Prove that if $x \geq 0$, $\sqrt[6]{x} = \sqrt[12]{x^2}$.
Sample: $\sqrt[6]{x} = x^{\frac{1}{6}}$; $\sqrt[12]{x^2} = x^{\frac{2}{12}} = x^{\frac{1}{6}}$

18. Prove that if $y \geq 0$, $\sqrt[5]{y} \cdot \sqrt[3]{y} = \sqrt[15]{y^8}$.
Sample: $\sqrt[5]{y} \cdot \sqrt[3]{y} = y^{\frac{1}{5}} \cdot y^{\frac{1}{3}} = y^{\frac{1}{5}+\frac{1}{3}} = y^{\frac{8}{15}}$; $\sqrt[15]{y^8} = y^{\frac{8}{15}}$

In 19 and 20, write the expression using a single radical sign.

19. $\sqrt[3]{r} \cdot \sqrt[4]{r}$ $\sqrt[12]{r^7}$ 20. $\sqrt[6]{a} \cdot \sqrt[5]{b}$ $\sqrt[30]{a^5b^6}$

LESSON MASTER 8-6 B

Questions on SPUR Objectives

Vocabulary

1. Complete the following: When we *rationalize* the denominator of a fraction, we rewrite the fraction in an equivalent form so that ___?___.
Sample: **the denominator does not contain any irrational numbers**

2. What is the *conjugate* of the expression $m + \sqrt{n}$? → $m - \sqrt{n}$

Skills Objective D: Rewrite or simplify expressions with radicals.

In 3–18, rationalize the denominator. Assume variables under the radical sign are positive.

3. $\dfrac{1}{\sqrt{3}}$ → $\dfrac{\sqrt{3}}{3}$

4. $\dfrac{2}{\sqrt{7}}$ → $\dfrac{2\sqrt{7}}{7}$

5. $\dfrac{6}{\sqrt{6}}$ → $\sqrt{6}$

6. $\dfrac{5}{2\sqrt{10}}$ → $\dfrac{\sqrt{10}}{4}$

7. $\dfrac{4}{\sqrt{x}}$ → $\dfrac{4\sqrt{x}}{x}$

8. $\dfrac{1}{\sqrt{x^3}}$ → $\dfrac{\sqrt{x}}{x^2}$

9. $\dfrac{5a}{\sqrt{a}}$ → $5\sqrt{a}$

10. $\dfrac{3e}{\sqrt{e^7}}$ → $\dfrac{3\sqrt{e}}{e^3}$

11. $\dfrac{8n}{\sqrt{6n^5}}$ → $\dfrac{4\sqrt{6n}}{3n^2}$

12. $\dfrac{9}{c\sqrt{c}}$ → $\dfrac{9\sqrt{c}}{c^2}$

13. $\dfrac{7}{3+\sqrt{2}}$ → $3 - \sqrt{2}$

14. $\dfrac{4}{8-\sqrt{5}}$ → $\dfrac{32+4\sqrt{5}}{59}$

15. $\dfrac{x}{\sqrt{x}+1}$ → $\dfrac{x\sqrt{x}-x}{x-1}$

16. $\dfrac{4}{6-\sqrt{r}}$ → $\dfrac{24+4\sqrt{r}}{36-r}$

17. $\dfrac{5+\sqrt{3}}{5-\sqrt{3}}$ → $\dfrac{14+5\sqrt{3}}{11}$

18. $\dfrac{6}{\sqrt{10}-\sqrt{7}}$ → $2\sqrt{10}+2\sqrt{7}$

In 19 and 20, write the expression in radical form with a rational denominator. Assume that the variables are positive.

19. $5^{\frac{3}{2}}\cdot a^{-\frac{1}{2}}$ → $\dfrac{5\sqrt{5a}}{a}$

20. $b^{-\frac{7}{2}}c$ → $\dfrac{c\sqrt{b}}{b^4}$

141 ▶

▶ **LESSON MASTER 8-6 B** *page 2*

21. Show that $(\sqrt{50}-7)$ is 14 less than its reciprocal.

Sample: $\dfrac{1}{\sqrt{50}-7} - 14 = \dfrac{1(\sqrt{50}+7)}{(\sqrt{50}-7)(\sqrt{50}+7)} - 14$

$= \dfrac{\sqrt{50}+7}{50-49} - 14 = \dfrac{\sqrt{50}+7}{1} - 14 = \sqrt{50}-7$

In 22–24, use the triangle at the right. Write the ratio with a rationalized denominator.

22. $\dfrac{PR}{QR}$ → $\sqrt{3}$

23. $\dfrac{PR}{QP}$ → $\dfrac{\sqrt{3}}{2}$

24. $\dfrac{QR}{QP}$ → $\dfrac{1}{2}$

In 25 and 26, use the square at the right. Write the ratio with a rationalized denominator.

25. $\dfrac{CD}{AC}$ → $\dfrac{\sqrt{2}}{2}$

26. $\dfrac{AC}{CD}$ → $\sqrt{2}$

In 27 and 28, rationalize the numerator.

27. $\dfrac{2-\sqrt{5}}{3}$ → $\dfrac{-1}{6+3\sqrt{5}}$

28. $\dfrac{6+4\sqrt{2}}{9}$ → $\dfrac{2}{27-18\sqrt{2}}$

Review Objective A, Lesson 7-2

In 29–37, evaluate and write in standard form.

29. $(-5)^2$ → 25
30. $(15)^3$ → 3375
31. $(-1)^{19}$ → -1
32. $(-12)^2$ → 144
33. $2^3 \cdot 7^3$ → 2744
34. $6^3 \cdot 6^2$ → 7776
35. $1.9 \cdot 10^5$ → 190,000
36. $44{,}066 \cdot 10^0$ → 44,066
37. $(9.1 \cdot 10^2)(3.4 \cdot 10^3)$ → 3,094,000

142

LESSON MASTER 8-7 B

Questions on SPUR Objectives

Vocabulary

1. Complete the following: When x is negative and n is ___?___, $\sqrt[n]{x}$ stands for the real nth root of x. → **odd**

Skills Objective C: Evaluate radicals.

2. Calculate $(-7)^n$ for all integer values of n from -4 to 4.

$\frac{1}{2401}$	$-\frac{1}{343}$	$\frac{1}{49}$	$-\frac{1}{7}$	1
-7	49	-343	2401	

In 3–8, *multiple choice*. Tell which of the following describes the expression.

(a) defined, real positive number
(b) defined, real negative number
(c) defined, nonreal number
(d) not defined

3. $\sqrt[3]{-20}$ → b
4. $\sqrt{-18}$ → c
5. $\sqrt{12}$ → a
6. $\sqrt[6]{-64}$ → d
7. $\sqrt[4]{5}$ → a
8. $\sqrt[11]{-9}$ → b

In 9–16, write as a decimal or a simple fraction.

9. $\sqrt[3]{-64}$ → -4
10. $\sqrt[9]{-1}$ → -1
11. $\sqrt[5]{100{,}000}$ → 10
12. $\sqrt[5]{3125}$ → 5
13. $\sqrt[3]{-27} \cdot \sqrt[3]{-64}$ → 12
14. $\sqrt[3]{-1} + \sqrt[7]{-128}$ → -3
15. $\sqrt[9]{-2^{18}}$ → -4
16. $\sqrt[9]{(-2)^{18}}$ → 4

143 ▶

▶ **LESSON MASTER 8-7 B** *page 2*

Properties Objective G: Apply properties of radicals and nth-root functions.

In 17–20, for what values of n is the expression defined?

17. $\sqrt[8]{n}$ → $n \geq 0$
18. $\sqrt[9]{n}$ → n is any real number.
19. $n^{\frac{4}{3}}$ → $n \geq 0$
20. $\sqrt[n]{-18}$ → n is any odd number.

21. If a is negative, is $a^3 = \sqrt{a^6}$? Why or why not?
Sample: No, if a is negative, a^3 is negative; but $\sqrt{a^6}$ is positive.

Representations Objective I: Make and interpret graphs of inverses of relations.

22. a. Sketch the graph of $y = x^4$ for $-8 \leq x \leq 8$.
b. Sketch the graph of $y = \sqrt[4]{x}$ for $-8 \leq x \leq 8$.

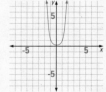

c. Is $y = \sqrt[4]{x}$ the inverse of $y = x^4$? Why or why not?
Sample: No; the graphs of the functions are not reflection images of each other over the line $y = x$.

144

LESSON MASTER 8-8 B

Questions on SPUR Objectives

Vocabulary

1. Suppose Equation A implies Equation B. If a solution to Equation B is *not* a solution to Equation A, the solution is called ___?___.

extraneous

Skills Objective E: Solve equations with radicals.

In 2–11, find all real solutions.

2. $\sqrt[4]{a} = 4$

$a = 256$

3. $\sqrt[5]{w} = -3$

$w = -243$

4. $8\sqrt[5]{x} = -4$

$x = -\frac{1}{32}$

5. $\frac{8}{5} \cdot \sqrt[6]{m} = 8$

$m = 15{,}625$

6. $18 - \sqrt[4]{u} = 9$

$u = 6561$

7. $5\sqrt[3]{y} - 2 = -\sqrt[3]{y}$

$y = \frac{1}{27}$

8. $\sqrt[4]{r+3} = -5$

no real solution

9. $\sqrt{2m - 6} = 18$

$m = 165$

10. $22 + \sqrt[7]{c+2} = 21$

$c = -3$

11. $8 + \sqrt[6]{2b} = 3$

no real solution

Uses Objective H: Solve real-world problems which can be modeled by equations with radicals.

12. Find two points on the line $y = 4$ that are 5 units away from the point (2, 3).

$(2 \pm 2\sqrt{6},\ 4)$

13. Find two points on the line $x = -5$ that are 6 units away from the point (3, 0).

no points

14. Janet made a wooden-cube lamp table and veneered it with $\frac{1}{8}$-inch-thick walnut. The finished cube has volume of about 3725 cubic inches. What was the approximate length of an edge of the cube before it was veneered?

≈ 15.25 in.

15. The equation $d = 1.82 \sqrt[3]{r^2}$ approximates the average distance (in millions of miles) of a planet from the sun where r is the number of days in the planet's revolution. Venus is an average distance of 108.2 million miles from the sun. Find the number of days in Venus's revolution.

≈ 458 days

Review Objective G, Lesson 7-4

16. Mr. Machado invested $7,500 in a 5-year CD (certificate of deposit) that paid 6.8% compounded quarterly. If he leaves the money alone, how much will the CD be worth when it matures?

$10,507.04

17. Dana invested $2,600 in an account that pays 5.4% compounded daily (365 days a year). If she leaves the money alone, how much will be in the account after 3.5 years?

$3140.86

LESSON MASTER 9-1 B

Questions on SPUR Objectives

Vocabulary

1. Write the general equation for an *exponential function* and give the restrictions, if any, for each variable.

$f(x) = ab^x;\ a \neq 0,\ b > 0,\ b \neq 1$

Properties Objective D: Recognize properties of exponential functions.

In 2 and 3, an equation for a function is given. **a.** Give the domain of the function. **b.** Give the range of the function.

2. $f(x) = 9^x$

a. **all reals**

b. **positive reals**

3. $f(x) = 3(1.05)^x$

a. **all reals**

b. **positive reals**

Uses Objective F: Apply exponential-growth models.

4. The population N of a certain strain of bacteria grows according to the equation $N = 200 \cdot 2^{1.4t}$, where t is the time in hours.

a. How many bacteria were there at the beginning of the experiment?

200 bacteria

b. After how many hours will the number of bacteria double?

$\approx .7$ hour

c. Estimate the number of bacteria in 10 hours.

$\approx 3{,}276{,}800$ bac.

d. Estimate the number of bacteria 2 hours before the experiment began.

≈ 28.7 bacteria

5. In 1994, the number of weekly passes sold by Tri-Cities Transit was 98,481 and was growing at a rate of about 3.8% per year. At this rate, estimate the number of passes sold in each year.

a. 1997

$\approx 110{,}140$ passes

b. 1985

$\approx 70{,}401$ passes

---

6. Of the American cities with populations over 100,000, Mesa, Arizona, had the fastest growing population for the decade from 1980 to 1990. In 1980, its population was 152,404. In 1990, it was 288,091. Assume that the growth rate continues.

a. By what percent did the population of Mesa increase in the decade from 1980 to 1990? Round to the nearest percent.

89%

b. What was the growth rate for the decade?

1.89

c. Let $P(x) =$ the population x decades after 1980. Find a formula for $P(x)$.

$P(x) = 152{,}404(1.89)^x$

d. Estimate the population of Mesa in 2010.

1,028,920

e. Use the function $P(x)$ from part c to:

(i) estimate the year during which the population was 200,000.

1984

(ii) estimate the year during which the population will reach a half million.

1999

Representations Objective I: Graph exponential functions.

7. *Multiple choice.* Which equation has a graph that is an exponential curve?

(a) $y = 4x$ (b) $y = x^4$ (c) $y = 4^x$ (d) $y = \frac{x}{4}$

c

8. At the right, sketch a graph that could represent exponential growth.

Sample graph is given.

9. Locate at least five points on the graph of $y = .25 \cdot 3^x$ on the grid at the right.

Sample points are:

(0, .25), (1, .75), (2, 2.25), (3, 6.75), (-1, .083)

LESSON MASTER 9-2 B

Questions on SPUR Objectives

Vocabulary

1. What is true of the growth factor in situations of *exponential decay*?

The growth factor is between zero and 1.

2. What is *depreciation*?

Sample: a decrease in value of manufactured goods over time

Properties Objective D: Recognize properties of exponential functions.

In 3 and 4, an equation for a function is given. **a.** Give the domain of the function. **b.** Give the range of the function.

3. $f(x) = 0.9^x$

a. **all reals**
b. **positive reals**

4. $f(x) = 1.5(.08)^x$

a. **all reals**
b. **positive reals**

5. Give the equations of all asymptotes of the graph defined by $f(x) = 3(.44)^x$.

$y = 0$

6. *Multiple choice.* The reflection image over the y-axis of an exponential-decay curve is which of the following?

(a) same exponential-decay curve   (b) different exponential-decay curve

(c) exponential-growth curve   (d) none of these

c

7. Consider the exponential function with equation $y = ab^x$. Give an equation for its x-intercept and y-intercept.

no x-intercept   **$y = a$**

Uses Objective F: Apply exponential-decay models.

8. Suppose a new car bought in 1988 for $14,675 depreciates 15% each year.

a. Find an equation that gives the car's value x years after 1988.

$y = 14,675(.85)^x$

b. Predict the car's value in 1995.

$4704.47

▶ LESSON MASTER 9-2 B *page 2*

9. Consider the equation $L = .87^x$, which gives the percent of light that will pass through x thicknesses of a certain type of tinted glass. (L = lumens per square meter)

a. What percent of light will pass through a single thickness?

87%

b. What percent of light will pass through four thicknesses?

57.3%

c. What percent of light will pass through a half-thickness of the glass?

93.3%

d. Suppose a source emits light with an intensity of 1400 lumens per square meter. What is the intensity of the light passing through six thicknesses of the glass?

607 lumens/m²

10. Radium-226 (^{226}Ra) has a half-life of 1620 years.

a. Determine an equation for the percent of ^{226}Ra remaining in the original sample after x half-life periods.

$y = 100(.5)^x$

b. If you start with 4 g of ^{226}Ra, how much will remain after 5 half-life periods?

.125 g

c. How many years equal 5 half-life periods of ^{226}Ra?

8100 years

Representations Objective I: Graph exponential functions.

11. At the right, sketch a graph that could represent exponential decay.

Sample graph is given.

12. Locate at least five points on the graph of $y = .6^x$ on the grid at the right.

Sample points are:
(0, 1), (1, .6),
(2, .36), (-1, 1.6),
(-2, 2.7)

LESSON MASTER 9-3 B

Questions on SPUR Objectives

Vocabulary

1. Consider the number e.

a. After whom was it named?

Euler

b. Give its value to the nearest millionth.

2.718281

c. Fill in the blank: As n increases, the sequence of numbers ___?___ approaches e.

$(1 + \frac{1}{n})^n$

Properties Objective D: Recognize properties of exponential functions.

In 2 and 3, an equation for a function is given. **a.** Give the domain of the function. **b.** Give the range of the function.

2. $f(x) = e^{2x}$

a. **all reals**
b. **positive reals**

3. $g(x) = 3e^{-4x}$

a. **all reals**
b. **positive reals**

In 4–9, *multiple choice.* Which situation is described by the function?

(a) constant increase   (b) constant decrease

(c) exponential growth   (d) exponential decay

4. $f(x) = e^{-3x}$ **d**

5. $g(x) = 5ex$ **a**

6. $h(x) = -2ex + 1$ **b**

7. $u(x) = 4e^x$ **c**

8. $v(x) = e^{8x}$ **c**

9. $w(x) = e^{0.5x}$ **c**

Uses Objective F: Apply exponential-growth and exponential-decay models.

10. Suppose an initial amount of $20,000 grows at the rate of 13% per year. Use function notation to describe this continuous-change model.

$N(t) = 20,000e^{.13t}$

11. Suppose $1800 is invested at an annual interest rate of 7% compounded continuously, and the money is left untouched.

a. How much is in the account after 5 years?

$2554.32

b How much is in the account after 10 years?

$3624.75

c. Find the effective annual yield on the account.

≈ 7.25%

▶ LESSON MASTER 9-3 B *page 2*

12. A machine depreciates so that its value after t years is given by $N(t) = N_0e^{-.18t}$.

a. What is the annual rate of depreciation of the machine?

18%

b. If after 5 years the machine is worth $16,000, what was its original value?

$39,353.65

13. Suppose the accident rate in Julian County is continually decreasing at an annual rate of 3%.

a. If there were 5,706 accidents this year, write a function to give the number of accidents in t years.

$N(t) = 5706e^{-.03t}$

b. Estimate the number of accidents in 10 years.

4227 acc.

14. The amount L of Radium-226 (^{226}Ra) remaining after t years decreases according to the formula $L = Be^{-0.000428t}$. If 500 micrograms of ^{226}Ra are left after 8,000 years, how many micrograms were present initially?

15,345.97 micrograms

Representations Objective I: Graph exponential functions.

15. At the right is a graph of the function $N(t) = N_0e^{-rt}$. Is r positive or negative?

positive

16. a. Draw the graphs of $y = e^{3x}$ and $y = e^{-3x}$ on the grid at the right.

b. How are the graphs related?

Sample: The graphs are reflection images of each other over $x = 0$.

LESSON MASTER 9-4 B

Questions on SPUR Objectives

Vocabulary

1. Suppose the decade growth factor for a population is D and the annual growth factor is A. Write an equation that relates D and A.

$$D = A^{10}$$

Uses   Objective G: Fit an exponential model to data.

2. *Multiple choice.* For which set of data below is an exponential model most appropriate? Explain why.   **a**

(a)
x	0	1	2	3	4	5
y	5	40	320	2560	20,480	163,840

(b)
x	0	1	2	3	4	5
y	5	20	800	4000	20,000	120,000

(c)
x	0	1	2	3	4	5
y	5	15	60	300	1800	12,600

Sample: The growth factor between subsequent pairs of data points is the constant 8.

3. An experiment began with 200 of a certain type of bacteria. The bacteria grew exponentially, and 4 hours later there were 18,000.

   a. Fit an exponential model to these data. $y = 200\,(3.08)^x$

   b. After 12 hours, how many bacteria will be present? $\approx 145{,}760{,}100$ bac.

4. In a horticultural experiment, the monthly growth of a plant was monitored. The results of the experiment are in the table below.

Month	1	2	3	4	5	6
Growth (cm)	5.2	4.2	3.5	2.7	2.2	1.8

▶ LESSON MASTER 9-4 B *page 2*

a. Draw a scatterplot of these data at the right.

b. Let G be the amount of growth and m the number of months. Fit an exponential model to these data.
   Sample:
   $$G = 6.476(.8070)^m$$

5. The table at the right gives the population in Kuever County for the years 1870 through 1950.

Year	Population	Decade Growth Factor
1870	8,320	
1880	11,823	1.421
1890	16,848	1.425
1900	24,042	1.427
1910	34,188	1.422
1920	48,923	1.431
1930	69,666	1.424
1940	76,911	1.104
1950	98,831	1.285

a. For which years is it appropriate to fit the data to an exponential model? Explain your reasoning.

1870–1930; Sample: The growth factor is nearly constant in each decade.

b. Calculate the annual growth factor between 1890 and 1900.   **1.036**

c. Find an exponential model for the population of Kuever County for the years given in your answer in Part a.
   Sample: $y = 24{,}000 \cdot (1.036)^{x-1900}$

Review   Objective B, Lesson 8-2

In 6–11, find the inverse of the function described.

6. $f(x) = \{(7, 2), (-9, 0), (-1, 2), (5, 5)\}$ $\{(2, 7), (0, -9), (2, -1), (5, 5)\}$

7. $y = -8x$ $y = -\frac{1}{8}x$

8. $y = 7x + 4$ $y = \frac{x - 4}{7}$

9. $y = x^2 - 7x + 6$ $y = \frac{7 \pm \sqrt{25 + 4x}}{2}$

10. $y = |x|$ $y = \pm x,\ x \geq 0$

11. $y = -4x^2$ $y = \pm \frac{\sqrt{-x}}{2},\ x \leq 0$

LESSON MASTER 9-5 B

Questions on SPUR Objectives

Vocabulary

1. a. Write the following sentence as an equation. y is the logarithm of x to the base 10.
   $y = \log_{10} x$ or $y = \log x$

   b. Complete the following definition. y is the logarithm of x to the base 10 if and only if ___?___.
   $10^y = x$

2. What are *common logarithms*?
   logarithms to the base 10

Skills   Objective A: Determine values of common logarithms.

In 3–12, write the number as a decimal. Do not use a calculator.

3. $\log 10{,}000$ **4**

4. $\log (0.001)$ **-3**

5. $\log 10^{18}$ **18**

6. $\log 10$ **1**

7. $\log \frac{1}{1{,}000{,}000}$ **-6**

8. $\log (1 \text{ trillion})$ **12**

9. $\log 10^{.35}$ **.35**

10. $\log \sqrt[6]{10}$ $\frac{1}{6}$, or $1.\overline{6}$

11. $\log 10^{\frac{5}{4}}$ **1.25**

12. $\log \sqrt[4]{10^6}$ **1.5**

In 13–18, use a calculator. Give the logarithm to the nearest thousandth.

13. $\log 7$ **.845**

14. $\log 316$ **2.500**

15. $\log 6.31$ **.800**

16. $\log 298{,}055$ **5.474**

17. $\log 0.000069$ **-4.161**

18. $\log (29 \text{ million})$ **7.462**

Skills   Objective C: Solve common-logarithmic equations.

In 19–24, solve. Round solutions to the nearest ten-thousandth.

19. $\log x = 3$ $x = 1000$

20. $\log y = -4$ $y \approx .0001$

21. $\log z = 0$ $z = 1$

22. $\log w = 2.9$ $w \approx 794.3282$

23. $\log a = \frac{1}{3}$ $a \approx 2.1544$

24. $\log b = -3.55$ $b \approx .0003$

▶ LESSON MASTER 9-5 B *page 2*

Properties   Objective E: Identify and apply properties of common logarithms.

25. What are the domain and the range of the common logarithm function?
   domain   **positive reals**   range   **all reals**

26. What is the logarithm of 1? Justify your answer.
   zero; $10^0 = 1$

27. Use the definition of logarithm of x to the base 10 to explain why the log (-100) does not exist.
   Sample: There is no number y such that $10^y = -100$.

28. *True or false.* The common logarithm of a number is an exponent. Justify your answer.
   True; sample: y is the common logarithm of x if and only if $10^y = x$; y is an exponent.

29. The inverse of the function with equation $y = \log x$ is $y = $ ___?___ 10^x

Representations   Objective J: Graph common-logarithmic curves.

30. a. Complete the table of values at the right. Round to the nearest tenth.

x	.5	1	2	5	10	20
$y = \log x$	-.3	0	.3	.7	1	1.3

   b. Plot the points from Part a on the grid.

   c. Join the points with a smooth curve. What is this curve called?
   logarithmic curve

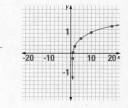

LESSON MASTER 9-6 B

Questions on SPUR Objectives

Vocabulary

1. **a.** How are the units spaced on a *linear scale*?

   Sample: The difference between successive units is the same.

   b. How are the units spaced on a *logarithmic scale*?

   Sample: The ratio between successive units is the same.

Skills Objective B: Use logarithms to solve exponential equations.
Objective C: Solve logarithmic equations.

In 2–5, use the formula $D = 10 \log \left(\frac{N}{10^{-12}} \right)$, which gives the measure in D decibels (dB) for a sound with intensity N given in w/m².

2. Find the relative intensity in decibels of a sound with intensity $3.16 \cdot 10^{-4}$ w/m². — $\approx 85\,dB$

3. Find the intensity, in w/m², of a sound having a relative intensity of 95 dB. — $\approx 3.16 \cdot 10^{-3}$ w/m²

4. Find the relative intensity in decibels of air conditioning in which the sound intensity is 10^{-6} w/m². — $60\,dB$

5. Find the intensity, in w/m², of a freight train having a relative intensity of 75 dB. — $\approx 3.16 \cdot 10^{-5}$ w/m²

In 6–11, use the formula $pH = -\log H^+$ to find the pH of a solution in which H^+ is the concentration of hydrogen ions (in moles/liter).

6. What is the pH of a solution that has a concentration of hydrogen ions of 10^{-9} moles/liter? — 9

7. What is the concentration of hydrogen ions in a solution with a pH of 5? — 10^{-5} moles/L

8. What is the pH of a solution that has a concentration of hydrogen ions of $5.62 \cdot 10^{-6}$ moles/liter? — 5.25

▶ LESSON MASTER 9-6 B *page 2*

9. What is the concentration of hydrogen ions in a solution with a pH of 2.5? Express your answer in scientific notation. — $\approx 3.2 \cdot 10^{-3}$ moles/L

10. What is the concentration of hydrogen ions in a sample of stream water with a pH of 7.8? Express your answer in scientific notation. — $1.6 \cdot 10^{-8}$ moles/L

11. A soil sample from a desert has a concentration of hydrogen ions of $3.16 \cdot 10^{-10}$ moles/liter. What is the pH? — 9.5

Uses Objective H: Apply logarithmic scales (pH, decibel), models, and formulas.

Use the formulas given in Exercises 6–11.

12. When exposed to noise levels of 80 dB for several hours, a person's hearing may be affected for half a day. However, even a single, short exposure to noises of 160 dB may cause physical damage inside the ear. This noise that damages the ear is how many times as intense as the noise that only temporarily affects hearing? — 10^8 times

13. The noise from a riveting machine measures 100 dB. The noise in a busy office measures 65 dB. How many times as intense is the noise from the machine as the noise from the office? — $10^{3.5}$ times

14. The noise level in a classroom measures 55 dB. If the noise level in the gym is 3 times as intense, how many decibels would it be? — $\approx 59.8\,dB$

15. The pH of rainwater is 5.6. Atmospheric pollutants have caused acid rain, which in some regions has a pH of 4.6. How many times as great is the concentration of hydrogen ions in acid rain as in the normal rainwater? — 10 times

16. A solution has a pH of 9.5. What would be the pH of a solution that has twice the concentration of hydrogen ions? — 9.2

17. A soil sample from garden A has a pH of 6.2. A sample from garden B has a pH of 6.8. The soil in garden B is how many times as alkaline as the soil in garden A? — ≈ 4 times

---

LESSON MASTER 9-7 B

Questions on SPUR Objectives

Vocabulary

1. Give a complete definition of *logarithm of m to the base b*.

   Sample: If $b > 0$ and $b \neq 1$, then $n = \log_b m$ if and only if $b^n = m$.

Skills Objective A: Determine values of logarithms.

In 2–17, write the number as a decimal.

2. $\log_5 125$ — 3
3. $\log_6 36$ — 2
4. $\log_2 128$ — 7
5. $\log_9 9$ — 1
6. $\log_8 \frac{1}{8}$ — -1
7. $\log_4 \frac{1}{64}$ — -3
8. $\log_9 3$ — $\frac{1}{2}$, or .5
9. $\log_{81} 3$ — $\frac{1}{4}$, or .25
10. $\log_{14} 1$ — 0
11. $\log_2 2^{21}$ — 21
12. $\log_6 \sqrt{6}$ — $\frac{1}{2}$, or .5
13. $\log_7 7^{\frac{4}{3}}$ — $\frac{4}{3}$, or 1.3
14. $\log_{100} .000001$ — -3
15. $\log_{12} \sqrt[4]{12^5}$ — $\frac{5}{4}$, or 1.25
16. $\log_5 (5^3)^2$ — 6
17. $\log_6 36^4$ — 8

Skills Objective C: Solve logarithmic equations.

In 18–29, solve. Round solutions to the nearest hundredth.

18. $\log_4 a = 7$ — $a = 16{,}384$
19. $\log_6 b = \frac{3}{5}$ — $b \approx 2.93$
20. $\log_{12} c = 0$ — $c = 1$
21. $\log_d \frac{1}{625} = -4$ — $d = 5$
22. $\log_y 28 = \log_5 28$ — $y = 5$
23. $\log_x 10 = \frac{1}{3}$ — $x = 1000$
24. $\log_z 7 = 2.35$ — $z \approx 2.29$
25. $\log_m 22 = \frac{2}{3}$ — $m \approx 103.19$
26. $\log_g 13 = 1$ — $g = 13$
27. $\log_n 100 = 4.25$ — $n \approx 2.96$
28. $\log_r 53 = .5$ — $r = 2809$
29. $\log_{15} w = -.08$ — $w \approx .81$

▶ LESSON MASTER 9-7 B *page 2*

Properties Objective E: Identify and apply properties of logarithms.

30. Write the equivalent logarithmic form for $p^r = s$. — $\log_p s = r$

In 31–34, write in exponential form.

31. $\log_4 16{,}384 = 7$ — $4^7 = 16{,}384$
32. $\log_{16} 64 = \frac{3}{2}$ — $16^{\frac{3}{2}} = 64$
33. $\log_8 2.55 \approx .45$ — $8^{.45} \approx 2.55$
34. $\log_9 \frac{1}{729} = -3$ — $9^{-3} = \frac{1}{729}$

In 35–38, write in logarithmic form.

35. $12^4 = 20{,}736$ — $\log_{12} 20{,}736 = 4$
36. $25^{3.5} = 78{,}125$ — $\log_{25} 78{,}125 = 3.5$
37. $14^{\frac{1}{2}} \approx 3.74$ — $\log_{14} 3.74 = \frac{1}{2}$
38. $.2^{-5} = 3125$ — $\log_{.2} 3125 = -5$

Representations Objective J: Graph logarithmic curves.

39. Locate at least 5 points on the graph of the equation $y = \log_4 x$.

40. The graph below has equation $y = \log_b x$. Find b.

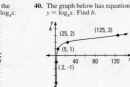

Sample points are given. — 5

41. Consider the graph of the equation $y = 8^x$. The reflection image of this graph over the line $x = y$ results in a graph described by what equation? — $y = \log_8 x$

Review Objective B, Lessons 7-2, 7-3, 7-6, 7-7, 7-8

In 42–47, simplify.

42. $a^4 \cdot a^3$ — a^7
43. $(m^6)^5$ — m^{30}
44. $\frac{u^{10}}{u^7}$ — u^3
45. $\left(\frac{x^{12}}{y^{15}} \right)^{\frac{1}{3}}$ — $\frac{x^4}{y^5}$
46. $(r^6)^{\frac{1}{2}}$ — r^3
47. $\sqrt[6]{w^{18}}$ — w^3

LESSON MASTER 9-8 B

Questions on SPUR Objectives

Skills Objective C: Solve logarithmic equations.

In 1–10, solve.

1. $\log x = 5 \log 4$
$x = 1024$

2. $\log_5 u = \frac{1}{3} \log_5 64$
$u = 4$

3. $\log m = \log 2 + \log 14$
$m = 28$

4. $\log 28 - \log 7 = \log y$
$y = 4$

5. $\log p = \log 6 + 3 \log 5$
$p = 750$

6. $\log_4 h = \frac{1}{2} \log_4 49 - \log_4 3$
$h = \frac{7}{3}$

7. $\log 6 + \log 10 = \log (5a)$
$a = 12$

8. $4 \log x = \log 32 - \log 2$
$x = 2$

9. $\frac{-1}{2} \log n = \log 1 - 2 \log 9$
$n = 6561$

10. $\log_8 \left(\frac{x}{2}\right) = 2 \log_8 5 + 3 \log_8 2$
$x = 400$

Properties Objective E: Identify and apply properties of logarithms.

In 11–18, write the number as a decimal.

11. $\log_{18} 18^{20}$ ___20___

12. $\log_{12} 3 + \log_{12} 4$ ___1___

13. $4 \log_3 9$ ___8___

14. $\log_6 72 - \log_6 2$ ___2___

15. $\log_{25} 7 - \log_{25} 35$ ___-.5___

16. $\frac{1}{5} \log_8 32{,}768$ ___1___

17. $7 \log_3 3 - 8 \log_3 3$ ___-1___

18. $\log \sqrt[8]{100}$ ___.25___

▶ **LESSON MASTER 9-8 B** *page 2*

In 19–24, name the general property illustrated.

19. $\log \left(\frac{24}{5}\right) = \log 24 - \log 5$
Quotient Property of Logarithms

20. $\log_{16} 16^{-9} = -9$
Log$_b$ of b^n Theorem

21. $\log 4 + \log 12 = \log 48$
Product Property of Logarithms

22. $6 \log_8 7 = \log_8 7^6$
Power Property of Logarithms

23. $\log \left(\frac{2}{3} \cdot 28\right) = \log \frac{2}{3} + \log 28$
Product Property of Logarithms

24. $\log \sqrt[4]{18^3} = \frac{3}{4} \log 18$
Power Property of Logarithms

Review Objective F, Lesson 9-3

25. Write the formula for continuously compounded interest and tell what each variable represents.
$A = Pe^{rt}$; P = **principal, or amount invested;**
r = **annual interest rate; t = number of years;**
A = **amount in account after t years.**

26. Suppose $3200 is invested at an annual interest rate of 8.2% compounded continuously, and the money is left untouched.

a. How much is in the account after 3 years? **$4092.48**

b. How much is in the account after 10 years? **$7265.60**

LESSON MASTER 9-9 B

Questions on SPUR Objectives

Vocabulary

1. Complete the following: Logarithms to the base ___?___ are called *natural logarithms*. ___e___

Skills Objective A: Determine values of natural logarithms.

In 2–5, write the number as a decimal. Do not use a calculator.

2. $\ln e^{14}$ ___14___

3. $\ln e^{\frac{4}{3}}$ ___$\frac{4}{3}$, or $1.\overline{3}$___

4. $5 \ln e^2$ ___10___

5. $\ln e^{-3}$ ___-3___

In 6–11, give the logarithm to the nearest hundredth.

6. $\ln 8$ ___2.08___

7. $\ln 0.44$ ___-.82___

8. $\ln 5{,}068$ ___8.53___

9. $\ln .05$ ___-3.00___

10. $\ln 1$ ___0___

11. $\ln (-9)$ ___not defined___

Properties Objective E: Identify and apply properties of natural logarithms.

In 12–15, write in exponential form.

12. $\ln 42 \approx 3.738$ ___$e^{3.738} \approx 42$___

13. $\ln 0.2 \approx -1.609$ ___$e^{-1.609} \approx 0.2$___

14. $\ln 2.4 \approx .875$ ___$e^{.875} \approx 2.4$___

15. $\ln 3{,}000 \approx 8.006$ ___$e^{8.006} \approx 3{,}000$___

In 16–19, write in logarithmic form.

16. $e^7 \approx 1097$ ___$\ln 1097 \approx 7$___

17. $e^{1.5} \approx 4.482$ ___$\ln 4.482 \approx 1.5$___

18. $e^{-\frac{1}{2}} \approx .607$ ___$\ln .607 \approx -\frac{1}{2}$___

19. $e^{\frac{7}{4}} \approx 5.755$ ___$\ln 5.755 \approx \frac{7}{4}$___

In 21–23, identify the property that justifies the equation.

20. $\ln e^{10} = 10$
Log$_b$ of b^n Theorem

21. $\ln 12 - \ln 2 = \ln 6$
Quotient Property of Logarithms

22. $50 \ln 6 = \ln 6^{50}$
Power Property of Logarithms

23. $\ln 15 = \ln 3 + \log 5$
Product Property of Logarithms

▶ **LESSON MASTER 9-9 B** *page 2*

Uses Objective H: Apply logarithmic models and formulas.

24. Suppose an account pays an annual interest rate r compounded continuously. The formula $t = \frac{\ln g}{r}$ can be used to determine the number of years t for the investment to grow to g times what it was, assuming that the money is left untouched.

a. How long will it take an investment to double if the account pays

(i) 5% compounded continuously? **13.86 years**

(ii) 7% compounded continuously? **9.9 years**

(iii) 10% compounded continuously? **6.93 years**

b. If $8,000 is invested at 8% compounded continuously, in how many years will the account be worth $12,000? **5.07 years**

c. What annual rate of interest compounded continuously would be necessary for an account to triple in

(i) 20 years? **5.5%**

(ii) 15 years? **7.3%**

(iii) 10 years? **11.0%**

(iv) 5 years? **22.0%**

Representations Objective J: Graph natural-logarithmic curves.

25. a. Complete the table of values at the right. Round to the nearest tenth.

x	.5	1	2	5	10	20
$y = \ln x$	-.7	0	.7	1.6	2.3	3.0

b. Plot the points from Part a on the grid.

c. Join the points with a smooth curve.

d. Draw the reflection image of your graph over the line $y = x$. What equation describes the reflection image?
___$y = e^x$___

LESSON MASTER 9-10 B

Questions on SPUR Objectives

Skills Objective B: Use logarithms to solve exponential equations.

In 1–12, solve. Round solutions to the nearest hundredth.

1. $64^x = 4096$
$x \approx 2$

2. $625^x = 125$
$x \approx .75$

3. $12^u = 400$
$u \approx 2.41$

4. $6^a = 3$
$a \approx .61$

5. $10^c = 2.77$
$c \approx .44$

6. $196^{w+1} = 537,824$
$w \approx 1.5$

7. $e^x = 24$
$x \approx 3.18$

8. $5e^n = 33$
$n \approx 1.89$

9. $(0.8)^y = e^2$
$y \approx -8.96$

10. $6.5 \cdot 10^8 = e^n$
$n \approx 20.29$

11. $11^{6y-3} = 80$
$y \approx .80$

12. $2^r = 0.0053$
$r \approx -7.56$

▶ **LESSON MASTER 9-10 B** *page 2*

Uses Objective F: Apply exponential-growth and exponential-decay models.

In 13–15, assume the money is left untouched in the account.

13. Jacob's college savings are invested in a bond that pays an annual interest of 6.2% compounded continuously. How long will it take the money to triple?
17.7 years

14. Marta invested $5,000 in an account that pays an annual interest of 8.1% compounded continuously. In how many years will there be $8,000 in the account?
5.8 years

15. At what rate of interest, compounded continuously, would you have to invest your money for it to double in 8 years?
8.7%

16. The equation $p = 100(0.5)^{\frac{x}{5730}}$ gives the percent p of Carbon 14 (^{14}C) remaining after an organism has been decomposing for x years. How many years will it take for there to be the given percent of ^{14}C remaining?

    a. 50% (Recall, this is called the *half-life*.)
    5730 years

    b. 75%
    ≈ 2378 years

    c. 30%
    ≈ 9953 years

17. The intensity L_t of light transmitted through a certain type of tinted glass t mm thick can be found with the formula $L_t = L_0 10^{-.034t}$, where L_0 is the intensity before entering the glass. How thick should the glass be in order to block 30% of the light?
≈ 4.56 mm

18. In 1995, the profits for Uptown Manufacturing were $763,000 and growing at a rate of about 4.5% annually. Assuming that profits continue to grow at this rate, during what year will the profits reach one million dollars?
2001

LESSON MASTER 10-1 B

Questions on SPUR Objectives

Vocabulary

1. Refer to the diagram at the right. Fill in the blank.

    a. The *leg adjacent* to θ is $\overline{AC}$.

    b. The *leg opposite* θ is $\overline{BC}$.

    c. The *hypotenuse* is $\overline{AB}$.

2. Fill in the blank with the name of a trigonometric ratio.

    a. the **tangent** of θ = $\frac{\text{length of leg opposite } \theta}{\text{length of leg adjacent to } \theta}$

    b. the **sine** of θ = $\frac{\text{length of leg opposite } \theta}{\text{length of hypotenuse}}$

    c. the **cosine** of θ = $\frac{\text{length of leg adjacent to } \theta}{\text{length of hypotenuse}}$

Skills Objective A: Approximate values of trigonometric functions using a calculator.

In 3–5, approximate each trigonometric value to the nearest thousandth.

3. Refer to the triangle at the right.

    a. sin θ **.385**

    b. cos θ **.923**

    c. tan θ **.417**

4. Refer to the triangle at the right.

    a. sin D **.6**   b. cos D **.8**

    c. sin E **.8**   d. cos E **.6**

    e. tan D **.75**   f. tan E **1.333**

▶ **LESSON MASTER 10-1 B** *page 2*

5. a. Measure the length of each side of the triangle at the right. Then estimate the trigonometric value.

    i. sin R   ii. cos R   iii. tan R
    .826   **.569**   **1.448**

    b. Measure ∠R in the triangle at the right. Then use that measure to find each trigonometric value.

    i. sin R   ii. cos R   iii. tan R
    .819   **.574**   **1.428**

6. Refer to the regular octagon at the right. Suppose the length of each side is 12 cm. Find the length of $\overline{BD}$.

    ≈ 22.2 cm

Uses Objective F: Solve real-world problems using the trigonometry of right triangles.

7. A ship sails 64 kilometers on a bearing of 20°. How far east of its original position is the ship?
≈ 21.9 km

8. Dennis sights the top of a rocket at 54° when he stands 65 ft away. He is 5 ft tall. About how tall is the rocket?
≈ 94.5 ft
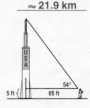

9. A straight water slide makes a 40° angle with the surface of the water. If the slide is 11.5 meters high, how long is it?
≈ 17.9 m

Sheet 1 (top-left)

Name _____

LESSON MASTER 10-2 B   Questions on SPUR Objectives

Vocabulary

Refer to the diagram at the right.
Complete the sentence with the
appropriate phrase.

1. a. ∠1 is called a(n)
   angle of depression

   b. ∠2 is called a(n)
   angle of elevation

   c. In geometry, ∠1 and ∠2 are called **alternate interior angles**

   d. How are the measures of ∠1 and ∠2 related?
   They are equal.

Skills Objective C: Determine the measure of an angle given its sine, cosine, or tangent.

In 2–5, find the measure of the acute angle θ
to the nearest degree.

2. sin θ = .42 **25°**
3. cos θ = $\frac{1}{2}$ **60°**
4. tan θ = 9.5 **84°**
5. sin θ = $\frac{\sqrt{3}}{2}$ **60°**

In 6–9, evaluate the functions to the nearest tenth.

6. cos⁻¹ .951 **18.0°**
7. tan⁻¹ .067 **3.8°**
8. sin⁻¹ .966 **75.0°**
9. cos⁻¹ $\frac{5}{13}$ **67.4°**

In 10 and 11, refer to the diagram at the right.
Find the measure to the nearest degree.

10. m∠A **23°**
11. m∠B **67°**

169 ▶

Sheet 2 (top-right)

Name _____

▶ **LESSON MASTER 10-2 B** *page 2*

Uses Objective F: Solve real-world problems using the trigonometry of right triangles.

12. A garage is 8 feet above the
    level street. The driveway
    from the street to the garage
    is 45 feet long. Find the
    driveway's angle of incline.
    ≈ 10.2°

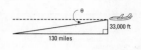

13. A plane flying at 33,000 ft
    is 130 miles from the
    airport when it begins to
    descend. If the angle of
    descent is constant, find
    this angle.
    ≈ 2.8°

14. If a tower 18 meters high casts a shadow
    9.5 meters long, what is the angle of
    elevation of the sun?
    ≈ 62.2°

15. A person on top of a building finds
    there is a 38° angle of depression to
    the head of an assistant who is
    170 cm tall. If the assistant is
    10 meters from the building, how
    tall is the building?
    ≈ 9.5 m

16. The base of a 24-ft ladder is placed 8 ft
    from a building.

    a. What angle does the ladder make
       with the level ground?
       ≈ 70.5°

    b. How high above the ground is the
       top of the ladder?
       ≈ 22.6 ft

170

Sheet 3 (bottom-left)

Name _____

LESSON MASTER 10-3 B   Questions on SPUR Objectives

Skills Objective B: Find exact values of trigonometric functions of multiples of 30° or 45°.

In 1–9, give the exact value.

1. cos 60° $\frac{1}{2}$
2. sin 60° $\frac{\sqrt{3}}{2}$
3. tan 60° $\sqrt{3}$
4. cos 45° $\frac{\sqrt{2}}{2}$
5. sin 45° $\frac{\sqrt{2}}{2}$
6. tan 45° 1
7. cos 30° $\frac{\sqrt{3}}{2}$
8. sin 30° $\frac{1}{2}$
9. tan 30° $\frac{\sqrt{3}}{3}$

In 10–13, find the trigonometric value and the
indicated length. Give the exact answer.

10.
   a. sin 30° $\frac{1}{2}$
   b. x **16**

11.
   a. cos 60° $\frac{1}{2}$
   b. y **9**

12.
   a. cos 45° $\frac{\sqrt{2}}{2}$
   b. a $\frac{5\sqrt{2}}{2}$

13.
   a. tan 60° $\sqrt{3}$
   b. m $4\sqrt{3}$

Properties Objective E: Identify and use definitions and theorems relating sines, cosines, and tangents.

In 14–21, fill in the blank with the measure of an acute angle.

14. sin 74° = cos **16°**
15. cos 19° = sin **71°**
16. sin 45° = cos **45°**
17. cos 7° = sin (90 − **7°**)
18. $\frac{\sin 23°}{\cos 23°}$ = tan **23°**
19. tan 68° = $\frac{\sin 68°}{\cos 68°}$
20. (sin 88°)² + (cos **88°**)² = 1
21. (sin **14°**)² + (cos 14°)² = 1

171 ▶

Sheet 4 (bottom-right)

Name _____

▶ **LESSON MASTER 10-3 B** *page 2*

In 22–26, assume the angle is acute.

22. If cos x = 0.49, then what is the value of sin x? **≈ .872**

23. If sin y = $\frac{\sqrt{5}}{3}$, then what is the value of cos y? **$\frac{2}{3}$, or ≈ .667**

24. If sin z ≈ .515, and cos z ≈ .857, what is the
    value of tan z? **≈ .601**

25. Suppose sin θ = $\frac{\sqrt{6}}{5}$.

    a. What is the value of cos θ? **$\frac{\sqrt{19}}{5}$**

    b. What is the value of tan θ? **$\frac{\sqrt{114}}{19}$**

26. Suppose cos θ = $\frac{\sqrt{10}}{10}$ and tan θ = 3, what is the
    value of sin θ? **$\frac{3\sqrt{10}}{10}$**

In 27–29, verify the property for the triangle
at the right.

27. (sin θ)² + (cos θ)² = 1

$$\text{Sample: } AB = \sqrt{2^2 + 3^2} = \sqrt{13}$$

$$(\sin θ)^2 + (\cos θ)^2 = \left(\frac{3}{\sqrt{13}}\right)^2 + \left(\frac{2}{\sqrt{13}}\right)^2$$

$$= \frac{9}{13} + \frac{4}{13} = 1$$

28. sin (90° − θ) = cos θ

Sample:
$$\sin (90° − θ) = \sin A$$
$$= \frac{2}{\sqrt{13}}$$
$$\cos θ = \frac{2}{\sqrt{13}}$$
$$\sin (90° − θ) = \cos θ$$

29. tan θ = $\frac{\sin θ}{\cos θ}$

Sample:
$$\frac{\sin θ}{\cos θ} = \frac{3/\sqrt{13}}{2/\sqrt{13}}$$
$$= \frac{3}{2}$$
$$\tan θ = \frac{3}{2}$$
$$\frac{\sin θ}{\cos θ} = \tan θ$$

172

ADVANCED ALGEBRA © Scott, Foresman and Company

289

LESSON MASTER 10-4 B

Questions on SPUR Objectives

Vocabulary

1. What is the *unit circle?*
   a circle with center at the origin and radius 1 unit

2. Let (x, y) be image of $(1, 0)$ under R_θ. What is the relationship between (x, y) and the sine and cosine of θ?
   Sample: $x = \cos\theta$ and $y = \sin\theta$.

Skills Objective B: Find exact values of trigonometric functions of multiples of 30° or 45°.

3. Explain how to find the exact value of cos 390° without using a calculator.
   Sample: cos 390° = cos (390° − 360°) = cos 30° = $\sqrt{3}/2$

4. Explain how to find the exact value of sin -300° without using a calculator.
   Sample: sin -300° = sin (360° − 300°) = sin 60° = $\sqrt{3}/2$

In 5–20, give the exact value. Do not use a calculator.

5. cos 360° **1**
6. sin 180° **0**
7. cos 270° **0**
8. cos (-180°) **-1**
9. sin (-90°) **-1**
10. cos (-90°) **0**
11. cos 720° **1**
12. sin (-270°) **1**
13. cos 540° **-1**
14. sin 540° **0**
15. sin (-330)° **$\frac{1}{2}$**
16. sin 450° **1**
17. cos (-450°) **0**
18. sin 405° **$\sqrt{2}/2$**
19. sin 3600° **0**
20. sin (-300°) **$\sqrt{3}/2$**

▶ **LESSON MASTER 10-4 B** *page 2*

Representations Objective I: Use the properties of a unit circle to find trigonometric values.

In 21–26, to the nearest thousandth, find the coordinates of the image of the point (1, 0) under the given rotation.

21. $R_{65°}$ **(.423, .906)**
22. $R_{10°}$ **(.985, .174)**
23. $R_{378°}$ **(.951, .309)**
24. $R_{400°}$ **(.766, .643)**
25. $R_{325°}$ **(.819, .574)**
26. $R_{-700°}$ **(.940, .342)**

In 27–29, use the diagram of a unit circle at the right.

27. Find cos θ. **.559**
28. Find sin θ. **.829**
29. Find θ to the nearest degree. **56°**

In 30–37, refer to the diagram at the right. Give the letter that could stand for the function value.

30. cos 180° **i**
31. sin 270° **l**
32. sin 28° **d**
33. cos 82° **e**
34. sin (-270°) **h**
35. cos 388° **c**
36. cos 450° **g**
37. sin (-278°) **f**

Review Objective F, Lesson 10-1

38. A loading-dock ramp makes a 20° angle with the ground. If the dock is 2.5 meters high, how long is the ramp? **≈ 7.3 m**

39. A person sights the top of the San Jacinto Monument at an angle of 85° when standing 50 feet from the base of the monument. If the person is 6 feet tall, about how high is the monument? **≈ 578 ft**

40. A rock dropped 182 ft from the top of the Leaning Tower of Pisa lands at a point 14 ft from the base of the tower. What angle does the tower make with the ground? **≈ 87°**

LESSON MASTER 10-5 B

Questions on SPUR Objectives

Skills Objective A: Approximate values of trigonometric functions using a calculator.

In 1–12, use a calculator to evaluate. Round the value to the nearest thousandth.

1. cos 98° **-.139**
2. sin 159° **.358**
3. cos 280° **.174**
4. cos 195° **-.966**
5. sin 250° **-.940**
6. sin 348° **-.208**
7. cos 410° **.643**
8. sin (-200°) **.342**
9. sin (-25)° **-.423**
10. cos 915° **-.966**
11. sin (-1300°) **.643**
12. cos (-640.5°) **.182**

Skills Objective B: Find exact values of trigonometric functions of multiples of 30° or 45°.

In 13–18, *true or false.* Do not use a calculator.

13. sin 390° = sin -30° **false**
14. cos 540° = cos 180° **true**
15. sin -300° = sin 60° **true**
16. cos 210° = cos 30° **false**
17. sin 240° = -sin 60° **true**
18. cos 300° = -cos 60° **false**

In 19–34, give the exact value.

19. sin 150° **$\frac{1}{2}$**
20. cos 225° **$\frac{-\sqrt{2}}{2}$**
21. cos 240° **$\frac{-1}{2}$**
22. sin 300° **$\frac{-\sqrt{3}}{2}$**
23. sin 135° **$\frac{\sqrt{2}}{2}$**
24. cos 315° **$\frac{\sqrt{2}}{2}$**
25. sin 480° **$\frac{\sqrt{3}}{2}$**
26. cos 570° **$\frac{-\sqrt{3}}{2}$**
27. cos 585° **$\frac{-\sqrt{2}}{2}$**
28. sin (-45°) **$\frac{-\sqrt{2}}{2}$**
29. cos (-60°) **$\frac{1}{2}$**
30. sin (-210°) **$\frac{1}{2}$**
31. cos (-150°) **$\frac{-\sqrt{3}}{2}$**
32. cos (-810°) **0**
33. sin (-3000)° **$\frac{-\sqrt{3}}{2}$**
34. cos (-585°) **$\frac{-\sqrt{2}}{2}$**

▶ **LESSON MASTER 10-5 B** *page 2*

Representations Objective I: Use the properties of a unit circle to find trigonometric values.

In 35–42, for the indicated point, tell if the value for sin θ or cos θ is *positive, negative,* or *neither.*

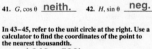

35. A, cos θ **pos.**
36. B, sin θ **pos.**
37. C, sin θ **pos.**
38. D, cos θ **neg.**
39. E, cos θ **neg.**
40. F, cos θ **neg.**
41. G, cos θ **neith.**
42. H, sin θ **neg.**

In 43–45, refer to the unit circle at the right. Use a calculator to find the coordinates of the point to the nearest thousandth.

43. P **(.848, -.530)**
44. Q **(-.643, .766)**
45. R **(-.438, -.899)**

In 46–49, give the letter in the diagram at the right that could represent the given value.

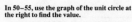

46. sin 138° **f**
47. sin (-270°) **d**
48. cos (-68°) **i**
49. cos 228° **g**

In 50–55, use the graph of the unit circle at the right to find the value.

50. sin θ **.438**
51. cos θ **-.899**
52. cos α **-.743**
53. sin α **-.669**
54. θ **154°**
55. α **-138°**

LESSON MASTER 10-6 B

Questions on SPUR Objectives

Uses Objective G: Solve real-world problems using the Laws of Cosines.

1. Ship *A* sights Ship *B* at a distance of 6.4 km, and Ship *A* sights Ship *C* at a distance of 7.7 km. The angle between the two sightings is 80°.

   a. In the space below, draw and label a diagram to represent this situation.

6.4 km 80° 7.7 km

B• •*C*

   b. How far apart are Ship *B* and Ship *C*? ≈ **9.1 km**

2. Refer to the drawing at the right. At what angle θ should a 36-inch-wide door be opened so that distance *a* is at least 15 inches?

   at least 24°

3. Refer to the drawing at the right. Maxine is designing a tent. If the two sides meet at a 40° angle, find *w*, the width of the tent along the ground.

   ≈ **5.5 ft**

4. Refer to the diagram at the right. If two planes leave Berlin, one flying toward London and the other flying toward Paris, by approximately what angle θ do their headings differ?

   ≈ **21.5°**

London 939 km
345 km   θ   Berlin
Paris   882 km

▶ **LESSON MASTER 10-6 B** *page 2*

Representations Objective H: Find missing parts of a triangle using the Law of Cosines.

5. Find *AB*. ≈ **8.8**

C
4 102° 7
A *B*

6. Find *DE*. ≈ **12.3**

E
13
D 59° *F*
12

7. Find m∠*G*. ≈ **59.3°**

G 6
15 *I*
13
H

8. Find *KJ*. ≈ **9.5**

K
7 85° 7 *J*
L

9. Find *MN*. ≈ **9.8**

M 24.5 *O*
20°
N 18

10. Find *PR*. ≈ **12.0**

P 8 *Q*
9
R

11. Find the measure of the angle.

∠*S* ≈ **34.9°** ∠*T* ≈ **64.1°**
∠*U* ≈ **81.0°**

S
145 132
T 84 *U*

12. Find *n*. ≈ **41.7**

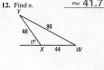

Y
86
48
n° *X* 44 *W*

LESSON MASTER 10-7 B

Questions on SPUR Objectives

Vocabulary

1. Define *triangulation*.

   Sample: Dividing a region into triangular regions, taking measurements and using trigonometry to determine other measures

Uses Objective G: Solve real-world problems usng the Law of Sines.

2. A bridge is to be built across a canyon from point *A* to point *B*. A surveyor drew the diagram at the right based on measurements taken at the site. Find the length of the bridge.

   ≈ **289.8 ft**

A
44°
B 57°
240 ft *C*

3. In the drawing at the right, *PS* is the height of a mountain. Find the given measure.

   a. m∠*QRP* **120°**
   b. m∠*RPQ* **22°**
   c. *PR* ≈ **296 m**
   d. *PS* ≈ **256 m**

P
38° 60°
Q 180 m *R* *S*

4. As shown at the right, a ship heading due west had to detour around an oil spill. At point *U*, the ship steered 45° off course, and sailed until it cleared the spill. Then at point *V* it turned back toward its original course and intersected it at a 36° angle at point *W*. If the original route from *U* to *W* is 32 km long, how many additional kilometers did the ship have to sail?

   ≈ **9.95 km**

V
36° oil spill 45°
W *U*
32 km

5. Fire stations *X* and *Y* are 45 mi apart. The ranger at station *X* sees a fire at point *Z* such that m∠*YXZ* = 30°. The ranger at station *Y* sees the fire such that m∠*XYZ* = 70°. How far is the fire from each station?

   X ≈ **42.9 miles** *Y* ≈ **22.9 miles**

▶ **LESSON MASTER 10-7 B** *page 2*

Representations Objective H: Find missing parts of a triangle using the Law of Sines.

6. Find *BC*. ≈ **19.1**

C
9 85° 28° *B*
A

7. Find *DE*. ≈ **15.0**

E
D 30° 62°
17 *F*

8. Find *KJ*. ≈ **19.6**

K
37°
J
100°
L 12

9. Find *NO*. ≈ **26.7**

N 22° *O*
10
M

10. Find *GH*. ≈ **49.7**

G 34
70° 70° *Y*
H

11. Find *TU*. ≈ **8.3**

S
37° 14
T 65° 61° *R*
U

Review Objective I: Lesson 6–3

In 12 and 13, assume parabola *B* is a translation image of parabola *A* at the right.

12. What translation maps parabola *A* onto parabola *B*? *T*₄, ₋₈

13. An equation for parabola *A* is *y* = *x*². Write an equation for parabola *B*.

   $y = (x - 4)^2 - 8$

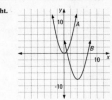

LESSON MASTER 10-8 B

Questions on SPUR Objectives

Vocabulary

1. Define *sine wave*.

A graph which can be mapped onto the
graph of $g(\theta) = \sin \theta$ by any composite of
translations, scale changes, or reflections

In 2 and 3, complete the definition.

2. If the graph of a function can be mapped onto itself
under a horizontal translation of positive magnitude,
then we call this type of function a ___?___.

periodic function

3. Situations that lead to sine
waves are called ___?___.

sinusoidal

Representations Objective J: Identify properties of the sine and cosine functions using their graphs.

4. Consider $R_\theta(0,1)$.

   a. What is the first coordinate of the image? **cos θ**

   b. What is the second coordinate of the image? **sin θ**

5. On the grid at the right,
graph the function
$f(x) = \sin x$ for
$-360° \leq x \leq 360°$.

6. On the grid at the right,
graph the function
$f(x) = \cos x$ for
$-360° \leq x \leq 360°$.

181 ▶

▶ **LESSON MASTER 10-8 B** *page 2*

7. Give the domain and the range of the sine function.

   domain **all real numbers** range **{x: -1 ≤ x ≤ 1}**

8. Give the domain and the range of the cosine function.

   domain **all real numbers** range **{x: -1 ≤ x ≤ 1}**

9. What is the y-intercept of

   a. the sine graph? **0**   b. the cosine graph? **1**

10. Give the least 4 nonnegative x-intercepts of

    a. the sine function. **0°, 180°, 360°, 540°**

    b. the cosine function. **90°, 270°, 450°, 630°**

11. Give the period of

    a. the sine function. **360°**   b. the cosine function. **360°**

12. Refer to the graph at
the right.

    a. Does this function
    seem to be periodic?
    If so, what is
    its period?
    yes; 360°

    b. Is the function graphed sinusoidal? Explain your reasoning.
    Sample: Yes; it can be mapped onto the
    graph of $g(\theta) = \sin \theta$ by a scale change $S_{1,.5}$.

    c. What equation might describe the graph? **$y = \frac{1}{2}\sin x$**

Review Objective C: Lesson 10-2

In 13–16, evaluate the function to the nearest tenth.

13. $\cos^{-1}.844$ **32.4°**   14. $\tan^{-1}.093$ **5.3°**

15. $\sin^{-1}.331$ **19.3°**   16. $\cos^{-1}\frac{7}{25}$ **73.7°**

182

LESSON MASTER 10-9 B

Questions on SPUR Objectives

Skills Objective C: Determine the measure of an angle given its sine or cosine.

**In 1–4, solve for all θ between 0° and 180°. Give θ to
the nearest degree.**

1. $\sin \theta = .788$ **52°, 128°**   2. $\sin \theta = .358$ **21°, 159°**

3. $\sin \theta = -.995$ **none**   4. $\sin \theta = .988$ **81°, 99°**

**In 5 and 6, give the exact values for all x between
0° and 180°.**

5. $\sin x = \frac{\sqrt{3}}{2}$ **60°, 120°**   6. $\sin x = 1$ **90°**

7. Suppose $\sin \theta = .891$. Find θ to the nearest degree if

   a. θ is acute. **63°**   b. θ is obtuse. **117°**

Properties Objective E: Identify and use theorems relating sines and cosines.

8. *Multiple choice.* If $\sin 34° = n$, then ___?___ **d**
   (a) $\sin 34° = 180 - n$ (b) $\sin 56° = n$
   (c) $\sin 146° = 180 - n$ (d) $\sin 146° = n$

9. *Multiple choice.* If $\sin 34° = n$, then ___?___ **b**
   (a) $\cos 34° = 180 - n$ (b) $\cos 56° = n$
   (c) $\cos 146° = n$ (d) $\cos 56° = -n$

10. If θ is between 0° and 180°, how many solutions does
the equation have?

    a. $\cos \theta = .58$ **1**   b. $\sin \theta = .58$ **2**

11. If $\sin \theta = 0.8$ and $0° < \theta < 180°$, give all possible
values for $\cos \theta$. **.6, -.6**

12. If $\sin \theta = 0.23$ and θ is obtuse, find $\cos \theta$ to
the nearest thousandth. **-.973**

183 ▶

▶ **LESSON MASTER 10-9 B** *page 2*

Uses Objective G: Solve real-world problems using the Law of Sines or the Law of Cosines.

13. In a state park, camp headquarters are 6 km from the ranger's station,
and the ranger's station is 4.5 km from the park entrance. The line
from the camp headquarters to the entrance forms a 48° angle with
the line joining camp headquarters and the ranger's station.

    a. At what angle does the line joining the entrance
    and the camp headquarters meet the line joining
    the entrance and the ranger's station? (Hint:
    There are two possibilities.) **≈82°, ≈98°**

    b. Find the distance from camp headquarters **≈4.6 km, ≈3.4 km**
    to the entrance. (Give both possibilities.)

Representations Objective H: Find missing parts of a triangle using the Law of Sines or the Law of Cosines.

**In 14–16, a triangle is described. a. Solve the triangle.
b. Sketch the triangle. Give all possibilities.**

14. $\triangle ABC$, with $m\angle B = 40°$, $AC = 6$, and $AB = 8$

$m\angle C \approx 59°$ $m\angle C \approx 121°$
$m\angle A \approx 81°$ $m\angle A \approx 19°$
$BC \approx 9.2$ $BC \approx 3.0$

15. $\triangle RST$, with $m\angle R = 102°$, $RS = 10$, and $ST = 18$

$m\angle T \approx 33°$
$m\angle S \approx 45°$
$RT \approx 13.0$

16. $\triangle XYZ$, with $m\angle X = 72°$, $XZ = 7.3$, and $YZ = 7$

$m\angle Y \approx 83°$ $m\angle Y \approx 97°$
$m\angle Z \approx 25°$ $m\angle Z \approx 11°$
$XY \approx 3.1$ $XY \approx 1.4$

184

LESSON MASTER 10-10 B

Questions on SPUR Objectives

Vocabulary

1. Define *radian*.

   Sample: the measure of an angle, an arc, or a rotation such that π radians = 180°

Skills Objective A: Approximate values of trigonometric functions using a calculator.

In 2–9, approximate to the nearest thousandth.

2. $\sin\left(\frac{5\pi}{9}\right)$ **.985**
3. $\tan\left(\frac{\pi}{8}\right)$ **.414**
4. $\cos\left(\frac{\pi}{12}\right)$ **.966**
5. $\sin\left(-\frac{4\pi}{15}\right)$ **-743**
6. $\tan(-2.3\pi)$ **-1.376**
7. $\cos(4.6\pi)$ **-.309**
8. $\sin 3$ **.141**
9. $\tan -5$ **3.381**

Skills Objective B: Find exact values of trigonometric functions of radian equivalents of multiples of 30° or 45°.

In 10–23, give the exact value.

10. $\cos\left(\frac{\pi}{6}\right)$ $\frac{\sqrt{3}}{2}$
11. $\sin\left(\frac{\pi}{4}\right)$ $\frac{\sqrt{2}}{2}$
12. $\cos\left(\frac{\pi}{2}\right)$ **0**
13. $\sin\left(\frac{3\pi}{4}\right)$ $-\frac{\sqrt{2}}{2}$
14. $\tan\left(-\frac{\pi}{4}\right)$ **-1**
15. $\cos 0$ **1**
16. $\sin\left(-\frac{\pi}{3}\right)$ $-\frac{\sqrt{3}}{2}$
17. $\tan\left(\frac{5\pi}{6}\right)$ $-\frac{\sqrt{3}}{3}$
18. $\sin 3\pi$ **0**
19. $\cos 12\pi$ **1**
20. $\sin\left(-\frac{3\pi}{2}\right)$ **1**
21. $\cos -4.5\pi$ **0**
22. $\cos\left(\frac{19\pi}{6}\right)$ $-\frac{\sqrt{3}}{2}$
23. $\sin\left(-\frac{23\pi}{3}\right)$ $\frac{\sqrt{3}}{2}$

▶ **LESSON MASTER 10-10 B** *page 2*

Skills Objective D: Convert angle measures from radians to degrees or degrees to radians.

In 24–35, convert to radians.

24. 135° $\frac{3\pi}{4}$
25. -180° $-\pi$
26. 36° $\frac{\pi}{5}$
27. -90° $-\frac{\pi}{2}$
28. 45° $\frac{\pi}{4}$
29. 720° 4π
30. 1° $\frac{\pi}{180}$
31. 60° $\frac{\pi}{3}$
32. -30° $-\frac{\pi}{6}$
33. -540° -3π
34. 225° $\frac{5\pi}{4}$
35. 660° $\frac{11\pi}{3}$

In 36–47, convert to degrees.

36. $\frac{\pi}{8}$ **22.5°**
37. 3π **540°**
38. -4π **-720°**
39. $\frac{\pi}{2}$ **90°**
40. $\frac{5\pi}{6}$ **150°**
41. 1.5π **270°**
42. 9.46 **≈542°**
43. $\frac{11\pi}{12}$ **165°**
44. $\frac{8\pi}{3}$ **480°**
45. 6 **≈344°**
46. $-\frac{\pi}{4}$ **-45°**
47. $\frac{7\pi}{8}$ **157.5°**

Representations Objective I: Use the properties of a unit circle to find trigonometric values.

In 48–55, refer to the diagram at the right. Give the letter that could represent the given function value.

48. $\cos \pi$ **e**
49. $\sin \frac{3\pi}{2}$ **h**
50. $\sin \frac{\pi}{3}$ **b**
51. $\sin 3\pi$ **f**
52. $\cos \frac{3\pi}{4}$ **c**
53. $\cos -\frac{\pi}{12}$ **i**
54. $\sin -\frac{5\pi}{4}$ **d**
55. $\sin 2.75\pi$ **d**

LESSON MASTER 11-1 B

Questions on SPUR Objectives

Vocabulary

1. Give an example of a *polynomial in x* written in standard form.

   Sample: $4x^3 - 3x^2 + x - 8$

Properties Objective E: Use technical vocabulary to describe polynomials.

In 2–7, a polynomial is given. **a.** Write the polynomial in standard form. **b.** Give the degree of the polynomial. **c.** Name the leading coefficient. **d.** Give the number of terms.

2. $9v^2 + 7v^3$
   a. $7v^3 + 9v^2$
   b. 3
   c. 7
   d. 2

3. $8m^2 + 4 - 6m$
   a. $8m^2 - 6m + 4$
   b. 2
   c. 8
   d. 3

4. $c^5 - 2c^3 - c^2 - 5$
   a. $c^5 - 2c^3 - c^2 - 5$
   b. 5
   c. 1
   d. 4

5. $12 - 6p$
   a. $-6p + 12$
   b. 1
   c. -6
   d. 2

6. $-14r^7 + 6r^{19} - r^3 + 4r^{10}$
   a. $6r^{19} + 4r^{10} - 14r^7 - r^3 - r$
   b. 19
   c. 6
   d. 5

7. $12e^4$
   a. $12e^4$
   b. 4
   c. 12
   d. 1

▶ **LESSON MASTER 11-1 B** *page 2*

Uses Objective H: Use polynomials to model real-world situations.

8. For five years, Mr. Volaskis invested $1600 per year in a retirement account paying *r*% compounded annually. No additional money was added or withdrawn.

   a. Write a polynomial expression to give the total amount in his account at the end of the fifth year. $(x = 1 + r)$

   $1600x^5 + 1600x^4 + 1600x^3 + 1600x^2 + 1600x$

   b. Determine how much is in his account if it earned 4.8% each year.   **$9228.43**

9. A parents' organization saved the fun-fair profits in a special fund for new playground equipment. The money was left untouched and earned *r*% interest compounded annually. The table shows the deposits.

Date	Deposit
6/89	$ 800
6/90	1150
6/91	1200
6/92	750
6/93	1130
6/94	980

   a. Write a polynomial expression for the amount in the account after the 6/94 deposit. $(x = 1 + r)$

   $800x^6 + 1150x^5 + 1200x^4 + 750x^3 + 1130x^2 + 980x$

   b. Evaluate how much was in the account after 6/94, if $r = 3.7\%$.   **$6829.45**

Representations Objective J: Graph polynomial functions.

In 10 and 11, a polynomial function is given. **a.** Evaluate $f(-2)$, $f(0)$, and $f(1)$. **b.** Sketch the graph of the polynomial function on the given window.

10. $f(x) = -4x^4 + 12x^2 - 3x + 20$
    a. **10, 20, 25**
    b.
    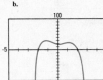

11. $P(x) = x^5 + 4.5x - 7$
    a. **-48, -7, -1.5**
    b.
    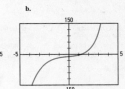

LESSON MASTER 11-2 B

Questions on SPUR Objectives

Skills Objective A: Use the Extended Distributive Property to multiply polynomials.

In 1–8, expand and write in standard form.

1. $(x^3 + 6)(x - 3)$
$x^4 - 3x^3 + 6x - 18$

2. $(2 + 4n^4)^2$
$16n^8 + 16n^4 + 4$

3. $(e + 9)(e + 4)(e - 9)$
$e^3 + 4e^2 - 81e - 324$

4. $(5x + 3)^2(2x - 8)$
$50x^3 - 140x^2 - 222x - 72$

5. $(-y^2 + 6)(y^4 + 2y^2 - 3)$
$-y^6 + 4y^4 + 15y^2 - 18$

6. $b(6b - 5)(2b^3 + 1)$
$12b^5 - 10b^4 + 6b^2 - 5b$

7. $(2u + 1)(3u - 4)(-u^2 + 1)$
$-6u^4 + 5u^3 + 10u^2 - 5u - 4$

8. $(g^2 - 2g + 2)(g^2 + 2g - 4)$
$g^4 - 6g^2 + 12g - 8$

In 9–12, multiply and simplify.

9. $(x + 3y)(2x - 2xy + y)$
$2x^2 - 2x^2y + 7xy - 6xy^2 + 3y^2$

10. $(4w + 3)(-2w - 5x + 7)$
$-8w^2 - 20wx + 22w - 15x + 21$

11. $(r + s)(r + 5s)(r - 3s)$
$r^3 + 3r^2s - 13rs^2 - 15s^3$

12. $(a + b + c)(a - b + c)$
$a^2 + 2ac - b^2 + c^2$

Properties Objective E: Use technical vocabulary to describe polynomials.

13. Give an example of each.

a. monomial — Sample: $-5n$

b. binomial — Sample: $3m + 4$

c. trinomial — Sample: $2x^2 + 3x - 9$

In 14 and 15, give the degree of the polynomial.

14. $12a^2b^4 + 3ab^3 + b^2$ — 6

15. $-9m^7n - 4m^4n^3 + m^2n^2 - 16$ — 8

Uses Objective I: Use polynomials to describe geometric situations.

In 16 and 17, consider the largest of the rectangles in the diagram. a. Give its dimensions. b. Find its area.

16.

a. $2a + 2b$, $a + b + 4c$

b. $2a^2 + 4ab + 2b^2 + 8ac + 8bc$

17.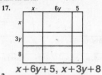

a. $x + 6y + 5$, $x + 3y + 8$

b. $x^2 + 9xy + 13x + 18y^2 + 63y + 40$

18. Refer to the largest rectangular solid to the right.

a. What are its dimensions?
$v + 5$, $3u + 2$, $u + v + 2$

b. What is its volume?
$3u^2v + 3uv^2 + 15u^2 + 23uv + 2v^2 + 40u + 14v + 20$

c. What is its surface area?
$6u^2 + 14uv + 2v^2 + 56u + 22v + 48$

19. An open box is folded from a sheet of tag board 55 cm by 70 cm, after removing squares of side x from each corner.

a. At the right, sketch a diagram of this situation.

b. Write a formula for the volume $V(x)$ of the box.
$V(x) = 3850x - 250x^2 + 4x^3$

c. Write a formula for the surface $S(x)$ area of the box.
$S(x) = 3850 - 4x^2$

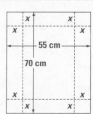

55 cm

70 cm

LESSON MASTER 11-3 B

Questions on SPUR Objectives

Vocabulary

1. For real numbers a, b, and c, if $ax^2 + bx + c = 0$, then what is the quantity $b^2 - 4ac$ called? — **discriminant**

2. a. What does it mean if we say a polynomial is *prime* over the set of polynomials with rational coefficients? *
Sample: It cannot be factored into polynomials of lower degree whose coefficients are rational numbers.

b. What does it mean if we say a polynomial is *prime* over the set of polynomials with real coefficients?
Sample: It cannot be factored into polynomials of lower degree whose coefficients are real numbers.

Skills Objective B: Factor polynomials using common-monomial factoring, perfect-square patterns, or patterns for the difference of squares.

In 3–7, fill in the blanks.

3. $6g^2h - 15gh^2 = 3gh(\underline{2g} - \underline{5h})$

4. $16x^3y + 20x^2 = \underline{4x^2}(4xy + 5)$

5. $a^3b^4c^7 - a^2b^2c^5 + a^2b^2c^4 = a^2b^2c^4(\underline{ab^2c^3} - \underline{c} + \underline{1})$

6. $-18x^3y^2z^2 + 14x^2y^2 - 30y^2z = \underline{-2y^2}(9x^3z^2 - 7x^2 + 15z)$

7. $4(a + 2b) - (a + 2b)^2 = (a + 2b)(\underline{4} - \underline{a - 2b})$

In 8–15, multiple choice. Which of the following describes the polynomial?

(a) perfect square   (b) difference of squares

(c) sum of squares   (d) none of the above

8. $a^2 - 81$ — b

9. $c^2 + 14c + 49$ — a

10. $r^2 + 144$ — c

11. $2m^2 + 8m + 16$ — d

12. $36x^2 - 60x + 25$ — a

13. $49 - 9u^2$ — b

14. $x^6 - 1$ — b

15. $25e^2 + 10e + 4$ — d

In 16–23, factor over the set of polynomials with rational coefficients, if possible. If this is not possible, write *prime*.

16. $8a^2 - 2a - 3$
$(4a - 3)(2a + 1)$

17. $m^2 + 2m + 6$
prime

18. $x^2 - 100$
$(x + 10)(x - 10)$

19. $4n^3 + 20n^2 - 24n$
$4n(n + 6)(n - 1)$

20. $a^2b^4c^2 - 81d^2$
$(ab^2c + 9d)(ab^2c - 9d)$

21. $49g^2 + 42g + 9$
$(7g + 3)^2$

22. $4e^2 - ef - 3f^2$
$(4e + 3f)(e - f)$

23. $9x^3 - 30x^2 + 25x$
$x(3x - 5)^2$

24. a. Write $r^4 - 1$ as the product of two binomials.
$(r^2 + 1)(r^2 - 1)$

b. Write $r^4 - 1$ as the product of three binomials.
$(r^2 + 1)(r + 1)(r - 1)$

25. Factor $4x^2 - 5$ over the set of real numbers.
$(2x + \sqrt{5})(2x - \sqrt{5})$

26. Factor $4y^2 + 1$ over the set of complex numbers.
$(2y + i)(2y - i)$

Review Objective K, Lesson 6-10

In 27–29, suppose D is the discriminant for a quadratic function $f(x) = ax^2 + bx + c$. Tell if $D = 0$, $D > 0$, or $D < 0$ for the graph of $f(x)$.

27.
$D < 0$

28.
$D = 0$

29.
$D > 0$

In 30–33, give the number of x-intercepts of the graph of the parabola.

30. $y = 16x^2 - 24x + 9$ — 1

31. $y = -x^2 - 5x - 12$ — 0

32. $y = 3x^2 - 10x + 8$ — 2

33. $y + 3 = 8x^2 - 10x$ — 2

LESSON MASTER 11-4 B

Questions on SPUR Objectives

Representations Objective K: Estimate zeros of functions of polynomials using tables or graphs.

In 1 and 2, the graph of a polynomial function is shown.
a. Give the minimum number of x-intercepts.
b. Estimate the value of each x-intercept.

1.

a. __3__
b. $\approx$ -3.9, $\approx$ -.4, $\approx$ 1.6

2.
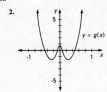
a. __4__
b. $\approx$ -.48, $\approx$ -.08, $\approx$ .08, $\approx$ .48

In 3 and 4, the graph of a polynomial function is shown.
a. Give the minimum number of x-intercepts.
b. Give the minimum number of solutions to the equation $h(x) = 60$. Between which pair of consecutive integers does each solution occur?
c. Give the minimum number of solutions to the equation $h(x) = -20$. Between which pair of consecutive integers does each solution occur?

3.

a. __1__
b. 3; -6, -5; -2, -1; 1, 2
c. 1; 2, 3

4.

a. __0__
b. 2; -1, 0; 3, 4
c. 0

▶ **LESSON MASTER 11-4 B** *page 2*

In 5–8, estimate the real zeros of the function described to the nearest tenth.

5. $f(x) = x^3 + 2x^2 - 4x - 1$
  -3.2, -.2, 1.4

6. $g(x) = -3x^5 + 6x^4 + 2x^3 - 3x^2 + 8x - 5$
  -1.2, .6, 2.3

7. $h(t) = 2t^4 - 8t^2 + 4$
  -1.8, -.8, .8, 1.8

8. $P(n) = n^6 - 4n^5 + 3n^2$
  0, 1, 4

9. a. Complete the table of values for the function $k(x) = .5x^4 - 2x^3 + 5$

x	k(x)
-5	567.5
-4	261
-3	99.5
-2	29
-1	7.5
0	5
1	3.5
2	-3
3	-8.5
4	5
5	67.5

  b. From the table, how many real zeros does the function have?
  __2__
  c. Between which two consecutive integers do the zeros occur?
  1 and 2, 3 and 4
  d. How could you use a graph to justify your answers in Parts b and c?
  Sample: Graph the function. Then count and read the x-intercepts.
  e. Use technology to find each zero to the nearest tenth.
  1.6, 3.8

In 10 and 11, solve each system. Round solutions to the nearest tenth.

10. $\begin{cases} y = -x^3 + 5x + 2 \\ y = 5 \end{cases}$
  (-2.5, 5), (.7, 5), (1.8, 5)

11. $\begin{cases} y = .5x^4 - 3x^2 \\ y = 2x - 3 \end{cases}$
  (.7, -1.5), (2.6, 2.2)

LESSON MASTER 11-5 B

Questions on SPUR Objectives

Skills Objective C: Find zeros of polynomial functions by factoring.

In 1–9, find the exact zeros of the polynomial function described.

1. $f(x) = (x + 1)(x - 3)(3x + 2)$ __$-1, 3, -\frac{2}{3}$__

2. $g(x) = 4x(2x + 9)$ __$0, -\frac{9}{2}$__

3. $h(a) = a^2 - 10a + 25$ __5__

4. $d(x) = x^2 - 64$ __8, -8__

5. $j(x) = x^3 + 18x^2 + 81x$ __0, -9__

6. $e(n) = 15n^3 - 45n^2 - 60n$ __0, 4, -1__

7. $g(x) = x^4 - 36x^2$ __0, 6, -6__

8. $h(a) = 4a^3 - 4a$ __0, 1, -1__

9. $d(x) = 18x^3 + 57x^2 - 21x$ __$0, \frac{1}{3}, -\frac{7}{2}$__

Skills Objective D: Determine an equation for a polynomial function from data points.

In 10–13, write equations for three different polynomial functions with the given zeros. Samples are given.

10. 0, -5, and 3
  $y = x(x+5)(x-3)$
  $y = x^2(x+5)(x-3)$
  $y = 2x(x+5)(x-3)$

11. 0, 9, and -9
  $y = x(x+9)(x-9)$
  $y = x^2(x+9)(x-9)$
  $y = 5x(x+9)(x-9)$

12. $\frac{3}{2}, \frac{5}{4}$, and -2
  $y = (2x-3)(4x-5)(x+2)$
  $y = (x-\frac{3}{2})(x-\frac{5}{4})(x+2)$
  $y = x(2x-3)(4x-5)(x+2)$

13. -3, 0, 3.5, and 7
  $y = 2x(x+3)(x-3.5)(x-7)$
  $y = x(2x+6)(2x-7)(2x-14)$
  $y = 4x^2(x+3)(x-3.5)(x-7)$

▶ **LESSON MASTER 11-5 B** *page 2*

Properties Objective F: Apply the Zero-Product Theorem and the Factor Theorem.

14. Consider the two polynomial functions with equations $f(x) = 3x(x + 4)(2x - 1)$ and $g(x) = x^2(x + 4)(2x - 1)$. What do the graphs of the two equations have in common?
  They have the same x-intercepts, 0, -4, and $\frac{1}{2}$.

15. Suppose $f(x) = (x + a)(x + b)(x - 2c)$. What are the zeros of the function f?
  -a, -b, 2c

16. The graph of a polynomial function contains the points $(a, 0)$, $(b, 0)$, $(0, c)$, (d, e), and $(f, 0)$. Give as many factors of the polynomial as you can.
  $(x - a), (x - b), (x - f)$

17. The graph of a polynomial equation does not cross the x-axis. Can the polynomial be factored? Explain your reasoning.
  Sample: No; if it were factorable with a factor $(x - r)$, then r is a root and an x-intercept.

Representations Objective J: Graph polynomial functions.

18. At the right is the graph of a fourth-degree polynomial with leading coefficient 1 and integer zeros.
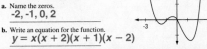
  a. Name the zeros.
  -2, -1, 0, 2
  b. Write an equation for the function.
  $y = x(x + 2)(x + 1)(x - 2)$

Representations Objective K: Estimate zeros of functions of polynomials using graphs.

19. Consider the polynomial equation $y = x^3 - 2x^2 - 3x$.

  a. Sketch a graph of the polynomial.
  b. Use the graph to factor the polynomial.
  $y = x(x + 1)(x - 3)$

LESSON MASTER 11-6 B

Skills Objective B: Factor polynomials
Objective C: Find zeros of polynomial functions by factoring.

In 1–9, a polynomial is given. **a.** Factor the polynomial over the set of *complex* numbers. **b.** Check your answers by multiplying the factors.

1. $x^2 + 4x - 357$

a. $(x - 17)(x + 21)$
b. $x^2 - 17x + 21x - 357 = x^2 + 4x - 357$

2. $10z^2 + 51z + 27$

a. $(5z + 3)(2z + 9)$
b. $10z^2 + 45z + 6z + 27 = 10z^2 + 51z + 27$

3. $y^2 - 3$

a. $(y + \sqrt{3})(y - \sqrt{3})$
b. $y^2 - y\sqrt{3} + y\sqrt{3} - 3 = y^2 - 3$

4. $n^2 + 4n + 7$

a. $(n + 2 + i\sqrt{3})(n + 2 - i\sqrt{3})$
b. $(n + 2)^2 - 3i^2 = n^2 + 4n + 4 + 3 = n^2 + 4n + 7$

5. $6m^3 - 17m^2 + 5m$

a. $m(3m - 1)(2m - 5)$
b. $m(6m^2 - 15m - 2m + 5) = 6m^3 - 17m^2 + 5m$

6. $2a + 3a^2 - 10$

a. $3(a + \frac{1 + \sqrt{31}}{3})(a + \frac{1 - \sqrt{31}}{3})$
b. $3(a^2 + \frac{a + a\sqrt{31}}{3} + \frac{a - a\sqrt{31}}{3} + \frac{1 - 31}{9}) = 3a^2 + 2a - 10$

7. $c^3 - 17c$

a. $c(c + \sqrt{17})(c - \sqrt{17})$
b. $c(c^2 - 17) = c^3 - 17c$

8. $16g^2 + 8\sqrt{5}g + 5$

a. $(4g + \sqrt{5})^2$
b. $16g^2 + 2(4g\sqrt{5}) + 5 = 16g^2 + 8\sqrt{5}g + 5$

9. $8d^3 - 2d^2 - 3d$

a. $d(4d - 3)(2d + 1)$
b. $d(8d^2 + 4d - 6d - 3) = 8d^3 - 2d^2 - 3d$

In 10–13, an equation is given. **a.** Find all real solutions. **b.** Check your answer by graphing.

10. $0 = x^2 - 17$

a. $x = \sqrt{17}$ or $x = -\sqrt{17}$
b.

11. $24x^2 + 53x - 7 = 0$

a. $x = \frac{1}{8}$ or $x = -\frac{7}{3}$
b.

12. $x^2 + x + 4 = 0$

a. $x = -\frac{1}{2} \pm \frac{i\sqrt{15}}{2}$
b.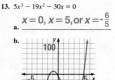

13. $5x^3 - 19x^2 - 30x = 0$

a. $x = 0, x = 5,$ or $x = -\frac{6}{5}$
b.

In 14 and 15, an equation is given. **a.** Solve. **b.** Check the solution by substituting into the original equation.

14. $m^2 + 10 = 0$

a. $m = i\sqrt{10}$ or $m = -i\sqrt{10}$
b. Checks are not shown.

15. $2k^3 - 13k^2 + 20k = 0$

a. $k = 0, k = 4,$ or $k = \frac{5}{2}$
b.

LESSON MASTER 11-7 B

Properties Objective G: Apply the Rational Zero Theorem.

1. Suppose $8m^6$ is the first term of a polynomial function written in standard form and 7 is the last term. Let $\frac{p}{q}$ be a rational number in lowest terms and let $\frac{p}{q}$ be a zero of the polynomial function.

a. Fill in each blank with a number: p is a factor of __?__ and q is a factor of __?__ .

7, 8

b. Give three possible values for $\frac{p}{q}$.

Samples: $\frac{7}{8}, \frac{1}{2}, \frac{1}{4}$

In 2–5, use the Rational Zero Theorem to factor the polynomial.

2. $x^3 - 2x^2 - 21x - 18$

$(x + 1)(x + 3)(x - 6)$

3. $6y^3 - 13y^2 + y + 2$

$(2y - 1)(3y + 1)(y - 2)$

4. $15z^3 - 22z^2 - 5z$

$z(3z - 5)(5z + 1)$

5. $9a^5 - 30a^4 - 81a^3 + 30a^2$

$3a^2(a - 5)(a + 2)(3a - 1)$

In 6–13, a polynomial is given. **a.** Use the Rational Zero Theorem to list all possible rational zeros of the given polynomial. **b.** Find all rational zeros.

6. $f(x) = 2x^3 - x^2 - 2x + 1$

a. $\pm 1, \pm\frac{1}{2}$
b. $1, -1, \frac{1}{2}$

7. $g(x) = 125x^3 - 1$

a. $\pm 1, \pm\frac{1}{5}, \pm\frac{1}{25}, \pm\frac{1}{125}$
b. $\frac{1}{5}$

8. $q(x) = 3x^2 + 2x + 8$

a. $\pm 1, \pm 2, \pm 4, \pm 8, \pm\frac{1}{3},$ $\pm\frac{2}{3}, \pm\frac{4}{3}, \pm\frac{8}{3}$
b. none

9. $h(x) = 10x^2 - 11x + 3$

a. $\pm 1, \pm 3, \pm\frac{1}{2}, \pm\frac{1}{5}, \pm\frac{1}{10}, \pm\frac{3}{2},$ $\pm\frac{3}{5}, \pm\frac{3}{10}$
b. $\frac{1}{2}, \frac{3}{5}$

10. $f(x) = x^5 - 12x^4 + 36x^3 - x^2 + 12x - 36$

a. $\pm 1, \pm 2, \pm 3, \pm 4, \pm 6,$ $\pm 9, \pm 12, \pm 18, \pm 36$
b. $1, 6$

11. $t(x) = 8x^5 - 32x^4 + x^2 - 4$

a. $\pm 1, \pm 2, \pm 4, \pm\frac{1}{2}, \pm\frac{1}{4}, \pm\frac{1}{8}$
b. none

12. $t(x) = 2x^6 + 6x^5 + 3x + 21$

a. $\pm 1, \pm 3, \pm 7, \pm 21, \pm\frac{1}{2},$ $\pm\frac{3}{2}, \pm\frac{7}{2}, \pm\frac{21}{2}$
b. none

13. $s(x) = x^6 + 4x^5 - x - 4$

a. $\pm 1, \pm 2, \pm 4$
b. $1, -4$

Representations Objective J: Graph polynomial functions.

14. Consider $g(x) = -3x^5 + 20x^2 - 8$.

a. Use the Rational Zero Theorem to list all possible rational zeros.

$\pm 1, \pm 2, \pm 4, \pm 8, \pm\frac{1}{3}, \pm\frac{2}{3},$ $\pm\frac{4}{3}, \pm\frac{8}{3}$

b. Graph the polynomial function at the right.

c. Use Parts **a** and **b** to find all rational zeros.

15. Consider $h(x) = 4x^6 + 6x^2 + 5$.

a. Use the Rational Zero Theorem to list all possible rational zeros.

$\pm 1, \pm 5, \pm\frac{1}{2}, \pm\frac{5}{2}, \pm\frac{1}{4}, \pm\frac{5}{4}$

b. Graph the polynomial function at the right.

c. Use Parts **a** and **b** to find all rational zeros.

Review Objective C, Lessons 6-7 and 6-8

In 16–19, find all solutions.

16. $2x^2 + 9x - 1 = 0$

$x = \frac{-9 \pm \sqrt{89}}{4}$

17. $4n^2 - 6n - 7 = 0$

$n = \frac{3 \pm \sqrt{37}}{4}$

18. $6m^2 + 7m = 5$

$m = \frac{1}{2}$ or $m = -\frac{5}{3}$

19. $4a - 10 = 3a^2$

$a = \frac{2 \pm i\sqrt{26}}{3}$

LESSON MASTER 11-8 B

Questions on SPUR Objectives

Vocabulary

1. Suppose r is a *root* of a polynomial function and has *multiplicity 3*. What does this mean?
   Sample: $(x - r)^3$ is a factor of the polynomial.

2. Give an example of a polynomial function in **Samples are given.** factored form that has
   a. 5 as a double root. $f(x) = (x - 5)^2$
   b. 3 as a root with mutiplicity 4. $g(x) = (x - 3)^4(2x + 1)$

Properties   Objective F: Apply the Fundamental Theorem of Algebra.

3. State the Fundamental Theorem of Algebra.
   Every polynomial equation $P(x) = 0$ of any degree with complex-number coefficients has at least one complex-number solution.

4. Consider the equation $8x^4 - i\sqrt{2}\,x^2 + 3 + 2i = 0$.
   a. What is the minimum number of complex roots of the equation?   **1**
   b. What is the maximum number of different roots of the equation?   **4**

5. Consider the equation $(2x - 1)^5(x^2 - 5)(x^2 + 4) = 0$.
   a. What is the minimum number of complex roots of the equation?   **1**
   b. What is the maximum number of roots of the equation?   **9**
   c. Find all the rational roots and state the multiplicity of each.
      $x = \frac{1}{2}$, **multiplicity 5**

▶ **LESSON MASTER 11-8 B** *page 2*

d. Find all the irrational roots and the multiplicity of each.
   $x = \sqrt{5}$, **multiplicity 1**; $x = -\sqrt{5}$, **multiplicity 1**

e. Find all the nonreal roots and the multiplicity of each.
   $x = 2i$, **multiplicity 1**; $x = -2i$, **multiplicity 1**

f. Without graphing, tell how many times the equation crosses the x-axis. Explain your reasoning.
   Sample: 3 times; there are three different real roots.

Culture   Objective L: Be familiar with the history of the solving of polynomial equations.

6. Match each name with his contribution towards solving all polynomial equations.

a. Évariste Galois	**e**	In the 16th century, discovered how to solve any quartic equation
b. Niccolo Tartaglia	**d**	In the 18th century, proved the Fundamental Theorem of Algebra
c. Omar Khayyam	**g**	In the 16th century, discovered how to solve some types of cubic equations exactly
d. Karl Friedrich Gauss		
e. Ludovico Ferrari	**h**	In 1799, provided most of the proof that a general quintic equation cannot be solved by formulas
f. Niels Abel		
g. Scipione Del Ferro	**f**	In 1824, completed the proof that a general quintic equation cannot be solved by formulas
h. Paolo Ruffini	**b**	In 1535, discovered a method for solving all cubic equations exactly
	c	In the 12th century, showed how to solve many cubic equations
	a	In 19th century, described a method for determining which polynomial equations of degree 5 or more can be solved using formulas

---

LESSON MASTER 11-9 B

Questions on SPUR Objectives

Skills   Objective D: Determine an equation for a polynomial function from data points.

In 1–7, a set of ordered pairs or a sequence is given.
a. Determine whether the given values can be described by a polynomial function of degree 5 or less.
b. If so, give its degree.

1.

x	1	2	3	4	5	6	7	8
y	6	13	32	69	130	221	348	517

   a. **yes**   b. **3**

2.

x	5	6	7	8	9	10	11	12
y	-27,500	-8896	27,228	91,072	196,196	360,000	604,204	955,328

   a. **yes**   b. **5**

3.

x	-4	-3	-2	-1	0	1	2	3
y	1407	1539	1674	1814	1960	2113	2271	2440

   a. **no**   b. _____

4.

x	-18	-12	-6	0	6	12	18	24
y	-304	-124	-16	20	-16	-124	-304	-556

   a. **yes**   b. **2**

5.

x	0	5	10	15	20	25	30	35
y	0	-5	-80	-405	-1280	-3125	-6480	-12,005

   a. **yes**   b. **4**

6. the sequence in which $a_1 = 7$ and $a_n = a_{n-1} + 4$
   a. **yes**   b. **1**

7. the sequence in which $a_1 = 3$ and $a_n = 4a_{n-1} - 2$
   a. **no**   b. _____

▶ **LESSON MASTER 11-9 B** *page 2*

8. Can the method of finite differences be used with this set of data? Explain why or why not.

x	0	4	12	24	40	60	84	112
y	23	34	45	56	67	78	89	100

   Sample: No; the x-values do not form a linear sequence.

9. Suppose there is a polynomial formula of degree ≤ 5 for the nth term of the sequence 14, 71, 182, 365, 638, 1019, 1526, 2177, ... Use the method of finite differences to predict the next term.   **2990**

Uses   Objective H: Use polynomials to model real-world situations.

10. As part of an experiment, Chiang held a paper tube to her eye and estimated the number of grid squares she could see through the tube when the tube was held at various distances above a sheet of grid paper. Her results are given in the table.

Distance Above Paper (cm)	1	2	3	4	5	6
Number of Squares Visible	30	39	50	63	78	95

   a. What degree equation would you use to best model the data? Explain your answer.
      2nd degree; second differences are equal.

   b. Predict how many squares Chiang could view when the tube is held 7 cm above the paper.   **114 squares**

Review   Objective A, Lesson 5-4

In 11 and 12, solve the system.

11. $\begin{cases} \frac{1}{3}x - y = 6 \\ \frac{1}{2}x + 2y = -5 \end{cases}$
    $x = 6, y = -4$

12. $\begin{cases} 2a + b - c = -9 \\ 3a + 3b + 2c = 4 \\ a + 2b - 2c = -12 \end{cases}$
    $a = -2, b = 0, c = 5$

Page 205

LESSON MASTER 11-10 B

Questions on SPUR Objectives

Skills Objective D: Determine an equation for a polynomial function from data points.

In 1 and 2, the data in the table can be modeled by a polynomial equation of the form $y = ax^2 + bx + c$.
a. List three equations which can be used to solve for a, b, and c.
b. Solve the system to find a formula which models the data.

1.

x	1	2	3	4	5	6	7	8
y	6	15	28	45	66	91	120	153

a. $a+b+c=6,\ 4a+2b+c=15,\ 9a+3b+c=28$

b. $y = 2x^2 + 3x + 1$

2.

x	1	2	3	4	5	6	7	8
y	-7	-16	-31	-52	-79	-112	-151	-196

a. $a+b+c=-7,\ 4a+2b+c=-16,\ 9a+3b+c=-31$

b. $y = -3x^2 - 4$

In 3 and 4, write a polynomial formula which models the data.

3.

x	1	2	3	4	5	6	7	8
y	4	6	6	4	0	-6	-14	-24

$y = -x^2 + 5x$

4.

x	1	2	3	4	5	6	7	8
y	8	15	34	71	132	223	350	519

$y = x^3 + 7$

5. The data below can be modeled by an equation of the form $y = ax^4 + cx^2$. Find the equation.

x	0	1	2	3	4	5	6	7
y	0	3	24	99	288	675	1368	2499

$y = x^4 + 2x^2$

Page 206

▶ **LESSON MASTER 11-10 B** *page 2*

Uses Objective H: Use polynomials to model real-world situations.

6. A statue is to be erected at the top of a number of square concrete steps as shown below. The top square is 10 ft by 10 ft by .5 ft. The second one is 20 ft by 20 ft by .5 ft. The third is 30 ft by 30 ft by .5 ft. Each additional square step is 10 ft longer on a side.

a. How many cubic feet of concrete are needed for
   i. the top step? **50 cu ft**   ii. the 2nd step? **200 cu ft**
   iii. the 3rd step? **450 cu ft**   iv. the 4th step? **800 cu ft**
   v. the 5th step? **1250 cu ft**

b. Complete the table below. Be sure to give the *total* number of cubic feet of concrete needed.

Number of Steps	1	2	3	4	5
Cubic Feet of Concrete	50	250	700	1500	2750

c. Write an equation to model the data.

$f(n) = \frac{50}{3}n^3 + 25n^2 + \frac{25}{3}n$

d. Use your equation to predict how many cubic feet of concrete would be needed for 8 stairs.   **10,200 cu ft**

Page 207

LESSON MASTER 12-1 B

Questions on SPUR Objectives

Vocabulary

In 1 and 2, refer to the parabola below.

1. Identify the following.
   a. *focus*   **G**
   b. *directrix*   **j**
   c. *vertex*   **X**
   d. *axis of symmetry*   **k**

2. Explain what is true about all the points on the parabola. You may sketch additional points or segments and refer to them in your explanation.

   Sample: For every point P on the parabola, the distance from P to G is equal to the distance from P to j.

Skills Objective B: Write equations for parabolas given sufficient conditions.

In 3–5, write an equation for the parabola satisfying the given conditions.

3. focus $(0, -4)$ and directrix $y = 4$ $y = -\frac{1}{16}x^2$

4. focus $(3, 0)$ and directrix $x = -3$ $y^2 = 12x$

5. Given $F = (6, 0)$ and line m with equation $x = -6$, write an equation for the set of points equidistant from F and m. $y^2 = 24x$

Properties Objective E: Find points on a parabola using its definition.

6. Find five points on the parabola with directrix w and focus U including the vertex of the parabola.
   Four sample points are given in addition to the vertex.

Page 208

▶ **LESSON MASTER 12-1 B** *page 2*

Properties Objective F: Identify characteristics of parabolas.

In 7–9, an equation for a parabola is given. a. Tell whether the parabola opens up or down. b. Give the focus. c. Give the vertex. d. Give the directrix.

7. $y = -\frac{1}{5}x^2$ a. **down**   b. $\left(0, -\frac{5}{4}\right)$ c. $(0, 0)$ d. $y = \frac{5}{4}$

8. $y = 8x^2$ a. **up**   b. $\left(0, \frac{1}{32}\right)$ c. $(0, 0)$ d. $y = -\frac{1}{32}$

9. $y = -4(x+2)^2$ a. **down**   b. $\left(-2, -\frac{1}{16}\right)$ c. $(-2, 0)$ d. $y = \frac{1}{16}$

Properties Objective G: Classify curves as parabolas using algebraic or geometric properties.

10. The graph of a parabola has focus $F = (2, 1)$ and directrix d with equation $y = -1$.
    a. *Multiple choice.* Choose the points that lie on the parabola.
       (a) $A = (4, 1)$ (b) $B = (-2, 4)$
       (c) $C = (-1, 2)$
       a, b

    b. Explain how you determined your answer in Part a.
       Sample: The equation for the parabola is $y = \frac{1}{4}(x - 2)^2$; points A and B satisfy the equation, but point C does not.

Representations Objective J: Graph parabolas given sentences for them and vice versa.

11. a. Graph the parabola with equation $y = -\frac{1}{8}x^2$.
    b. Plot and label the focus.
    c. Plot and label the directrix.

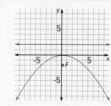

LESSON MASTER 12-2 B

Questions on SPUR Objectives

Vocabulary

1. Write a definition for *circle*, including the meanings of *radius* and *center*.

   Sample: A circle is the set of all points in a plane at a given distance—its radius—from a fixed point—its center.

Skills Objective B: Write equations for circles given sufficient conditions.

In 2–7, write an equation for the circle satisfying the conditions.

2. center at (0, 0), radius 9
   $$x^2 + y^2 = 81$$

3. center at (0, 0), radius .4
   $$x^2 + y^2 = .16$$

4. center at (3, -1), radius 3
   $$(x-3)^2 + (y+1)^2 = 9$$

5. center at (-2, -6), radius 11
   $$(x+2)^2 + (y+6)^2 = 121$$

6. center at (8, 0), radius $\frac{8}{5}$
   $$(x-8)^2 + y^2 = \frac{64}{25}$$

7. center at (2, 5), radius $\sqrt{7}$
   $$(x-2)^2 + (y-5)^2 = 7$$

Properties Objective F: Identify characteristics of circles.

In 8–11, identify the center and radius of each circle.

8. $(x-4)^2 + (y+6)^2 = 36$
   center **(4, -6)**
   radius **6**

9. $x^2 + y^2 = 80$
   center **(0, 0)**
   radius **$4\sqrt{5}$**

10. $(x+2)^2 + (y+4.5)^2 = 1$
    center **(-2, -4.5)**
    radius **1**

11. $(x-.6)^2 + (y+.9)^2 = 2.25$
    center **(.6, -.9)**
    radius **1.5**

Properties Objective G: Classify curves as circles using algebraic or geometric properties.

12. a. *True or false.* The points $(4, 4\sqrt{3})$, $(-4\sqrt{2}, 4\sqrt{2})$, (0, 8), and (-8, 0) all lie on the same circle with center (0, 0).
    true

    b. Explain how you determined your answer in Part a.
    Samples: By the Distance Formula, every point is 8 units from (0, 0); all points satisfy the equation for the circle, $x^2 + y^2 = 64$.

Uses Objective H: Use circles to solve real-world problems.

13. A sprinkler shoots a 10-foot stream of water in all directions. Consider a graph in which each unit represents one foot. Place the sprinkler at the origin.

    a. Write an equation to represent the boundary of the sprinkled area.
    $$x^2 + y^2 = 100$$

    b. A prize rose bush is located 8 ft east and 6 ft north of the sprinkler. Will the rose bush get sprinkled? Explain your thinking.
    Sample: Yes; the point (8, 6) satisfies the equation of the circle.

Representations Objective J: Graph circles given sentences for them and vice versa.

14. Graph the circle with equation $(x + 2)^2 + (y - 3)^2 = 9$.

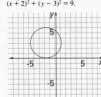

15. Write an equation for the circle graphed below.

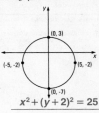

$$x^2 + (y + 2)^2 = 25$$

LESSON MASTER 12-3 B

Questions on SPUR Objectives

Vocabulary

1. Label the diagram at the right to identify the *boundary*, the *interior*, and the *exterior*.

exterior, interior, boundary

Skills Objective B: Write equations or inequalities for circles given sufficient conditions.

2. What equation describes the lower semicircle of the circle $x^2 + y^2 = 15$?
   $$y = -\sqrt{15 - x^2}$$

3. a. Write a sentence describing all points in the interior of a circle whose center is (3, 4) and whose radius is 7.
   $$(x-3)^2 + (y-4)^2 < 49$$

   b. Use your answer to part a to show that (6, -1) is in the interior of the circle.
   $$(6-3)^2 + (-1-4)^2 = 3^2 + (-5)^2 = 9 + 25$$
   $$= 34 < 49$$

Uses Objective H: Use circles to solve real-world problems.

4. A parade float 8 feet high and 5 feet wide approached a semicircular arch with a diameter of 18 feet.

   a. Will the float fit through the arch? Justify your answer.
   Sample: Yes; the equation for the arch is $x^2 + y^2 = 81$, and the points (2.5, 8) and (-2.5, 8) for the float are in the interior of the semicircle.

   b. Find the radius of the smallest arch through which the float could pass.
   ≈8.38 ft

5. A semicircular mirror is made from four smaller mirrors as shown at the right. What are the least dimensions possible for the rectangular mirror out of which each end piece is cut?
   2 ft, ≈3.46 ft

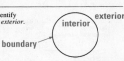

4 ft

2 ft 2 ft 2 ft 2 ft

---

6. A telephone company defines Zone 1 as a region within a 24-mile radius of the phone company's downtown office. For a flat rate of $56 per month, a city resident can make unlimited phone calls within Zone 1.

   Consider a graph in which each unit represents one mile. Place the office at the origin.

   a. Write an equation to represent the boundary of Zone 1.
   $$x^2 + y^2 = 576$$

   b. A resident made a call to a store located 20 miles east and 10 miles north of the office. Is the store located within Zone 1?
   yes

Representations Objective J: Graph quadratic relations for circles or circular regions given sentences for them and vice versa.

In 7–10, graph the relation.

7. $(x + 3)^2 + y^2 \leq 4$

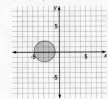

8. $x^2 + y^2 \geq 6$

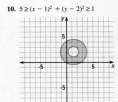

9. $(x + 2)^2 + (y - 4)^2 \leq 3$

10. $5 \geq (x - 1)^2 + (y - 2)^2 \geq 1$

LESSON MASTER 12-4 B

Questions on SPUR Objectives

Vocabulary

1. Refer to the ellipse at the right with foci P and Q.

   a. Write an equation relating the distances among points P, Q, A, and B.

   Sample: $AP + AQ =$
   $BP + BQ$

   b. Draw and label the vertices S and T of the ellipse.

   c. Draw the axes. Label the endpoints of each. Identify the major axis and the minor axis.

   major: $\overline{ST}$
   minor: $\overline{MN}$

   d. Draw and label the center C of the ellipse.

Skills Objective B: Write equations or inequalities for ellipses given sufficient conditions.

In 2–6, write an equation for an ellipse satisfying the conditions.

2. foci at (-7, 0) and (7, 0); focal constant 20
$$\frac{x^2}{100} + \frac{y^2}{51} = 1$$

3. foci at (0, 4) and (0, -4); focal constant 10
$$\frac{x^2}{9} + \frac{y^2}{25} = 1$$

4. foci at (0, 5) and (0, -5); major axis length 14
$$\frac{x^2}{24} + \frac{y^2}{49} = 1$$

5. foci at (-3, 0) and (3, 0); minor axis length $\sqrt{15}$
$$\frac{4x^2}{51} + \frac{4y^2}{15} = 1$$

6. center at origin; horizontal major axis 12, minor axis 8
$$\frac{x^2}{36} + \frac{y^2}{16} = 1$$

Properties Objective E: Find points on an ellipse using its definition.

7. Use the conic grid at the right with centers 8 units apart to draw the set of points P such that $PF_1 + PF_2 = 12$.

Properties Objective F: Identify characteristics of ellipses.

8. Consider the ellipse with equation $\frac{x^2}{?} + \frac{y^2}{?} = 1$. Identify

   a. the length of its major axis. **10**   b. the focal constant. **10**

   c. the foci. **$(0, \sqrt{7}), (0, -\sqrt{7})$**   d. the vertices. **$(0, 5), (0, -5)$**

   e. Is the major axis horizontal or vertical? **vertical**

Properties Objective G: Classify curves as ellipses using algebraic or geometric properties.

9. Does the point $(-5, 4\sqrt{3})$ lie on the ellipse with foci at (-6, 0) and (6, 0) and focal constant 20? **yes**

Uses Objective H: Use ellipses to solve real-world problems.

10. Grinsby's collar is on a 24-foot rope tied loosely around two trees which are 14 feet apart. A metal loop on the collar allows it to slide freely along the full length of the rope. Consider a graph in which each unit represents one foot. Place the origin halfway between the trees and place the trees on the x-axis. Write an equation to represent the boundary of Grinsby's play area.

    $$\frac{x^2}{144} + \frac{y^2}{95} = 1$$

Representations Objective J: Graph ellipses given sentences for them and vice versa.

11. Sketch the graph of $\frac{x^2}{?} + \frac{y^2}{?} = 1$.

12. a. Write a sentence for the shaded region below.

    $$\frac{x^2}{16} + \frac{y^2}{1} < 1$$

    b. Is $(3, -\frac{\sqrt{3}}{2})$ in the shaded region? **no**

LESSON MASTER 12-5 B

Questions on SPUR Objectives

Skills Objective C: Find the area of an ellipse.

In 1–5, find the area of the ellipse satisfying the given conditions.

1. Its equation is $\frac{x^2}{?} + \frac{y^2}{?} = 1$.   **$55\pi$**

2. Its equation is $\frac{x^2}{?} + \frac{y^2}{?} = 1$.   **$100\sqrt{7}\pi$**

3. It has foci (0, 5) and (0, -5) and focal constant 14.   **$14\sqrt{6}\pi$**

4. It has foci (-2, 0) and (2, 0) and minor axis length 6.   **$3\sqrt{13}\pi$**

5. It has the image of the unit circle under $S_{5,6}$.   **30π**

6. Which has a greater area: a circle of diameter 8 or an ellipse with axes of length 6 and 10?   **the circle**

7. Find the area of the shaded region at the right between a circle and ellipse with the same center.

   90π

Properties Objective G: Classify curves as circles or ellipses using algebraic or geometric properties.

In 8–11, a scale change is given. a. Write an equation for the image of the circle $x^2 + y^2 = 1$ under the scale change. b. Tell if the image is a noncircular ellipse.

8. $S_{5,3}$
   a. $\frac{x^2}{25} + \frac{y^2}{9} = 1$
   b. **yes**

9. $S_{2,2}$
   a. $\frac{x^2}{4} + \frac{y^2}{4} = 1$
   b. **no**

10. $S: (x, y) \to (5x, 5y)$
    a. $\frac{x^2}{25} + \frac{y^2}{25} = 1$
    b. **no**

11. $S(x, y) = (.3x, 1.5y)$
    a. $\frac{x^2}{.09} + \frac{y^2}{2.25} = 1$
    b. **yes**

---

12. Complete the following: An ellipse is a circle if its major and minor axes are ___?___.   **equal in length**

13. Suppose you want to find the area of a circle. Can you use the formula for the area of an ellipse, $A = \pi ab$? Explain why or why not?

    Sample: Yes; you can use r for both a and b.

Uses Objective H: Use ellipses to solve real-world problems.

14. A mirror shaped like an ellipse has major axis 14 in. and minor axis 9 in. Find the area of the mirror.   **≈ 99 sq. in.**

15. A pond shaped like an ellipse is bordered by a 4-ft wide walkway. The walkway is bordered by fence shaped like an ellipse. The major and minor axes of the fence are 48 ft and 32 ft.

    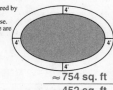

    a. Find the area of the pond.   **≈ 754 sq. ft**

    b. Find the area of the walkway.   **≈ 452 sq. ft**

Review Objective I, Lesson 2-6

16. Consider the equation $y = \frac{24}{x}$.

    a. What type of variation is described by the equation?   **inverse**

    b. Graph the equation in the window $-5 \le x \le 5$, $-150 \le y \le 150$. Sketch the graph at the right.

    c. What type of curve describes the graph?   **hyperbola**

    d. Identify all asymptotes of the graph.   **x-axis, y-axis**

Page 1 (Lesson Master 12-6 B)

LESSON MASTER 12-6 B — Questions on SPUR Objectives

Vocabulary

1. Refer to the hyperbola at the right with foci P and Q.

   a. Write an equation relating the distances among points P, Q, A, and B.

   Sample: $\overline{AQ} - \overline{AP} = \overline{BQ} - \overline{BP}$

   b. Draw and label the vertices S and T of the hyperbola.

   c. Sketch and label the asymptotes j and k of the hyperbola.

Skills Objective B: Write equations or inequalities for hyperbolas given sufficient conditions.

In 2–5, write an equation for the hyperbola satisfying the conditions.

2. foci at $(-4, 0)$ and $(4, 0)$; focal constant 6

$$\frac{x^2}{9} - \frac{y^2}{7} = 1$$

3. foci at $(-10, 0)$ and $(10, 0)$; focal constant 14

$$\frac{x^2}{49} - \frac{y^2}{51} = 1$$

4. vertices at $(-5, 0)$ and $(5, 0)$; containing the point $(10, 3)$

$$\frac{x^2}{25} - \frac{y^2}{3} = 1$$

5. vertices at $(-8, 0)$ and $(8, 0)$; foci at $(-12, 0)$ and $(12, 0)$

$$\frac{x^2}{64} - \frac{y^2}{80} = 1$$

Properties Objective E: Find points on a hyperbola using its definition.

6. Use the conic grid at the right with centers 6 units apart to draw the set of points P such that $|PF_1 - PF_2| = 4$.

Page 2 (Lesson Master 12-6 B page 2)

Properties Objective F: Identify characteristics of hyperbolas.

In 7 and 8, an equation is given for a hyperbola. a. Name its foci. b. Name its vertices. c. Give equations of its asymptotes.

7. $\frac{x^2}{?} - \frac{y^2}{?} = 1$

   a. $(-13, 0), (13, 0)$
   b. $(-12, 0), (12, 0)$
   c. $y = \frac{5}{12}x, \; y = -\frac{5}{12}x$

8. $\frac{x^2}{?} - y^2 = 1$

   a. $(-\sqrt{11}, 0), (\sqrt{11}, 0)$
   b. $(-\sqrt{10}, 0), (\sqrt{10}, 0)$
   c. $y = \frac{\sqrt{10}}{10}x, \; y = -\frac{\sqrt{10}}{10}x$

Properties Objective G: Classify curves as hyperbolas using algebraic or geometric properties.

9. a. *Multiple choice.* Choose all of the points that lie on the hyperbola with foci $(-15, 0)$ and $(15, 0)$ and focal constant 24.   **b, c**

   (a) $A(0, 9)$ (b) $B(12\sqrt{3}, 9\sqrt{2})$ (c) $C(-12, 0)$ (d) $D(24, 15)$

   b. Explain how you determined your answer in Part a.

   Sample: The equation of the hyperbola is $\frac{x^2}{144} - \frac{y^2}{81} = 1$; points B and C satisfy the equation, but points A and D do not.

Representations Objective J: Graph hyperbolas given sentences for them and vice versa.

10. Sketch the graph of $\frac{x^2}{?} - \frac{y^2}{?} = 1$

11. Write an equation for the hyperbola below.

$$\frac{x^2}{16} - \frac{y^2}{25} = 1$$

Page 3 (Lesson Master 12-7 B)

LESSON MASTER 12-7 B — Questions on SPUR Objectives

Skills Objective A: Rewrite an equation for a conic section in the general form of a quadratic equation in two variables.

In 1–6, rewrite in the form $Ax^2 + Bxy + Cy^2 + Dx + Ey + F = 0$.

1. $\frac{x^2}{?} - \frac{y^2}{?} = 1$ $\quad 4x^2 - 25y^2 - 100 = 0$

2. $y = 4(x - 2)^2 - 5$ $\quad 4x^2 - 16x - y + 11 = 0$

3. $(x + 8)(y - 7) = 30$ $\quad xy - 7x + 8y - 86 = 0$

4. $\frac{x^2}{?} + \frac{y^2}{?} = 1$ $\quad x^2 + 4y^2 - 100 = 0$

5. $y = \pm 2\sqrt{x^2 - 3}$ $\quad 4x^2 - y^2 - 12 = 0$

6. $xy = 72$ $\quad xy - 72 = 0$

Skills Objective B: Write equations for hyperbolas given sufficient conditions.

7. a. Find an equation for the hyperbola with foci at $(8, 8)$ and $(-8, -8)$ and focal constant 16. $\quad xy = 32$

   b. Find three points on the hyperbola.
   Samples: $(4, 8), (2, 16), (-8, -4)$

   c. Verify that $(-6, -4)$ is *not* on the hyperbola.
   Sample: $-6(-4) = 24 \neq 32$

Properties Objective F: Identify characteristics of hyperbolas.

8. Identify the asymptotes of the hyperbola with equation $xy = 12$. $\quad x\text{- and } y\text{-axes}$

9. *True or false.* The graph of $y = \frac{k}{x}$ is a rectangular hyperbola.   **true**

10. Consider the hyperbola with equation $xy = 15$. Name its

   a. foci. $(-\sqrt{30}, -\sqrt{30}), (\sqrt{30}, \sqrt{30})$
   b. asymptotes. $x\text{-axis}, y\text{-axis}$
   c. focal constant. $2\sqrt{30}$

Page 4 (Lesson Master 12-7 B page 2)

Properties Objective G: Classify curves as hyperbolas using algebraic or geometric properties.

11. Tell whether or not the graph of the equation is a hyperbola.

   a. $y = 6x$ **no**   b. $xy = -10$ **yes**   c. $y = \frac{12}{x}$ **yes**

   d. $y = \frac{x}{24}$ **no**   e. $x^2 + y^2 = 1$ **no**   f. $x^2 - y^2 = 1$ **yes**

Uses Objective H: Use hyperbolas to solve real-world problems.

12. Mrs. Hastings is cutting h hair ribbons, each l inches long from a spool of 240 inches of ribbon. Give the equation for the conic section which describes the relationship between h and l. $\quad hl = 240$

Representations Objective J: Graph hyperbolas given sentences for them and vice versa.

13. Sketch the graph of $y = -\frac{20}{x}$.

14. Sketch the graph of $xy \geq 32$.

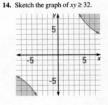

15. Refer to the hyperbola at the right.

   a. Write an equation for the hyperbola. $\quad xy = 10$

   b. Identify its foci.
   $(2\sqrt{5}, 2\sqrt{5}), (-2\sqrt{5}, -2\sqrt{5})$

$(-5, -2)$

Name _____

LESSON MASTER 12-8 B

Questions on SPUR Objectives

Vocabulary

1. What is a *quadratic system?*
   A system with at least one quadratic sentence

2. What is a *quadratic-linear system?*
   A quadratic system with at least one linear sentence

Skills Objective D: Solve systems of one linear and one quadratic equation by substitution.

In 3–8, solve the system.

3. $\begin{cases} cd = 32 \\ 3c + d = 4 \end{cases}$
   no real solutions

4. $\begin{cases} y = 4x \\ y = 2x^2 \end{cases}$
   (0, 0), (2, 8)

5. $\begin{cases} y = x^2 \\ 2x + 3y = 12 \end{cases}$
   $\left(\dfrac{-1 + \sqrt{37}}{3}, \dfrac{38 - 2\sqrt{37}}{9}\right)$
   $\left(\dfrac{-1 - \sqrt{37}}{3}, \dfrac{38 + 2\sqrt{37}}{9}\right)$

6. $\begin{cases} y = v^2 + 9 \\ y = \frac{1}{4}v \end{cases}$
   no real solutions

7. $\begin{cases} xy = 169 \\ 3x + 4y - 91 = 0 \end{cases}$
   $\left(\dfrac{52}{3}, \dfrac{39}{4}\right)$, (13, 13)

8. $\begin{cases} m^2 + n^2 = 200 \\ n - m = 20 \end{cases}$
   (-10, 10)

221 ▶

Name _____

▶ **LESSON MASTER 12-8 B** *page 2*

Uses Objective I: Use systems of quadratic equations to solve real-world problems.

9. A rectangular playground has an area of 2800 m² and a perimeter of 220 m. Find the dimensions of the playground.
   40 m, 70 m

Representations Objective K: Solve systems of quadratic equations graphically.

In 10–12, give two equations whose graphs illustrate the situation.
   Samples are given.

10. a hyperbola and a line that intersect in exactly two points
    $xy = 8$ $x = y$

11. a circle and a line that intersect in exactly one point
    $x^2 + y^2 = 16$ $x = -4$

12. a parabola and a line that have no points in common
    $y = x^2$ $y = x - 4$

In 13 and 14, graph the system and approximate the solutions.

13. $\begin{cases} 16x^2 + 9y^2 = 144 \\ y = 2x \end{cases}$

14. $\begin{cases} xy = 50 \\ y = -4x + 2 \end{cases}$

$\approx$ (1.7, 3.3), $\approx$ (-1.7, -3.3)   no solutions

222

Name _____

LESSON MASTER 12-9 B

Questions on SPUR Objectives

Skills Objective D: Solve systems of two quadratic equations by substitution or linear combination.

In 1–6, solve the system by substitution or linear combination.

1. $\begin{cases} x^2 + y^2 = 6 \\ 4x^2 - y^2 = 9 \end{cases}$
   $(\sqrt{3}, \pm\sqrt{3})$, $(-\sqrt{3}, \pm\sqrt{3})$

2. $\begin{cases} ab = 48 \\ a^2 + b^2 = 160 \end{cases}$
   (4, 12), (-4, -12), (12, 4), (-12, -4)

3. $\begin{cases} y^2 + 4x^2 = 40 \\ y^2 - 4x^2 = 8 \end{cases}$
   $(\pm 2, 2\sqrt{6})$, $(\pm 2, -2\sqrt{6})$

4. $\begin{cases} x^2 - y = 5 \\ x^2 + y^2 = 2 \end{cases}$
   no real solutions

5. $\begin{cases} r^2 + s^2 = 16 \\ s = r^2 + 4 \end{cases}$
   (0, 4)

6. $\begin{cases} y = d^2 - 6 \\ 2d^2 + y^2 = 27 \end{cases}$
   $(\pm 1, -5)$, $(\pm 3, 3)$

Uses Objective I: Use systems of quadratic equations to solve real-world problems.

7. An architect has designed a rectangular gallery with a floor area of 2352 sq. ft. The architect's clients want the floor area to be 2700 sq. ft, which can be accomplished by adding 3 ft to the width and 4 ft to the length in the original plans.

   a. Write a system of equations to describe this situation.
   $\begin{cases} lw = 2352 \\ (l + 4)(w + 3) = 2700 \end{cases}$

   b. What are the dimensions of the gallery in the original plan?
   42 ft, 56 ft

8. At football games last year, the snack shop took in $1200 in soft-drink sales. This year the price per drink was raised 15¢, 300 fewer drinks were sold, and $1365 was brought in. Find the price of the soft drinks and the number sold.

   a. last year. **50¢, 2400 drinks**

   b. this year. **65¢, 2100 drinks**

223 ▶

Name _____

▶ **LESSON MASTER 12-9 B** *page 2*

9. Monitoring Station A determines that the center of an earthquake is 40 miles away. Station B, 20 miles west, and 35 miles south of Station A, finds that it is 15 miles from the center. Find all possible locations of the center relative to Station A.
   $\approx$ 31 miles west and 25 miles south of Station A; $\approx$ 6 miles west and 40 miles south of Station A

Representations Objective K: Solve systems of quadratic equations graphically.

In 10–12, give equations whose graphs fit the situation. **Samples are given.**

10. a hyperbola and an ellipse that intersect in exactly two points
    $\dfrac{x^2}{9} - \dfrac{y^2}{16} = 1$ $\dfrac{x^2}{9} + \dfrac{y^2}{16} = 1$

11. a circle and a parabola that intersect in exactly three points
    $x^2 + y^2 = 25$ $y = -x^2 + 5$

12. a parabola and a hyperbola that have no points in common
    $y = x^2 + 5$ $\dfrac{x^2}{16} - \dfrac{y^2}{9} = 1$

13. Graph $\begin{cases} x^2 + y^2 = 100 \\ xy = 32 \end{cases}$ and approximate the solutions.
    $\approx$ (9.4, 3.4),
    $\approx$ (3.4, 9.4),
    $\approx$ (-9.4, -3.4),
    $\approx$ (-3.4, -9.4)

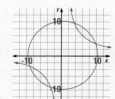

224

LESSON MASTER 13-1 B

Questions on SPUR Objectives

Vocabulary

1. What is a *series*?

   Sample: an indicated sum of the terms of a sequence.

Skills Objective A: Calculate values of a finite arithmetic series.

In 2–9, evaluate the given arithmetic series.

2. $5 + 10 + 15 + \ldots + 75$ — **600**

3. $-10 + -14 + -18 + \ldots + -94$ — **-1144**

4. $-11 + -5 + 1 + \ldots + 37$ — **117**

5. the sum of the first 80 positive integers — **3240**

6. the sum of the first 50 odd positive integers — **2500**

7. the sum of the first 50 even positive integers — **2550**

8. the sum of the first 35 terms of the sequence defined by $\begin{cases} a_1 = 12 \\ a_n = a_{n-1} + 3 \end{cases}$, for integers $n \geq 2$ — **2205**

9. the sum of the first 100 terms of the sequence defined by $\begin{cases} a_1 = -5 \\ a_n = a_{n-1} - 2 \end{cases}$, for integers $n \geq 2$ — **-10,400**

10. Consider the series $1 + 2 + 3 + \ldots + k$.
    a. How many terms are there? — **k terms**
    b. Suppose the sum is 15,753. Find k. — **k = 177**

11. Consider the series $2 + 4 + 6 + \ldots + n$.
    a. How many terms are there? — **$\frac{n}{2}$ terms**
    b. Suppose the sum is 1806. Find n. — **n = 84**

12. Consider the series $1 + 3 + 5 + \ldots + m$.
    a. How many terms are there? — **$\frac{m+1}{2}$ terms**
    b. Suppose the sum is 484. Find m. — **m = 43**

Uses Objective G: Solve real-world problems using arithmetic series.

13. A garden in the park is planted with 68 marigolds in the first row, 72 in the second row, and 4 more in each successive row. If the garden has 11 rows of marigolds, how many marigolds are there in all? — **968 marigolds**

14. A health club offers a special rate to encourage new members to continue their membership. The first month's fees are $70. Each successive month's fees drop $2 during the first year.
    a. What is the total amount of membership fees the first year? — **$708**
    b. During which month did the total reach $500? — **7th month**

15. Setsuo jogged 6 blocks the first day, 7 blocks the second day, and continued to jog an additional block every day. In how many days will he have jogged a total of 35 miles? (Use 1 mile = 12 blocks.) — **24 days**

Review Objective C, Lesson 7-5

In 16–20, give the first five terms of the geometric sequence described.

16. constant ratio -8, first term 3 — **3, -24, 192, -1536, 12,288**

17. constant ratio $\frac{2}{3}$, first term 2187 — **2187, 1458, 972, 648, 432**

18. third term 500, fourth term 2500 — **20, 100, 500, 2500, 12,500**

19. $g_n = 12(4)^{n-1}$, for integers $n \geq 1$ — **12, 48, 192, 768, 3072**

20. $\begin{cases} g_1 = 16 \\ g_n = -2g_{n-1} \end{cases}$, for integers $n \geq 2$ — **16, -32, 64, -128, 256**

In 21 and 22, a sequence is given. a. Could the sequence be geometric? b. If yes, give its constant ratio.

21. $9, 18, 27, 36, \ldots$
    a. **no**
    b.

22. $\frac{11}{6}, 11, 66, 396, \ldots$
    a. **yes**
    b. **6**

LESSON MASTER 13-2 B

Questions on SPUR Objectives

Skills Objective B: Calculate values of a finite geometric series.

1. Find the sum of the first 12 terms of the geometric series with first term 8 and common ratio 2. — **32,760**

2. Find the sum of the first 5 terms of the geometric series with first term 16 and common ratio $\frac{1}{4}$. — **21.3125**

3. Find the sum of the first 8 terms of the geometric series with first term -5 and common ratio -1.5. — **≈ 49.26**

4. Find the sum of the first 10 terms of the sequence defined by $\begin{cases} g_1 = 32 \\ g_n = .75g_{n-1} \end{cases}$, for integers $n \geq 2$ — **≈ 120.79**

5. Find the sum of the first 6 terms of the sequence defined by $\begin{cases} g_1 = 40 \\ g_n = -3g_{n-1} \end{cases}$, for integers $n \geq 2$ — **-7280**

6. Find the sum of the first 9 terms of the sequence defined by $\begin{cases} g_1 = -10 \\ g_n = -g_{n-1} \end{cases}$, for integers $n \geq 2$ — **-10**

In 7–11, a geometric series is given. a. Tell how many terms are in the series. b. Give the value of the series.

7. $81 + 27 + 9 + 3 + 1 + \frac{1}{3} + \frac{1}{9}$
   a. **7 terms**
   b. **$\approx 121.\overline{4}$**

8. $1 + 2 + 4 + 8 + \ldots + 512$
   a. **10 terms**
   b. **1023**

9. $6 + 24 + 96 + \ldots + 6 \cdot 4^{11}$
   a. **12 terms**
   b. **33,554,430**

10. $.005 + .01 + .02 + .04 + \ldots + .005 \cdot 2^8$
    a. **9 terms**
    b. **2.555**

11. $10 + -40 + 1600 + \ldots + 10(-4)^{22}$
    a. **23 terms**
    b. **$\approx 1.4 \cdot 10^{14}$**

12. $1 - 1.5 + 2.25 - \ldots + 1.5^{10}$
    a. **11 terms**
    b. **≈ 35.0**

13. $1 + m + m^2 + m^3 + \ldots + m^{17}$
    a. **18 terms**
    b. **$\frac{m^{18} - 1}{m - 1}$**

Uses Objective G: Solve real-world problems using geometric series.

14. On each January 3rd for 19 years, Mrs. Redstar deposited $500 in a college account that earned an annual yield of 5.5%
    a. Write a geometric series that represents the value of the fund on January 3rd of the 20th year. You may use "..."as needed.
    $500(1.055)^{19} + 500(1.055)^{18} + \ldots + 500(1.055)^2 + 500(1.055)$
    b. Evaluate the series in Part a. — **$16,934.16**
    c. If the account had earned 5% rather than 5.5%, how much less would there have been in the account on January 3rd of the 20th year? — **$901.18**

15. The output of a certain industrial machine decreased 2.5% each year. In 1986, the machine produced 6,300,000 thingumajigs. Find the total number of thingumajigs produced from 1986 through 1995. — **$\approx 56,364,936$**

16. At the right is a glass designer's plan for a stained-glass window. The designer will need to use leading for each segment shown in the diagram. The length of the side of the largest square is 100 cm.
    a. What is the perimeter of
       i. the largest square? — **400 cm**
       ii. the next largest square? — **$200\sqrt{2}$ cm**
       iii. the third largest square? — **200 cm**
    b. Write a geometric series that represents the total length of leading needed for the window. **Sample:**
    $400 + 200\sqrt{2} + 200 + 100\sqrt{2} + 100 + 50\sqrt{2} + 50$
    c. Find the total length of leading needed. — **≈ 1245 cm**

LESSON MASTER 13-3 B

Questions on SPUR Objectives

Vocabulary

1. a. Explain the meaning of $\sum\limits_{i=1}^{9} 4^i$.

   Sample: $4^1 + 4^2 + 4^3 + 4^4 + 4^5 + 4^6 + 4^7 + 4^8 + 4^9$

   b. What is the name of the Greek letter Σ? **sigma**

   c. What is the variable i called? **index variable, or index**

2. Explain the meaning of 12!.

   Sample: $12 \cdot 11 \cdot 10 \cdot 9 \cdot 8 \cdot 7 \cdot 6 \cdot 5 \cdot 4 \cdot 3 \cdot 2 \cdot 1$

3. What is a *permutation*?

   an arrangement of objects in a row

Skills Objective C: Use summation (Σ) or factorial (!) notation.

In 4–12, rewrite using Σ-notation or !-notation.

4. $5 + 10 + 15 + 20 + 25 + 30 + 35 + 40$ $\sum\limits_{i=1}^{8} 5i$

5. $7 \cdot 6 \cdot 5 \cdot 4 \cdot 3 \cdot 2 \cdot 1$ $7!$

6. $-2 + 4 + -8 + \ldots + 256$ $\sum\limits_{i=1}^{8} -2^i$

7. $60 + 70 + 80 + \ldots + 940$ $\sum\limits_{i=6}^{94} 10i$

8. $1 \cdot 2 \cdot 3 \cdot 4 \cdot 5 \cdot 6 \cdot 7 \cdot 8 \cdot 9 \cdot 10 \cdot 11 \cdot 12$ $12!$

9. $6 \cdot 5 \cdot 4 \cdot 3 \cdot 2 \cdot 1 \cdot 5 \cdot 4 \cdot 3 \cdot 2 \cdot 1$ $(6!)(5!)$

10. The sum of the cubes of the integers from 1 to 12 $\sum\limits_{i=1}^{12} i^3$

11. $98 + 198 + 298 + \ldots + 1498$ $\sum\limits_{i=1}^{15} 100i - 2$

12. $\dfrac{5 \cdot 4 \cdot 3 \cdot 2 \cdot 1}{8 \cdot 7 \cdot 6 \cdot 5 \cdot 4 \cdot 3 \cdot 2 \cdot 1}$ $\dfrac{5!}{8!}$

In 13–15, evaluate.

13. 8! **40,320**   14. 5! · 3! · 7! **3,628,800**   15. $\dfrac{18!}{14!}$ **73,440**

In 16–19, a series is given. a. Write the terms of the series.
b. Evaluate the series.

16. $\sum\limits_{i=1}^{20} 11i$ a. $11 + 22 + 33 + \ldots + 220$

   b. **2310**

17. $\sum\limits_{i=1}^{8} .3^i$ a. $.3 + .09 + .027 + \ldots + .00006561$

   b. $\approx .43$

18. $\sum\limits_{i=1}^{500} (4i + 3)$ a. $7 + 11 + 15 + \ldots + 2003$

   b. **502,500**

19. $\sum\limits_{i=-2}^{4} (6 \cdot 10^i)$ a. $.06 + .6 + 6 + \ldots + 60,000$

   b. **66,666.66**

Skills Objective D: Calculate permutations of n objects, n at a time.

20. a. List all the permutations of the letters S, M, A, R, T with the third term S.

MASRT	AMSRT	RTSMA	TMSAR
MASTR	AMSTR	RTSAM	TMSRA
MRSAT	ARSMT	RMSAT	TASMR
MRSTA	ARSTM	RMSTA	TASRM
MTSAR	ATSMR	RASMT	TRSMA
MTSRA	ATSRM	RASTM	TRSAM

   b. How many permutations are possible? **24 permutations**

21. How many permutations of the digits 1, 4, 6, 7, 9 are possible? **120 permutations**

Uses Objective H: Solve problems involving permutations of n objects.

22. In how many ways can 12 children line up at the water fountain? **479,001,600 ways**

23. In how many ways can 30 CDs be stacked in a "tower" CD rack? $\approx 2.6525 \cdot 10^{32}$ **ways**

24. In how many different orders can a cast of 10 be listed on a program? **3,628,800 ways**

25. A student takes 6 classes plus lunch in a 7-period day. In how many different orders can the student take the classes if lunch must be 4th period? **720 orders**

LESSON MASTER 13-4 B

Questions on SPUR Objectives

Vocabulary

1. Let S be a data set of n numbers.

   a. For what purposes are statistical measures of S used?
   to describe S

   b. What is the *mean* of S?
   the average of all terms of S

   c. What is the *median* of S?
   the middle term of S when the terms are placed in increasing order

   d. What is the *mode* of S?
   the number which occurs most often in S

   e. Complete the following: The *standard deviation* of S measures the ___?___ of the elements in S. **spread**

Uses Objective I: Use measure of central tendency or dispersion to describe data or distributions.

In 2–5, a set of temperatures in degrees Fahrenheit is given.
For each set, find a. the mean, b. the median, and c. the mode.

2. daily highs for one week in July:
   88, 91, 94, 94, 87, 89, 84

   a. ≈ 89.57 b. **89**   c. **94**

3. daily lows for one week in January:
   3, 0, -6, -11, -6, -3, -6

   a. ≈ -4.14 b. **-6**   c. **-6**

4. monthly highs for one year:
   33, 39, 48, 56, 69, 84, 96, 101, 89, 78, 52, 40

   a. ≈ 65.42 b. **62.5**   c. **none**

5. monthly lows for one year:
   -12, 8, 20, 31, 48, 61, 65, 74, 48, 20, 14, 8

   a. ≈ 32.08 b. **25.5**   c. **8, 20, 48**

In 6–9, use the heights in inches of the girls in two Brownie troops listed at the right.

Troop 416: 39, 35, 36, 42, 44, 41, 37, 42
Troop 38: 42, 42, 37, 38, 42, 36, 37, 42

For each troop, find a. the mean, b. the median, and c. the mode for the data.

6. Troop 416 a. **39.5** b. **40** c. **42**

7. Troop 38 a. **39.5** b. **40** c. **42**

8. What do you notice about your answers in Questions 6 and 7?
Both sets have the same mean, median, and mode.

9. Compute the standard deviation of the data for each troop.

   a. Troop 416 ≈ 3.04 b. Troop 38 ≈ 2.55

   c. What do your answers to Parts a and b tell you about the heights of the girls in the two Brownie troops?
   The heights in Troop 416 are more widely dispersed.

10. The graph shows the number of sit-ups done by the members of a karate team.

    Sit-Ups Done by Karate Kids

    a. Find the indicated measure of central tendency for the data in the graph.

    mean ≈ 75.71 median **80**

    mode **40** standard deviation ≈ 29.81

    b. Which of these measures best describes the data? Explain your answer.
    Sample: The mean is the best measure because it reflects all the data; the median gives only the middle element; the mode gives only the most frequent element; the standard deviation gives only the spread.

Four worksheet panels arranged in a 2x2 grid.

Top-Left Panel

LESSON MASTER 13-5 B   **Questions on SPUR Objectives**

Vocabulary

4. Complete the following: $\binom{n}{r}$ denotes the ___?___
element in row ___?___ of Pascal's triangle. $(r+1)st, n$

Skills   Objective D: Calculate combinations.

2. Write $\frac{7 \cdot 6 \cdot 5 \cdot 4 \cdot 3 \cdot 2 \cdot 1}{4 \cdot 3 \cdot 2 \cdot 1 \cdot 3 \cdot 2 \cdot 1}$ in the form $\binom{n}{r}$. $\binom{7}{4}$ or $\binom{7}{3}$

3. Write $\binom{9}{7}$ using factorial symbols. $\dfrac{9!}{7!2!}$

In 4–15, calculate.

4. $\binom{8}{3}$ 56   5. $\binom{6}{5}$ 6   6. $\binom{7}{6}$ 7

7. $\binom{8}{0}$ 1   8. $\binom{8}{8}$ 1   9. $\binom{18}{7}$ 31,824

10. $\binom{10}{1}$ 10   11. $\binom{24}{23}$ 24   12. $\binom{24}{1}$ 24

13. $\binom{16}{3}$ 560   14. $\binom{16}{13}$ 560   15. $\binom{29}{0}$ 1

Properties   Objective F: Recognize properties of Pascal's triangle.

16. Row 0 and row 5 of Pascal's triangle are given below.
Fill in rows 1–4 and 6–10.

1

Row 1   1   1

Row 2   1   2   1

Row 3   1   3   3   1

Row 4   1   4   6   4   1

Row 5   X   5   10   10   5   1

Row 6   1   6   15   20   (15)   6   1

Row 7   1   7   21   35   35   21   7   1

Row 8   1   8   28   56   70   56   28   8   1

Row 9   1   9   36   84   126   126   84   36   9   1

Row 10   1   10   45   120   210   252   210   120   45   10   1

Top-Right Panel

▶ **LESSON MASTER 13-5 B** *page 2*

In 17–20, refer to Pascal's triangle in Question 16.   See page 233.

17. Draw a circle around the element denoted by $\binom{6}{4}$.

18. Draw a square around the element denoted by $\binom{10}{5}$.

19. Draw a triangle around the element denoted by $\binom{7}{1}$.

20. Draw an X through the element denoted by $\binom{5}{0}$.

21. Verify that for $n = 8$, $\binom{8}{4} + \binom{8}{5} = \binom{n+1}{5}$.

$$\binom{8}{4} + \binom{8}{5} = \frac{8!}{4!(4!)} + \frac{8!}{5!(3!)} = 70 + 56 = 126$$

$$\binom{8+1}{5} = \frac{9!}{5!(4!)} = 126$$

22. Refer to row 9 of Pascal's triangle in Question 16.
Write 84 two different ways using $\binom{n}{r}$ notation. $\binom{9}{3}, \binom{9}{6}$

23. Show that $\binom{52}{12} = \binom{52}{40}$.

$$\binom{52}{12} = \frac{52!}{12!(40!)} =$$
$$\frac{52!}{40!(12!)} = \binom{52}{40}$$

24. Show that $12! = 12 \cdot 11!$.

$$12! = 12 \cdot 11 \cdot 10 \cdot 9 \cdot$$
$$8 \cdot 7 \cdot 6 \cdot 5 \cdot 4 \cdot 3 \cdot 2 \cdot 1 =$$
$$12(11 \cdot 10 \cdot 9 \cdot 8 \cdot 7 \cdot$$
$$6 \cdot 5 \cdot 4 \cdot 3 \cdot 2 \cdot 1) =$$
$$12 \cdot 11!$$

Review   Objective A, Lesson 11-2

In 25–30, multiply and write the product in standard form.

25. $(a + b)^2$ $a^2 + 2ab + b^2$

26. $(x + 3)^2$ $x^2 + 6x + 9$

27. $(4m^2 + 3m - 2)(6m - 1)$ $24m^3 + 14m^2 - 15m + 2$

28. $(y - 2)(y + 3)(y - 5)$ $y^3 - 4y^2 - 11y + 30$

29. $(a + b)^3$ $a^3 + 3a^2b + 3ab^2 + b^3$

30. $(x + 3)^3$ $x^3 + 9x^2 + 27x + 27$

Bottom-Left Panel

LESSON MASTER 13-6 B   **Questions on SPUR Objectives**

Vocabulary

1. What is a *binomial expansion*?
the result of writing a power of a binomial as a polynomial

Skills   Objective E: Expand binomials.

2. a. Expand $(a + b)^6$.
$a^6 + 6a^5b + 15a^4b^2 + 20a^3b^3 + 15a^2b^4 + 6ab^5 + b^6$

   b. Let $a = 2m$ and $b = 3n^2$. Substitute these values for a and b in the polynomial you wrote in Part **a** to expand $(2m + 3n^2)^6$.
$(2m)^6 + 6(2m)^5(3n^2) + 15(2m)^4(3n^2)^2 + 20(2m)^3(3n^2)^3 + 15(2m)^2(3n^2)^4 + 6(2m)(3n^2)^5 + (3n^2)^6$

   c. Simplify Part **b**.
$64m^6 + 576m^5n^2 + 2160m^4n^4 + 4320m^3n^6 + 4860m^2n^8 + 2916mn^{10} + 729n^{12}$

   d. Use your answer in Part **a** to expand $(5x^2 - y)^6$.
$15,625x^{12} - 18,750x^{10}y + 9375x^8y^2 - 2500x^6y^3 + 375x^4y^4 - 30x^2y^5 + y^6$

In 3–9, expand the binomial.

3. $(x^4 + 5)^3$ $x^{12} + 15x^8 + 75x^4 + 125$

4. $(3e - 7f)^4$ $81e^4 - 756e^3f + 2646e^2f^2 - 4116ef^3 + 2401f^4$

5. $(m - n^4)^5$ $m^5 - 5m^4n^4 + 10m^3n^8 - 10m^2n^{12} + 5mn^{16} - n^{20}$

Bottom-Right Panel

▶ **LESSON MASTER 13-6 B** *page 2*

6. $(2r + 4s)^7$ $128r^7 + 1792r^6s + 10,752r^5s^2 + 35,840r^4s^3 + 71,680r^3s^4 + 86,016r^2s^5 + 57,344rs^6 + 16,384s^7$

7. $(x^4 - 1)^8$ $x^{32} - 8x^{28} + 28x^{24} - 56x^{20} + 70x^{16} - 56x^{12} + 28x^8 - 8x^4 + 1$

8. $(a^3 + b^7)^4$ $a^{12} + 4a^9b^7 + 6a^6b^{14} + 4a^3b^{21} + b^{28}$

9. $(u - .5)^6$ $u^6 - 3u^5 + 3.75u^4 - 2.5u^3 + .9375u^2 - .1875u + .015625$

10. Consider $(1 + .06)^9$.

    a. Find the sum of the first three terms of the expansion.   1.6696

    b. Find $(1 + .06)^9$ using a calculator. ≈ 1.68948

    c. Do you think your answer to Part **a** is a reasonable estimate of $(1 + .06)^9$? Why or why not?   Sample: Yes; they are equivalent to the nearest tenth.

In 11–14, convert to an expression in the form $(a + b)^n$.

11. $\sum_{r=0}^{n} \binom{n}{r} x^{n-r} 5^r$ $(x + 5)^n$

12. $\sum_{r=0}^{n} \binom{n}{r} (6p)^{n-r} (q)^r$ $(6p + q)^n$

13. $\sum_{r=0}^{n} \binom{n}{r} (2k)^{n-r} (3w)^r$ $(2k + 3w)^n$

14. $\sum_{i=0}^{n} \binom{n}{i} \left(\frac{d}{2}\right)^{n-i} (-e)^i$ $\left(\frac{d}{2} - e\right)^n$

Properties   Objective F: Recognize properties of Pascal's triangle.

15. Explain the connection between Pascal's triangle and binomial expansion.
Sample: For the expansion of $(a + b)^n$, all powers of a from a^n to a^0 occur in order; in each term, the exponents of a and b add to n; if the power of b is r then the coefficient of the term is $\binom{n}{r}$.

LESSON MASTER 13-7 B

Questions on SPUR Objectives

Vocabulary

1. What is a *combination*?
   any choice of *r* objects taken from *n* objects.

Skills Objective D: Calculate combinations.

2. Consider the set {H, A, L, F}.
   a. Use exponential notation to tell how many subsets of this set there are. 2^4
   b. List the subsets.
   { } {H} {A} {L} {F} (HA) (HL) (HF) (AL) (AF) (LF) {HAL} {HAF} {HLF} {ALF} {HALF}
   c. Check that your answers in Parts a and b agree.
   $2^4 = 16$; there are 16 subsets in the list.
   d. Use $\binom{n}{r}$ notation and tell how many subsets have 2 elements. $\binom{4}{2}$
   e. Circle the subsets in Part b that have 2 elements.
   f. Check that your answers in Parts d and e agree.
   $\binom{4}{2} = 6$; there are 6 subsets circled.

3. Suppose a set has 7 elements. How many subsets have
   a. 2 elements? 21   b. 4 elements? 35   c. 7 elements? 1

4. Suppose a set has 12 elements. How many subsets have
   a. 0 elements? 1   b. 5 elements? 792   c. 7 elements? 792

5. a. Calculate $_8C_2$. 28
   b. What does $_8C_2$ stand for?
   number of 2-element subsets of an 8-element set

▶ **LESSON MASTER 13-7 B** *page 2*

Properties Objective F: Recognize properties of Pascal's triangle.

6. a. Calculate $_6C_0 + _6C_1 + _6C_2 + _6C_3 + _6C_4 + _6C_5 + _6C_6$. 64
   b. How is Part a related to Pascal's triangle?
   Sample: The addends are the elements in row 6 of Pascal's triangle.

Uses Objective H: Solve problems involving combinations.

7. Jennie has 12 close friends, but her mother will allow her to invite only 6 of them for a sleep over. In how many different ways can she make up her guest list? 924 ways

8. Paul wants to take some tapes on a bus trip to Washington, D.C. His carrying case holds 16 tapes. In how many ways can he choose the 16 tapes from his collection of 74 tapes? $\approx 6.73 \times 10^{15}$ ways

9. Consider 10 points in a plane such that no three are collinear.
   a. How many segments have these points as endpoints? 45 segments
   b. How many triangles have these points as vertices? 120 triangles
   c. Look at your answers to Parts a and b. Since each triangle has three sides, why are there not three times as many segments as there are triangles? Sample: Some segments are sides of more than than one triangle.

10. Home Harvest Nursery carries 88 varieties of flowers, 12 varieties of ground cover, and 31 varieties of vegetables. The company is planning a newspaper advertisement.
    a. Page 1 of the advertisement will show 8 different types of flowers. In how many different ways can the flowers be chosen? $\approx 6.43 \times 10^{10}$ ways
    b. Page 2 will show 4 different types of ground cover. In how many different ways can the ground cover be chosen? 495 ways
    c. Page 3 will show vegetables. How many different displays of at least one type of vegetable are possible? $\approx 2.15 \times 10^9$ ways

---

LESSON MASTER 13-8 B

Questions on SPUR Objectives

Vocabulary

1. a. Give an example of two *independent events*.
   Sample: Roll 6 on a die; roll 4 on a die.
   b. Give an example of two events that are *not* independent.
   Sample: Pick a card from a deck; keep the card and pick another card.

2. a. Give an example of two *mutually-exclusive events*.
   Sample: Roll 2 on a die; roll 3 on a die.
   b. Give an example of two events that are *not* mutually exclusive.
   Sample: Roll 2 on a die; roll an even number on a die.

3. List all of the features of a *binomial experiment*.
   A trial is repeated *n* times, where $n \geq 2$. The trials are independent. For each trial, there are only 2 outcomes—success or failure. Each trial has the same probability of success.

Uses Objective J: Solve problems using probability.

In 4–7, consider tossing a coin with $P(H) = 0.6$. You toss the coin 5 times.

4. a. Calculate the probability of 0 tails. .07776
   b. Calculate the probability of exactly 1 tail. .2592
   c. Calculate the probability of exactly 2 tails. .3456
   d. Calculate the probability of exactly 3 tails. .2304
   e. Calculate the probability of exactly 4 tails. .0768
   f. Calculate the probability of exactly 5 tails. .01024

5. In Question 4, which events are mutually exclusive? Explain your reasoning.
   Sample: All are mutually exclusive as no two of them can occur at the same time.

▶ **LESSON MASTER 13-8 B** *page 2*

6. a. Calculate the probability of at least 3 tails. .31744
   b. Calculate the probability of at most 3 tails. .91296

7. In Question 6, are the events in Parts a and b mutually exclusive? Explain your reasoning.
   Sample: No; getting 2 tails is a part of each event.

In 8 and 9, consider a 5-question multiple-choice quiz with three possible answers per question. If each question is answered by guessing, the probability of correctly answering any one question is $\frac{1}{3}$.

8. What is the probability of correctly answering exactly 3 questions? $\approx .165$

9. What is the probability of scoring at least 75% on the quiz? $\approx .041$

In 10–13, suppose you are shooting ten baskets from the free-throw line. Recently you've had a 70% probability of making each basket. If this pattern continues, give the probability that you will get

10. exactly 5 baskets. $\approx .103$ 11. exactly 7 baskets. $\approx .267$
12. exactly 10 baskets. $\approx .028$ 13. at least 7 baskets. $\approx .650$

In 14–17, suppose a fair coin is tossed 12 times. Give the probability of each event.

14. exactly 2 heads $\approx .016$ 15. exactly 6 heads $\approx .226$
16. exactly 10 tails $\approx .016$ 17. no more than 2 tails $\approx .019$

18. Suppose a fair coin is tossed 5 times.
    a. What could the quantity $\binom{5}{4}$ represent? Samples are given.
    the number of ways 4 heads could occur
    b. What could the quantity 2^5 represent?
    the number of possible outcomes.
    c. What could the quantity $\binom{5}{4}(.5)^4(.5)^1$ represent?
    the probability of getting exactly 4 heads

LESSON MASTER 13-9 B — Questions on SPUR Objectives

Vocabulary

1. What is a *lottery*?

   a game or procedure in which prizes are distributed among people by pure chance

Uses Objective J: Solve problems using probability.

2. In the Guess-the-Number booth at the state fair, players select a 4-digit number using any combination of the numbers, 1 through 6, rolled on a die.

   a. What is the probability of picking the correct 4-digit number?

   $\frac{1}{1296} \approx .00077$

   b. What are the odds against winning?

   1295 to 1

   c. If the winner wins $1000, and it costs 50¢ to play, does the Guess-the-Number booth gain money, lose money, or break even in the long run? Explain your reasoning.

   Sample: the booth loses money, because for 1296 tickets sold, $648 is taken in but $1000 is paid to a winner.

3. In the state fair's Spin 6 game, a wheel with the numbers 1 through 36 is spun 6 times. Prizes are given for anyone who picks 3 out of the 6 numbers, 4 out of 6, 5 out of 6, or 6 out of 6.

   a. What is the probability of picking exactly 3 out of the 6 numbers?

   $\frac{1}{24} \approx .0417$

   b. What is the probability of picking exactly 4 out of the 6 numbers?

   $\frac{1}{299} \approx .0033$

   c. What is the probability of picking exactly 5 out of the 6 numbers?

   $\frac{1}{10,821} \approx .0000924$

   d. What is the probability of picking exactly 6 out of the 6 numbers?

   $\frac{1}{1,947,792} \approx .0000005$

▶ LESSON MASTER 13-9 B *page 2*

e. The prizes in Spin 6 are $150 for picking exactly 3 out of 6 numbers, $2000 for 4 out of 6, and $75,000 for 5 out of 6.

   i. Based on the probabilities found in Parts **a** through **c**, do these prize amounts seem reasonable? Why or why not?

   Sample: Yes; probability of picking 4 is $\approx \frac{1}{12}$ that of picking 3, and prize for 4 is $\approx$ 13 times prize for 3; probability of picking 5 is $\approx \frac{1}{36}$ that of picking 4, and prize for 5 is 37.5 times prize for 4.

   ii. *Multiple choice.* Based on the other prize amounts and the probabilities found in Parts **a** through **d**, which prize would be appropriate for someone who chooses 6 out of 6 numbers correctly? Explain your choice. **b**

   (a) $5 million　(b) $13\frac{1}{2} million　(c) $20 million

   Sample: The probability of picking 6 is about $\frac{1}{180}$ that of picking 5; 180 times the prize money for 5 is $13.5 million.

4. At the after-prom party, 5 balls are chosen from 20 balls numbered from 1 to 20. Each couple may choose one game ticket. Enough prizes were donated to be able to award one prize to roughly every 25 couples. If a prize is given to each couple who pick 3 out of 5 numbers, will there be enough prizes? Explain your reasoning.

   Sample: No; $\binom{5}{3}\binom{15}{2} / \binom{20}{5} \approx .06772 \approx \frac{1}{15}$, so one in about every 15 couples will win.

Review Objective I, Lesson 8-2

5. *Multiple choice.* List all of the graphs that represent a function whose inverse is also a function. **c, d**

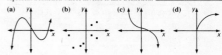

LESSON MASTER 13-10 B — Questions on SPUR Objectives

Vocabulary

1. What is a *probability function*?

   a function which maps a set of events onto their probabilities

2. What is a *binomial probability distribution*?

   a probability function that results from calculations of binomial probabilities

3. Complete the following: Suppose a fair coin is tossed 14 times. When the probabilities are graphed as a function of the number of heads, the graph approaches a curve called ___?___.

   a normal curve

4. When test scores are *normalized*, what is true about the distribution of the scores?

   Sample: The scores are distributed on a normal curve.

Uses Objective I: Use measures of central tendency or dispersion to describe data or distributions.

In 5–8, ACT scores range from 1 to 36, with a mean near 21 and a standard deviation near 5. Assume the scores are normally distributed.

5. About what percent of students have a score above 21?

   $\approx 50\%$

6. About what percent of students have a score below 16?

   $\approx 15.9\%$

7. About what percent of students have a score above 31?

   $\approx 2.3\%$

8. About what percent of students have scores between 16 and 26?

   $\approx 68.2\%$

▶ LESSON MASTER 13-10 B *page 2*

Representations Objective L: Graph and analyze binomial and normal distributions.

In 9–10, consider the function P with $P(n) = \frac{\binom{7}{n}}{2^7}$.

9. Complete the table of values and graph P.

10. What name is given to P?

   probability function or binomial distribution

n	$P(n)$
0	$\frac{1}{128}$
1	$\frac{7}{128}$
2	$\frac{21}{128}$
3	$\frac{35}{128}$
4	$\frac{35}{128}$
5	$\frac{21}{128}$
6	$\frac{7}{128}$
7	$\frac{1}{128}$

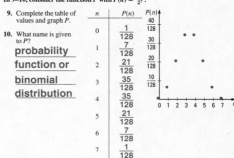

In 11–13, consider the normal distribution with mean 15 and standard deviation 4.

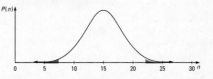

11. About what percent of the data are greater than 11? $\approx 84.1\%$

12. About what percent of the data are between 7 and 23? $\approx 95.4\%$

13. a. Shade the portions of the graph representing data more than two standard deviations away from 15.

   b. About what percent of the graph should you have shaded in Part a? $\approx 4.6\%$

LESSON MASTER 13-11 B

Questions on SPUR Objectives

Vocabulary

In 1–5, a situation involving sampling is described.
a. Describe the population. b. Identify the sample.

Samples are given.

1. A company is testing brakes to see how many miles can be driven before they need replacing.
   a. the set of all brakes manufactured
   b. the set of brakes being tested

2. The school board is interviewing citizens to see how they will vote on an upcoming bond referendum.
   a. the set of all voting citizens in its district
   b. the set of voting citizens being interviewed

3. The owner of a restaurant is asking its customers to list their favorite desserts.
   a. the set of all restaurant customers
   b. the set of customers being surveyed

4. A frozen-foods company is checking the weight of its pot pies.
   a. the set of all pot pies made by the company
   b. the set of pot pies being checked

5. A polling company is asking teenagers about their favorite electronics stores.
   a. the set of all teenagers in a given region
   b. the set of teenagers being surveyed

Uses Objective K: Give reasons for sampling.

6. List at least three reasons for sampling.
   Sample: Sampling saves time; it prevents destroying an entire population; it is necessary when the population is very large or infinite.

7. A juice company fills 6,000 cans of juice a day and randomly checks 1% of the cans to be sure they are properly filled.
   a. What is the population size in this situation?   6,000 cans
   b. What is the sample size in this situation?   60 cans

8. The Quincy Clock Company manufactures 2000 travel alarm clocks, 5000 stopwatches, and 3000 wall clocks each month. Suggest how the company might use stratified random sampling to test the accuracy of the timepieces.
   Sample: Randomly choose 10 travel alarm clocks, 25 stopwatches, and 15 wall clocks; or choose $2x$ travel alarms, $5x$ stopwatches, and $3x$ wall clocks.

9. A spinner has 5 congruent regions numbered 1 through 5. It is hoped that the spinner is fair. The spinner is spun 500 times in an experiment, and the experiment is repeated many times.
   a. If the spinner is fair, what is the mean number of times a 2 should appear?   100 times
   b. What is the standard deviation? ≈ 8.94
   c. 68% of the time the number of 2s should be between what two numbers?   91 and 109

10. Suppose that 25% of the households are tuned to a particular TV show. Consider all the random samples of 1500 people.
    a. For these samples, what is the mean number of people tuned to the show?   375 people
    b. What is the standard deviation? ≈ 16.77
    c. 95% of the time the samples will have between what two numbers of people watching the show?   341 and 409

11. At MacKenzie Motors, 20% of the new-car orders are for black cars. Consider a random-number table.
    a. Which digits could represent black cars?   Sample: 0, 1
    b. Start in the row that matches the day of the month on which you were born and the column that represents the month. Read the next 200 digits and compute the percent of orders for black cars in this simulation.   Answers will vary.